W9-AOJ-581

Discard

MAR 16 '18

Discard

LOGIC: A Modern Introduction to Deductive Reasoning

LOGIC: A Modern Introduction to Deductive Reasoning

D. B. Terrell
University of Minnesota

Holt, Rinehart and Winston, Inc.

New York Chicago San Francisco Toronto London

LIBRARY - SEMINARY OF
ST. VINCENT DE PAUL
BOYNTON BEACH, FLA.

Copyright © 1967 by HOLT, RINEHART AND WINSTON, Inc.

All Rights Reserved

Library of Congress Catalog Card Number: 67–11810

2600708

Printed in the United States of America

1 2 3 4 5 6 7 8 9

16337

Preface

The general aim of this book is to provide some basic insight into the techniques of modern logic while preserving a degree of relevance to the process of reasoning. It does not offer a study of deductive systems for their own sake but a study of deductive reasoning ordered and organized by systems. I have attempted to accomplish this objective by combining the familiarity and common sense that is the great virtue of classical logic with the rigor and self-consciousness contributed by modern logic.

This text is intended to offer a unified approach to the old and to the new logic and to avoid radical shifts from one context to another. An integrated treatment of traditional and modern logic is not characteristic of most textbooks that undertake to incorporate both. Discussions of traditional logic have tended to remain fixed in a fairly established pattern, despite occasional variations. The usual discussion of traditional methods stresses criticism while the treatment of modern logic stresses proof. The result is that the student who has learned well what has been said about traditional logic may still find it difficult to orient himself to what appears to be not only new symbols and procedures in modern logic but also an entirely new set of objectives. While this is not a disastrous obstacle and most students are able to overcome it, there is no need for such a difficulty to exist.

Here, the treatment of traditional logic in Part One attempts to acquaint the student with the strategies of a logical system. He is introduced first to the notion of a language constructed according to definite formation rules and then to rules of inference applicable to reasoning in that language. He is shown their relevance to the reasoning process; they are not introduced by fiat, as if laying down the rules of a peculiar game.

A secondary objective, the relevance of logical techniques to elementary computer design and programming, is first illustrated in the preliminary model that serves to introduce the idea of formal logic. There it is cited only as a possibility. Later, in Appendix 2, a "flow chart" or "block diagram" of a program for determining the logical relationship of any two statements in the language of traditional logic is presented.

Following the basic forms and rules of classical logic is a gradual expansion of their applicability to a widening range of arguments. This procedure is determined partly by the conviction that when the logic of Aristotle is presented halfheartedly as a concession to academic tradition, it is a waste of time. It must be taken seriously as an instrument for the analysis and critical evaluation of arguments in order to justify the attention it receives.

The quest for an integrated approach to diverse parts of logic is also responsible for the organization of Part Three. It involves two major innovations that are aimed at making validity tests and proof procedures easier for the ordinary student to master. They contribute to a more unified treatment of propositional logic and elementary quantification than is characteristic of most logic texts.

The first innovation, the evaluation chart, is used to test validity by truth value analysis and makes the procedure more mechanical and foolproof. By taking account of the relationship between quantified statements and multiple conjunctions or disjunctions, the use of evaluation charts becomes applicable to arguments involving quantification and truth-functional compounds. The other innovation, in the chapter on quantification, is the introduction of quantified versions of the basic rules of inference for sentential logic. This technique makes it possible for proofs involving quantified statements to draw on already familiar sets of rules.

Part Two dealing with informal fallacies would usually have no place in a text devoted solely to deductive logic. Deductive reasoning has, however, its psychological as well as its logical side. Consequently, the two chapters that comprise Part Two are included. They emphasize the linguistic and psychological sources of errors in reasoning. The approach taken has made it feasible to regroup and, in some cases, even to rename the various errors in reasoning that make up the common list of fallacies. The introduction of a classification called "fallacies of grammatical analogy" both sheds new light on certain classical fallacies and brings to bear some of the ideas underlying contemporary linguistic philosophy.

A small number of exercises sufficient to illustrate the methods developed in the text follow many of the sections within each Chapter. Appendix 1, "The Aberdeen Debate," offers an opportunity to apply the content of the text to an extended debate, held in Aberdeen, Scotland, in the seventeenth century.

For more extensive and demanding material on which the student can perfect the use of the technique he has learned, *Logic: Explanatory Exercises* by Terrell and Baker is recommended. It includes a large number of exercises keyed to this book.

The many graduate students at the University of Minnesota who have assisted me in teaching introductory logic have all contributed to the development of this book and deserve the author's gratitude. They are, however, too numerous to identify individually. Special thanks are due Robert Baker, now at the State University of Iowa and my collaborator on *Logic: Explanatory Exercises;* William S. Boardman of Lawrence University; Richard LaCroix of the University of Akron; and Candido P. Zanoni and his colleagues in the course on Functions and Problems of Logic at the General College of the University of Minnesota. They all made valuable suggestions based on an experimental version of the textbook prepared for classroom use at the University of Minnesota.

I wish to express my appreciation also to the International Business Machines, Inc., and to the late Wendy N. Gaunt of the IBM Minneapolis Education Center for the time she devoted to examining an earlier version of Appendix 2 and for the suggestions she made for improving it. I thank, too, the Haverford College Library for providing the photograph of the title page of the original pamphlet edition of the Aberdeen Debate that is reproduced in Appendix 1.

Minneapolis, Minn.   D.B.T.
January 1967

Contents

PART TWO

PART THREE

PART ONE

Chapter 1

THE NATURE
AND FUNCTION
OF LOGIC

1.1 LOGIC AND REASONING

What logic is and what it does has been the subject of much misunderstanding. This has been true not only of those who have made no special study of the subject but also of those who have studied it most closely. Most experts are agreed that logic had its first great exponent in Aristotle, although this does not mean that everything Aristotle said about logic is to be accepted as final or that the approach he took to the subject and the account he gave of it fixed its boundaries for all time. Most experts would agree that the outstanding modern work on logic is the tremendously technical *Principia Mathematica* by Bertrand Russell and Alfred North Whitehead. However, no matter how the logical system and the theories presented in that work have tended to dominate the thinking of modern logicians, there is still room for criticism and discussion. There are differences of opinion in which reasonable and knowledgeable experts are to be found on both sides; that is the way it goes with any attempt to answer basic questions, to resolve fundamental issues. We would meet the same situation if we started by asking, "What is science?" or "What is mathematics?" Fortunately, it is possible to carry out many of the important

3

functions of all of these human activities without finding any ultimately satisfactory answer to such questions; that is true of logic as well.

Nevertheless, it is useful to have at least a rough idea of what logic is and what it does (or attempts to do) before beginning a study of it. What follows is one man's opinion, cast in elementary terms and hence somewhat oversimplified, about the nature and purpose of logic—the subject matter of this book. We begin by making a statement that can claim general agreement:[1] Logic is about reasoning.

It is in the account of what reasoning is and how logic has to do with it that the possibilities of controversy arise. I shall attempt to set forth an account of my views here in as nontechnical a way as possible, keeping the controversial elements at a minimum. Still, they will be there; unfortunately, in an introductory textbook there can be no opportunity to define adequately the issues and examine the merits and demerits of the various answers to them.

We are considered to be reasoning when we give reasons. There are some philosophers who believe that we know certain facts to be true directly and without proof—they are alleged to be *intuited* by reason and to require no justifications to be made for them. Whether or not this view is correct is a matter to be settled by students of the theory of knowledge. We mention it here only to be rejected as far as logic is concerned; even if reason (or Reason) does reveal any truths directly, this function of reason is not the one with which logic is concerned. In fact, logic is not interested in *how* we know whether a belief is true—that is the problem of the theory of knowledge—nor even *whether* a given belief is true—which is usually a matter to be dealt with by some special discipline such as physics or history. Logic is not interested in beliefs by themselves but in beliefs that are related to each other in a special way: we say that one supports or provides evidence for the other, we advance the one as a reason for the other. That is reasoning in the sense in which logic is concerned with reasoning.

Sometimes, however, we do not give reasons in support of a belief. When two people disagree, they may not be disagreeing about the facts but about practical matters. Each party to the dispute may give reasons in favor of doing what he wishes to have done or thinks ought to be done. Certainly we must recognize that there is a difference between factual and

---

[1] But even this is an exaggeration. Some logical theorists would agree only as far as *applied* logic is concerned. They would say that there is a more fundamental system of *pure* logic that concerns not human reasoning but certain abstract relationships of which human beings can take account when they reason.

practical disagreements—"disagreements in belief" and "disagreements in attitude," as they have been called. It is one thing for two people to hold contradictory opinions; it is another for them to have conflicting desires or emotional attitudes. For example, a couple may both want to see a certain movie and still disagree about where it is being shown. That is a factual disagreement, a disagreement in belief. On the other hand, they may both know where the movie is playing and yet not share the desire to see it. That would be a practical disagreement or a disagreement in attitude. It would be a mistake to suppose that reasoning, that is to say giving reasons, is the monopoly of disagreements of the first kind. Whether the disagreement involves the facts—the biological consequences of atomic fall-out, for example—or decisions—whether to support or oppose the nuclear test ban, say—it is appropriate to give reasons. Just because there is disagreement about what to do, instead of what is true, does not mean that we are reduced to belaboring each other with clubs. Civilized men find it possible to reason with each other whether their disagreements arise in the realm of belief or in the realm of decision and attitude.

Sometimes the reasons offered in support of a belief or a decision are good reasons and sometimes they are not. It is the function of logic to make such discriminations only when the reasons are advanced in support of a belief. It is not the function of the logician as such to decide what are good reasons in support of a practical decision. To oppose atomic tests on the grounds of the biological danger of fallout is to adopt a practical attitude supported by a reason; whether this is a good and sufficient reason for the attitude, especially in view of the other conflicting reasons advanced in favor of the contrary point of view, is a matter for moralists to decide. Logic is about reasoning, but only that form of reasoning in which support is offered for a belief as to what is true or false, not reasoning in support of a decision to do or not to do something or an attitude for or against something.

1.2 LOGIC AND PSYCHOLOGY

The meaning of reasoning in the sense in which logic has to do with it will become clearer later on as we examine, analyze, and criticize examples of reasoning. Now it is important to consider the way in which logic has to do with reasoning. Psychology might also include the study of reasoning, just as it includes the study of perception and learning and motivation as different aspects of human thinking and behavior. Reasoning is something people do, and a completely comprehensive human psychology would have to be about it as well as about these other aspects of what people do. We would expect from the psychologist a description and explanation of the process of reasoning in various forms. We would expect from him a statement of the laws that govern such mental processes, laws that he has established by means of the usual methods of scientific investigation. These laws, however interesting they might be, would not be the laws of logic and they would form no part of the main body of logical theory. The reason for this is that, as scientist, the psychologist sets out to describe how we do reason and why we reason as we do. Strictly speaking, it is indifferent to him whether we reason correctly or incorrectly, whether we tend to be persuaded by good and sufficient reasons or by bad and flimsy ones. That distinction is the very essence of the way in which logic is about reasoning.

The logician does not care how we do reason, or why; he is concerned with how we must go about it if we are to reason correctly. The laws of logic are more like the laws of a community or moral laws than the laws of a science. They do not attempt to describe the facts but to prescribe rules that distinguish between what is correct and what is not. The difference between scientific and logical laws can be easily seen when we consider a case that does not conform to the law. If a scientific law is advanced and then a fact is discovered that conflicts with it, we say the law was wrong; a scientific law sets out to describe the facts as they are. When someone reasons in a way that conflicts with the principles of logic, we do not say that the principles are wrong; we conclude that he reasoned incorrectly. When it is said that logic is about reasoning, what is meant is that logic sets out to distinguish between correct and incorrect reasoning, not that it claims to describe the actual processes of human reasoning as psychological events. Logic has to do with the *critical evaluation* of reasoning, in that it attempts to discriminate between good reasoning and bad.

1.3 LOGIC AND COMMON SENSE

Everyone attempts to criticize reasoning at some time or another. Practically speaking, we are all incipient logicians whether or not we have ever studied logic. In most disagreements, unless no attempt is made to settle them by reasoning, there will be an occasion for saying, "That argument is no good at all!" or "I think it's an excellent argument!" or "Your reasoning is full of holes!" This represents the kind of approach to reasoning with which the logician, unlike the psychologist, is concerned (although I hasten to add that the vehemence my examples suggest is irrelevant to the point of these illustrations). Everyone has, to a greater or lesser degree, the ability to judge the correctness or incorrectness of a line of reasoning. That ability is part of what we mean by common sense.[2]

It is important to consider the relation between our practical common-sense abilities to criticize reasoning and the subject matter known as logic. Logic is not merely the unorganized sum total of our everyday criticisms made on the basis of common sense. Still, it is not inherently hostile to them and an enemy of common sense, as many have supposed. In a campaign speech he made on a certain occasion in 1937, Stanley Baldwin, the Prime Minister of Great Britain, proudly called attention to the British people and their history as providing us with a striking example of what could be accomplished by a people "who had never been guided by logic in anything they had done," who had accomplished all they had "without the aid of logic, but with the aid of common sense." Unfortunately for this point, which was the total and contemptible inferiority of logic to sound British common sense, he went on to say, "and so I deduce, and I hope it is a logical thing. . . ." In one paragraph, logic was viewed as the great rival and enemy of common sense and in the next as its ally. The view of this textbook is that Mr. Baldwin was correct the second time.[3]

It must be admitted that there seem to be reasons that support the view that logic and common sense are enemies. An ancient philosopher, Zeno, attempted to prove by sheer logic alone that motion was impossible and hence that what appears to our eyes to be motion is nothing but an illusion. Since then there have been other similar attempts to demonstrate, by sheer logic alone, philosophical theories that clash sharply with common sense. This interpretation rests on a mistake. It is impossible to prove anything by sheer logic alone except the correctness or incorrectness of arguments. That is the only sort of information that logic sets out to provide. Zeno attempted to demonstrate the unreality of motion by appeal to a certain argument, by reasoning, to be sure; but reasoning is not logic itself but the subject matter of logic, as we have seen.

How, then, are common-sense beliefs to be defended against the paradoxes of Zeno or anyone else? We may, as defenders of common sense, just dig in our heels and obstinately refuse to accept the conclusion of his reasoning, insisting that things *do* move no matter what any argument seems to prove. Alternatively, we may take a look at the argument and

---

[2] Another part of it is a set of beliefs that almost everyone thinks are true.

[3] These paragraphs are quoted at greater length in L. Susan Stebbing's *Thinking to Some Purpose.*

apply to it our common-sense ability to tell a correct argument from an incorrect one (as distinct from our conviction that its conclusion is false). The trouble with this procedure is that, although more reasonable than the first, it is not likely to get very far; after all, Zeno has advanced his argument and it is our judgment against his. There is one further attempt that could be made to resolve the issue. That would require the establishment of a commonly accepted set of systematic rules for the criticism of reasoning and then the application of them to the argument in question. If we can show by the application of general systematic rules of reasoning accepted by Zeno himself that there is a logical flaw in his argument, the question has been settled. But to do that is to resort to logic, for that is the real difference between our common-sense appraisals of reasoning and the methods of logic.

Where common sense is concerned with each particular argument as it comes up and makes no attempt to state the principles of its criticism, logic attempts to provide a systematic framework of principles by which we can carry out our criticism of any particular case that might arise. Logic is not so much an enemy of our common-sense judgment about correct and incorrect reasoning as it is an aid to it that reinforces and extends its power by providing explicit system and rule where there were none before. To our previous point to the effect that logic is about reasoning in the sense of criticizing it, we can now add the further specification that it is systematic in its procedures rather than piecemeal and haphazard. For elementary purposes, we can say that *what logic does is to establish a systematic framework of general rules for the analysis and criticism of reasoning*. Much more could be said about what is meant by reasoning and the words "systematic" and "critical." These are the key ideas to grasp in understanding what logic is and what it does. Nevertheless, what has been said so far will suffice for our present purposes. It is more important now to introduce and explain some of the technical terms that we shall find it convenient to use in talking about logic and carrying out its functions.

1.4 TECHNICAL TERMS

We shall not introduce all of the special vocabulary of logic in this section, just those words that have a relatively general application. All of the terms to be considered here are familiar words in common use; in the context of logical theory, they do not always have the same meaning they have in everyday speech. There are various reasons for this: sometimes there is no exact meaning for the word as it is ordinarily used, and the logician must impose a precision on it that it does not possess naturally. (The logician's special use of the term is no less natural or even original than the more widespread use. In fact, the logician's precise use of a certain word may be the original one; having been introduced for some special purpose in logical theory, the word has passed into common speech and lost a certain degree of precision in the process.) Sometimes the everyday use of a word undergoes a change in meaning; in logic, it is desirable to keep the meaning of important theoretical terms as stable and constant as possible. Whatever the reason may be for the difference between the logical use and the ordinary use of a word, it is important to recognize that such differences do exist and to understand the special technical meanings attached to them in logic.[4]

"Inference" is a term that may be going through a change of meaning. In what is regarded as its standard and correct usage, it refers to the process of going from one belief or set of beliefs (known or assumed to be true) to another belief supported by them. It is used in this sense in logic and refers to the process of reasoning itself, at least the kind of reasoning that was singled out as the subject matter of logic in Section 1.3. The statement or statements that constitute the starting point of an inference—statements expressing the belief or beliefs from which the further belief is derived and by which it is supported—are called the "premises." The statement expressing the belief derived from the premises is called the "conclusion." The premises are said to "imply" the conclusion. More and more frequently, the word "infer" is coming to be used in the same sense as "imply," so that premises are said to infer their conclusion. We shall preserve the distinction between these two words by using inference always to stand for the process of reasoning—people infer conclusions from premises—and implication to stand for the relationship between the premises and the conclusion they support—premises imply conclusions.

The premises and the conclusion of a process of reasoning make up an "argument." (It is to be noted that this word, as used for logical purposes, does not mean "dispute" as it most commonly does in everyday language.) Arguments, then, are the expressions of processes of reasoning. An argu-

---

[4] The definitions in the following paragraphs still leave much to be desired in this respect themselves. There are subtleties of philosophical opinion regarding the distinction between induction and deduction, to cite just one example, that have been slighted. A strong case has been made for saying that what distinguishes natural science is not a special kind of reasoning—inductive reasoning—but a special methodological application of deductive reasoning. The definitions are not offered as the last word of contemporary logical theory but only as first steps toward understanding some of the basic terms logicians use and some of the issues that can arise in connection with them.

ment, if it is fully explicit, must include at least one statement that serves as a premise and at least one statement that is intended to be a conclusion based on the premise(s). A set of statements in which none is supposed to be supported in any way by any of the others cannot constitute an argument.

We turn now to terms for the classification of processes of reasoning and the arguments that express them. The most basic distinction to be drawn is between "inductive" reasoning (or arguments) and "deductive" reasoning (or arguments), or "induction" and "deduction." There have been two points of view that have been advanced concerning the proper distinction between these two expressions. The traditional viewpoint has been that deductive reasoning is reasoning from the general to the particular and inductive reasoning is from the particular to the general. The more modern interpretation of the distinction is that in deductive reasoning, the conclusion is supposed to be *necessarily implied* by the premises; in inductive reasoning, the evidence is not supposed to support the conclusion with logical necessity but only to support it with a definite positive degree of probability.

The prevalent conviction of logical theorists and philosophers of science today is that the *way* in which the evidence supports the conclusion is of greater significance than the nature of the conclusion itself. The flaw in the traditional interpretation is that it overemphasizes the conclusion and the premises taken by themselves and neglects the relationship between them. We shall adopt here the modern distinction. We define deductive arguments as arguments advanced to prove their conclusions with logical necessity. Inductive arguments are such as are intended to support their conclusions with probability only. Another way to understand the distinction is that (assuming each argument accomplishes what it is supposed to accomplish) it is logically impossible for the premises of a deductive argument to be true and its conclusion false, while it is possible (but unlikely) that the premises of an inductive argument should be true while its conclusion is false.

So far nothing has been said about the critical evaluation of arguments, although it was explained previously that that is logic's function. We now turn, therefore, to the general expressions used in logical criticism. Deductive arguments, as such, are supposed to imply their conclusions with necessity. Of course, not every argument that is advanced as a deductive argument does so. That is, deductive reasoning, like any reasoning whatsoever, can be mistaken. When a deductive argument *does* support its conclusion with logical necessity, it is said to be "valid"; if not, it is "invalid." To say that an argument is deductively valid is to say that its conclusion cannot be false when its premises are true. It should not be understood as saying any more than this; it does not say that the premises or the conclusion *are* in fact true. An argument can be valid even though its premises and its conclusion are all false or the premises false (or one or more premises false) and the conclusion true. As long as we must say that if the premises were true, the conclusion would have to be true as well, validity is not affected by the actual truth or falsity of the argument's component parts.

From what has just been said about validity, it is clear that the mere validity of an argument does not insure the truth of its conclusion; valid arguments as such do not *prove* their conclusions. In order to prove a conclusion we must proceed from factual, that is, true premises. The word "sound" is usually applied to arguments that prove their conclusions. In order to be sound, an argument must both be valid and have true premises; an argument need not be sound in order to be valid. The word "correct" is sometimes used with the meaning here attached to "valid" and sometimes with the stronger meaning of "sound." Most often, it means "valid," as when we say, "His reasoning was correct, but his premises were mistaken."

To bring this long discussion of terminology to an end, we should consider the fact that neither validity nor soundness has anything to do—at least as far as definitions are concerned—with persuasive effect. What kinds of arguments are convincing is a matter of psychology that will vary from one person to another. That an argument is valid, or even sound, depends entirely on logic and the facts. Ordinarily, a valid argument, if lucidly stated, has some power to persuade, unless its premises are entirely ridiculous. If this were not so, it would not affect the validity of the argument in the least. As it happens, men are sometimes convinced by sound arguments, sometimes by unsound ones. What is responsible for the persuasive power of an argument is more a matter for the psychologist than for the logician.

1.5   A PRELIMINARY MODEL

The systematic rules of logic are formal rules. Instead of attempting to give an explanation or definition of logical formalism in Section 1.4 on terminology, we will illustrate what is meant by this aspect of logic. The example we will consider in this section involves the solution of a simple puzzle or problem in reasoning. The technique we use will serve as an elementary model of the more general and relatively more complicated techniques with which we will be concerned throughout most of the remainder of this book.

What is important is not so much the problem itself but the kind of problem it is. Nevertheless, we will, for the sake of realism and dramatic interest, consider a specific, although fictitious, case.

One Mrs. Sponsable has a problem: She and her husband (who runs a concert and lecture agency) are giving a party for six new clients, all of them promising figures in the world of entertainment and the arts. One is a painter, one a singer, one a pianist, one a poet, one a dancer, and one an actor. Mrs. Sponsable (who dabbles in water color herself) has spent all afternoon making appropriate place cards for the dinner table. Each one is especially suited for one of the guests, and she has left the names for the last. Unfortunately, the guest list she had her husband prepare cannot be found. She cannot reach his office, and the time for the party draws ever nearer. She can, however, remember the names: Mr. Allardyce, Miss Bennington, Mrs. Chancellor, Mr. Drew, Miss Ellenee, and Mr. O'Furioso. She found them easy to remember because of the alphabetical order (allowing a certain latitude in the case of Mr. O'Furioso). Who was the painter, who the poet, who the singer and so on eluded her recollection entirely. The best she could do was to recall a few bits of information and gossip. While Mrs. Chancellor was accompanying her husband on a lecture tour, they had discovered the singer, who had been singing "Mimi" in a University Opera Workshop production of *La Bohême*. The poet, Mrs. Sponsable recalled, was the painter's son-in-law. The pianist had been disappointed in love as a young man and was now a confirmed bachelor. Just recently, Miss Bennington had precipitated a major crisis by telling Mr. Allardyce's mother that his fiancée, the dancer, had worked for years as an exotic dancer in night clubs on the West Coast. Mr. Drew's left arm was paralyzed.

Mrs. Sponsable suspected that by putting these facts together she would be able to identify each of the six properly. In order to keep things straight, she set up the following chart:

	Painter	Actor	Pianist	Singer	Dancer	Poet
Mr. A.	___	___	___	___	___	___
Miss B.	___	___	___	___	___	___
Mrs. C.	___	___	___	___	___	___
Mr. D.	___	___	___	___	___	___
Miss E.	___	___	___	___	___	___
Mr. F.	___	___	___	___	___	___

Where she found it to be impossible for a certain individual to be the poet, or the painter, and so on, she put a *0* on the proper line; when she had succeeded in identifying one of them, she put a + on the appropriate line. She began by eliminating the women as possible candidates for identification as the actor. She continued by indicating that Mrs. Chancellor was not the singer, and Mr. Allardyce was not the pianist, and so on. When all but one had been eliminated in a given row, she put a + on the remaining line and *0*'s on all the other lines in the perpendicular row. Before long, each of the six members of the party had been successfully identified, and she proceeded with the task of making out the place cards.

It will be worthwhile, for a better understanding of the mechanics of logic, for us to reflect on the procedure followed in solving this problem. The most striking point to consider about the method Mrs. Sponsable used is her invention of the chart, which facilitated the solution not only by helping to keep the facts straight but also by making it possible to draw inferences in a particularly simple and mechanical way from the facts recorded on the chart. The final stages of the solution called for nothing more than the ability to apply two rules governing the distribution of *0*'s and +'s on the chart, without even understanding what they meant. One rule called for at least one + in each row or column; the other called for no more than one. The application of these rules could have been carried out by someone knowing nothing of Mrs. Sponsable's problem or of the significance of the chart and the signs she had devised in order to make its solution easier. Their application is a purely formal procedure. It is, in fact, the sort of thing that could easily be done by a machine.[5]

The invention of the chart, with the symbols to be used on it, represents the creation of an artificial language. The language has extremely limited resources. By using it, we can organize the data of the problem systematically and draw inferences by the application of formal principles. There are obvious advantages in being able to do so. However, the entire solution of the problem presented as a model could not be carried out on the chart by purely formal means because of the limitations of its language. For that reason, the solution can actually be broken down into three stages. On the chart, the only information that can be recorded is information to the effect that an individual is or is not a particular person. Before the chart

[5] An electrical device, for instance. Green and red lights could be used in the place of Mrs. Sponsable's +'s and *0*'s. Each square would contain one of each. Using fairly simple methods, the device could be wired so that as soon as five red lights are lit in any row or column, a green light would be lit up in the square remaining; and as soon as a green light is lit in any square, the red lights would light up in every other square in the same row or column.

could be used at all, therefore, it was necessary to arrive at information having that form. This was accomplished by "informal" or "unformalized" reasoning, that is, by reasoning that superficially at least did not appear to involve the application of any clear-cut and systematic formal rules. We could call this first step the stage of "common-sense" reasoning unaided by the explicit invocation of any general rules or principles of inference. The second stage is essentially a matter of translation. The information expressed in the English language (*Miss Bennington is not the actor, Mr. Allardyce is not the pianist,* and so on) is translated into the language of the chart (a *0* on the line where the row opposite Miss Bennington's name intersects with the column under *Actor;* a *0* on the line where the row opposite Mr. Allardyce intersects the column under *Pianist*). Once the distribution of marks on the chart makes it possible to do so, we can apply the two formal principles within the framework of the chart. This is the third stage of the solution; when it has been completed, the problem has been solved for anyone who understands the meaning of the marks on the chart. For someone who does not understand them, it will be necessary to translate them back into ordinary language.

Briefly summed up, the three stages of the solution are *informal reasoning, translation* (into a more formal and systematic language), and *formal reasoning.* Whether the reasoning is regarded as formal or not depends on whether it represents the explicit application of rules concerning the form or pattern of the symbols, rules that could be understood and applied without understanding the meaning of the symbols themselves. (Of course, the person who invents the language with its symbols must understand what they are intended to mean; the inventor, Mrs. Sponsable in our case, could easily have instructed someone else to apply the rules without explaining what she intended the symbols to mean.)

The consideration of these three stages immediately suggests to us the possibility of discovering formal principles that would have been applicable even to the inferences of the first stage—the informal stage. Why should not all reasoning, at least all deductive reasoning, be capable of being brought within the scope of a set of formal rules operating within the framework of a systematic language? The preliminary stage of informal reasoning could then be dispensed with and all inferences, once the initial premises have been expressed in the appropriate language, carried out in terms of the application of formal principles. This, with certain qualifications perhaps, we could express as the ideal of formal logic. To the extent that such an idea can be fulfilled, the designing of thinking machines and calculating machines becomes a possibility. Whether such devices are practically possible or not depends, of course, on technological considerations as well as on the progress of logical and mathematical theory. The attempt to construct logical machines goes back more than 200 years; only recently have technological developments, particularly in electronics, made feasible the actual construction of thinking machines of sufficient "intellectual" power to be useful (and led philosophers to pose the question: "Can they really think?").

The example of Mrs. Sponsable's place cards is obviously subject to narrow limitations. There is no intention of suggesting that it can serve as a general pattern into which, without further modifications, we can fit all deductive reasoning. We can use what has been discovered through the examination of this relatively simple model to make progress toward the creation of a more generally useful formal system than that represented by Mrs. Sponsable's chart. We shall consider two important historical attempts at a general system of formal logic, the "traditional" or Aristotelian system and the "modern" symbolic system. Nevertheless, there will be no pretense of following faithfully the historical presentation of these two systems. Instead, they will be developed in the light of the ideas that have emerged from the discussion in this chapter and in such a way as to bring out as much as possible the underlying similarities; such an approach depends on the possibility of truly comprehending, even at an elementary level, the idea of a logical system as such.

1.5 EXERCISES: FIVE LOGICAL PUZZLES

The problems that follow represent variations on old themes, some almost as old as the study of logic itself. If you have had no occasion to exercise your powers of reasoning recently, they provide an opportunity to do so. They are not easy problems, and any that you cannot solve right away should be attempted later on. Useful hints are scattered through the book; perhaps by the time you have finished it, you will have solved them all. (A large collection of similar puzzles has been assembled by C. R. Wylie, Jr., in *101 Puzzles in Thought and Logic,* Dover Publications, New York, 1957.)

A. THE THREE LITTLE PIGS. An Iowa farmer had a lot of smart hogs who could understand English and even answer questions that required either a Yes (Oink) or No (Oink Oink) answer. This is fairly bright as Iowa hogs go, but they had temperamental limitations. Some of them were stubborn and persistent liars and invariably answered falsely. The others were equally persistent in telling the truth. They all sulked and refused to answer if ever they were asked the same question twice. The farmer decided that while having a group of talking hogs was interesting enough all by itself, there really was not much use to it if you could not trust what they had to say. So he decided to pick out all the liars and sell them to a neighbor of his who had skinned him in a horse trade. He interrogated the entire herd, beginning with a large sow, Viola.

FARMER: Viola, do you lie to me?

VIOLA (voice muffled in feed-trough): Oink oink!

FARMER (to Herman, standing nearby): Herman, I could not exactly make out what Viola said. Did she say "No"?

HERMAN: Oink!

FARMER: Well, what about it? *Does* she lie?

HERMAN: Oink oink!

FARMER: Do you?

HERMAN: Oink oink!

FARMER (to next hog): Jewel, Viola and Herman tell me they don't tell lies. Is that so?

JEWEL: Oink oink!

FARMER: Do they, then?

JEWEL: Oink!

FARMER: And do you?

JEWEL: Oink oink!

Of the three hogs interviewed so far, which, if any, did the farmer sell to his neighbor?

B. AN OLD CHESS NUT. Twenty-four contestants entered a "knock-out" chess tournament—one in which losers are eliminated round by round until only one participant survives. It was foreseen that after the first three rounds had been completed, only three players would remain; one of them would therefore have to be given a bye for the semifinal round. An ingenious guessing game was proposed to determine who would have the advantage of the bye. The three semifinalists were to be seated in a triangle, with tables and boards behind them arranged in such a way that each could see the others' boards but not his own. Each was to attempt to guess the color of the pieces on his side of the board behind him, knowing only that they would not all have the white pieces but that otherwise the arrangement of colors would be determined by chance. A wrong guess would be penalized by immediate elimination and the remaining pair would advance to the final round. A correct guess would be rewarded with a bye, the winner of the game between the other two to be his opponent in the final round.

When it was pointed out that one of the players, a well-known and well-liked veteran of the tournament circuit named Keningson Dish, was blind, everyone supposed that the arrangement would have to be abandoned. But Mr. Dish himself refused to make any protest and airily dismissed his friends' observations that the procedure described, if he should advance as far as the semifinals, would unjustly favor his opponents. "I've been blind all my life," he said, "and

I've been playing in tournaments for more than fifty years without asking any favors. I don't intend to start now."

In fact, the blind Mr. Dish did survive the first three rounds and when he and the other two semifinalists had been seated according to the intended arrangement, after a minute or so it was he who broke the silence by calmly and correctly identifying the color of his pieces. What was their color and how did he know it? Was the method devised for determining the player who had a bye really to his disadvantage or not? Explain your answers.

C. THE BLIND BEGGAR AND THE PROUD PRINCESS (with a supporting cast of ladies and tigers). Once upon a time there was a blind beggar who decided he would marry the princess of the neighboring country. She was a young woman renowned for her spirit, beauty, fortune, and her haughty pride. She would speak to no one who was not of royal blood, not even her own ladies-in-waiting. The prospect of having for her husband one who had only a short time ago been a beggar, and blind as well, would be not at all pleasing. However, her father the king had decreed that he would give his daughter's hand to the cleverest man to present himself to claim it. The blind beggar, whose name was Hubris N. Carnet, was sure he was just the man. Along with three rivals, he presented himself at court as a claimant for the princess' hand.

There were only four candidates because the king had taken some pains to discourage any except those who were exceptionally brave or foolhardy or, as in the case of Hubris, exceptionally self-confident. Each suitor was assigned to one of four doors. Behind one door were three tigers, behind another two tigers and a lady, behind a third a tiger and two ladies and behind the remaining one, three ladies. The doors were labeled with signs that would have been correct had they been on the right doors, but not one of them was. One of the ladies was the princess, and the king promised that she would marry the first suitor who could identify her by asking just two questions that could be answered *yes* or *no*. The questions had to be directed to one of the ladies, but only from the princess herself could a truthful answer be expected. After hearing the answers to his questions, the suitor had to identify the princess. If he made an error, he would be fed to the tigers for their supper.

The blind man's friends attempted to dissuade him from what seemed to them his folly, but he insisted he would go on with it and wanted no special assistance. He only asked that each suitor be kept informed of the others' progress.

After the first hour, one suitor reported that he had heard two tigers growling behind his door and had reached a conclusion as to whether the other one was a lady or a tiger but did not yet choose to ask either of his questions. A short time later, another suitor reported that he had heard a lady scolding a tiger; he too knew whether the third individual was female or feline but did not choose to ask any questions yet. The third suitor said he had heard two ladies conversing but did not know whether there was a tiger or another lady with them, so he would wait also. As soon as he had heard the third report, the blind man addressed the king, "O, King, I cannot see nor have I heard any sounds, yet I am ready to ask my questions. There are two ladies behind the door before which I stand. If you will call them forth, I ask you to direct my questions to which of them first comes through the door." The king agreed, and the beggar asked the first of his two questions. At first the lady refused to answer at all, protesting that the question was unfair. The beggar insisted there had been no restrictions on what questions he might ask, but agreed to a compromise—if his first question was answered, he would ask no more like it. On this understanding, the test proceeded. When the beggar had heard the answers to both of his questions, he declared, "O, King, behind the door of the third suitor were three ladies, one of whom did not speak while her companions did. She is the princess and I claim her hand in marriage." And so she was, and so they were married and lived happily ever after.

How did Hubris know there were just two ladies behind his door? What questions did he ask and what answers did he receive? If he had received a different answer to his first question, would his second have been different? If he had received a different answer to his second question, whom would he have identified as the princess?

D. CHESS AND TAXES. Aleking, Bottlewink, Copperblank, Doll, and Euwin, all grand master chess champions, were invited to play in a special invitational tournament offering an uncommonly generous prize fund. First prize would be $5000, second $4000 and so on down to $1000 for fifth place. Furthermore, there would be a $1000 bonus for each game won in Round 1, $1200 for each game won in Round 2, and $400 for each draw. The tournament was to be a double round robin; that is, each player was to play every other player twice, once with the white and once with the black pieces. A win scored 1 point, a draw, ½ point and a loss, zero. The five all accepted their invitations, of course; not being accustomed to paying income taxes, none of them reported his winnings. Income Tax Investigator Montgomery Shock was assigned to the case; on the basis of the following bits of information, he was able to determine the amount of each player's income from the tournament:

1. No one lost all of his games or won all of his games in either round.
2. Each player had at least one win, at least one draw, and at least one loss.
3. There was a three-way tie for first place after Round 1, but there were no tie scores in Round 2 and no ties in the final standings.
4. The player who finished in the middle won at least one game from each of his opponents.
5. Aleking and Euwin were the only players to improve their scores from one round to the next.
6. Aleking was the only player to improve his rank.

7. Bottlewink had the same score in each round.
8. Doll's score in Round 2 was the same as Euwin's score in Round 1.
9. The players who finished in first and last place respectively drew both of their games with their nearest rivals.

E. WHO'S WHO IN FEUDAL HISTORY. Political historians of feudal Marplenum are confronted with sadly incomplete source material and a bewildering confusion of proper names and titles. There are some fragments of sources that refer to important figures by name only, others use title only, and some shift back and forth from one kind of designation to the other. It is impossible to form a clear picture of political events and alignments without sorting out the characters, and this is by no means easy. If there were two complete and parallel chronicles, with different systems of nomenclature, the identifications could be accomplished by direct comparison, but no such pair of documents is available. It *is* possible to work out a plausible scheme by deductive reasoning based on a few pieces of information in the chronicles together with a working assumption. A comparison of all the sources strongly suggests that there were just eight important historical figures involved and that the names and titles listed below belong to them. This is the working assumption. It is hoped that the various fragmentary sources can be correlated into one coherent chronicle by establishing which names correspond to which titles. The relevant information follows the two lists.

Duke and Duchess of Uskadara	Henry Maladroit
Marchioness of Halibut	Godfrey the Rude
Princess of Longines-Wittnauer	Clarence of Malmsey
Count of Beargarden	Philipp Longbotham
Earl of Bloomstown	Ulalume Hibbert
Electress of Ultramont	Joan Keelpot
The Young Pretender	Marguerite des Mains Blanches
	Isobel the Fair

1. One day Godfrey the Rude sore offended the Count of Beargarden, his host, by laying rough hands on Isobel, the Count's niece and a maid of but fourteen summers. He was slain by the Count's own hand. (Cedric MS. ca. 1347)
2. Ulalume bore twice as many children as her older sister, Marguerite. (*Ibid.*)
3. In 1343, Clarence of Malmsey, with a large army including many armed knights, invaded the land of Uskadara and demanded from the Duke tribute and fealty. (*Ibid.*)
4. The legitimate succession ended with Henry Maladroit, who had no brothers or sister, nor any children born in wedlock. He had arranged a marriage, however, between his natural son and Joan Keelpot. With her

family's support, the son laid claim to his father's title when it became vacant. When the "Young Pretender," for so he had been known for thirty years, died without ever having produced an heir, the claim was finally abandoned. (Allbran Chronicle, ca. 1360)

5. The Duke and Duchess of Uskadara were blessed, in their ten years of marriage, with seven healthy children, of whom one son and three daughters survived the Peasants' Revolt and the civil wars. (Allbran Chronicle)

6. The Electress of Ultramont counted among her children a king, three dukes, an earl, and a margrave. Her granddaughter was Princess of Longines-Wittnauer. (Taimpleace Fragment)

7. Philipp the Dullard, Phillip the Boor,
   Philipp Longbotham the Ould Batchelour. (Wall graffito, date uncertain but later than 1350.)

Chapter 2

THE FORMAL LANGUAGES
OF TRADITIONAL LOGIC

2.1 THE STRUCTURE OF STATEMENTS

In Chapter 1, we have considered a simple model of the solution of a problem by the application, for one stage of the reasoning process, of explicitly formulated principles. We applied the principles within the context of a chart and certain special symbols. One of the most important points to understand about the preliminary model is that the chart and symbols really constitute a language. It makes sense to speak of learning the meaning of the symbols on the chart and learning how to translate from the English language into "chartese" and vice versa. One of the chart's marked advantages was that once it had been constructed, it became possible to express a fact requiring a number of words in the English language by writing just one mark on an appropriate line on the chart: *Mrs. Chancellor is not the singer* (six marks in English) by one *0*. Of course, the *0* must be placed accurately, whereas the English sentence can be written anywhere without losing or altering its meaning. What this fact indicates is that part of what is expressed by special marks in the English language is expressed by position on the chart. The sheer structural features of the chart are of considerably more significance than are the corresponding features of the English language, that is, the order and relationship in which statements are made. On the chart as it is constructed, the *0* translatable as *Mrs. Chancellor is not the singer* must appear immediately below the *0* translatable as *Miss Bennington is not the singer;* these statements can be written side by side or one above the other, and so on, in English.

Nevertheless, the English statements are not entirely lacking in structure. The difference is rather that in the chart the basic structure is common to all of the marks by which statements are expressed; each one shares that structure with the others. In English, the basic structure recurs in each individual statement. This will become clearer if we examine more carefully what contributes to the meaningfulness of the marks made on the chart and then compare the results with what we discover on examining their written counterparts.

There are three distinct features that can be easily discerned in chartese. We began with a basic structure, the chart of lines. To these were added names and descriptions (Mr. Allardyce, *Pianist,* and so on). The names and descriptions fixed the subject matter identified by each respective line. Finally, marks (+'s and *0*'s), were placed on the lines. What they did was to indicate a relationship (identity or nonidentity) between the individuals named at the left of the rows and described at the head of the columns. For each of the seventy-two statements that can be made on the chart (thirty-six true ones and thirty-six false, two for each of the thirty-six lines in the chart), there is a distinctive position in the latticework, a distinctive subjective matter indicated by the names and descriptions, and a distinctive relationship indicated by one or the other of two marks. These three features combine to make a statement, true or false, about a definite subject matter.

In the English counterparts of the marks on the chart, there is no common structural background comparable to the latticework of the chart; there is a structure that is common to each of the sentences in the sense of being repeated in each one. We could represent the structure in this way:

$$[\qquad] \text{———} [\qquad].$$

In this structure, the spaces in brackets are to be filled in with the names and descriptions respectively. This corresponds to assigning names and descriptions to the rows and columns on the chart, that is, it determines the subject matter of the statement. The difference is that on the chart the subject matter of a whole class of statements is indicated all at once by assigning a certain name to the left row, for example, and so determining that the individual with that name is part of the subject matter of every statement made in that row. In English, the name must be separately included in each of the statements referring to that individual. When the subject matter has been identified by filling in the brackets, the relation-ship[1] that is indicated on the chart by using $+$ or 0 is indicated in English by using the expressions "is" or "is not." In both languages, then, we can say that there is (1) a discernible basic structure, (2) a way of identifying the subject matter of a given statement within the structure, and (3) a way of indicating the fact asserted to be true of that subject matter by the state-ment. How these functions are carried out will differ slightly from language to language. Whether they are all equally essential is another theoretical question that we need not attempt to settle; it is sufficient that we should be able to discern them in the examples of statements we have just been considering.

We are now in a position to see that there are two approaches we might take in devising a systematic language within which reasoning is to be governed by explicit principles. One way is exemplified by the chart that has provided our model. The chart was almost entirely artificial and ar-bitrary. We have now found that sentences in the English language also have a discernible structure, in some respects parallel to the structure of chartese. This makes it possible to create a serviceable language for logical purposes just by carefully selecting appropriate tools from within the re-sources of ordinary language. In this way, we can avoid giving up the support afforded by the familiar common-sense meaning of the statements (but this is an advantage that exacts a certain price, as we shall see).

In this chapter, we shall consider three different languages in which we can express the kinds of statements emphasized in traditional logic. The first language follows the methods just now suggested. Because it is derived from English, we shall call it "logical English." [2] Its sentences are all in English. They are selected to express the common meanings of many differents kinds of sentences in ordinary English. However, logical English lacks the variety of the ordinary language. It makes no concessions to style or grace of expression. It omits everything in English that is of merely literary or psychological importance but that makes no logical difference.

The other two languages we shall consider are artificially designed. One uses spatial patterns for its basic statement structures and is called the language of "Venn diagrams." The other is modeled on simple mathematical equations; we shall call it "algebraic notation." This chapter will present the important logical characteristics of statements in all three languages

---

[1] There are important objections to speaking of a "relationship" here, but the theo-retical issues involved need not be considered in an elementary textbook.

[2] It is not to be contrasted with *illogical* English but with *ordinary* English. It is just as possible to be illogical in logical English as it is in ordinary English, although perhaps not quite as easily.

as a basis for understanding the principles of reasoning that apply within
them.

2.2 THE STRUCTURE OF LOGICAL ENGLISH

We can treat logical English as a modification of the language used in
the preliminary model, the problem of Mrs. Sponsable's dinner party. To
each mark on the chart there corresponded a statement in English. We
have already observed that these statements in English have a characteristic
structure:

$$[\quad] \quad \text{————} \quad [\quad].$$

Statements are made within this structure by designating subject matter
inside the brackets and then writing "is" or "is not" in the underlined space:

> [Miss Bennington] is [the dancer].
> [Mrs. Chancellor] is not [the singer].

If we ignore the subject matter, we can say that there are just two kinds
of statements represented, "affirmative" and "negative." It is this difference
that is important to the purely logical aspects of the statements, for the rules
of logic are intended to be quite general and in their application are not to
be restricted to any given subject matter. The rules of reasoning that we
invoked in solving the problem on the chart applied to the lines without
any reference to subject matter at all (as indicated by the fact that they
applied indiscriminately to any row or column). The same should hold
true of rules of inference and principles of logical criticism intended to
have still wider scope.

The principal difference between the kind of statement considered in
the previous chapter and those that constitute the basic language of traditional logic is that the new system introduces a quantitative aspect absent
in the first. The statements involved in solving Mrs. Sponsable's problem
all concerned individuals, Mr. Allardyce, Miss Bennington, and so on. The
statements of logical English concern classes, for example, alligators,
basketballs, cabbages, diplomats, and so on. Classes are identified by expressions that (in principle, at least) could apply to more than just one
individual. In actual fact, they may apply to only one or even none, but
that is irrelevant to the logical status of the class. For example, the class
"pianists" includes a large number of individuals. The expression "pianist
invited to the party" might apply to just one individual in fact; in principle,

it might apply to more than one. Therefore, we must regard this expression as a general or class term and not as the name of one specific individual.

The quantitative aspect introduced by expressing the subject matter of a statement in terms of classes rather than individuals is this: sometimes, something is said to hold for all the members of a class, and sometimes it is said to hold for some (possibly no more than one). Contrast *All piano-playing bachelors are fortune hunters* with *Some piano-playing bachelors are fortune hunters*. We call the first a "universal statement" and the second a "particular statement." The class that is directly "quantified" in this way is the one mentioned first and is referred to as the "subject class." A quantified statement says that either all or some of its members have a certain relationship to (are included within or excluded from) another class. The latter is referred to as the "predicate class." The mark of a statement's quantity is written first, immediately preceding the subject class. In English, this quantitative difference is most frequently expressed by using the words "all" and "some." The affirmative or negative relationship is indicated by the expressions "are" and "are not." The one pair, by which we express the quantitative aspect (or "quantity") of the statement, comprises the "quantifiers" of the language. The expressions "are" and "are not" that express the affirmative or negative character of the relationship asserted (or "quality" of the statement) are called "copulas." (*Copula* is Latin for tie or connection.)

Each sentence in logical English must include two expressions intended to indicate the two classes that constitute its subject matter—its "terms," subject (*S*) and predicate (*P*)—a quantifier (*Q*) indicating its quantity, universal or particular; a copula (*C*), indicating whether the relationship asserted is affirmative or negative. The basic structure is:

$$Q \qquad [S] \qquad C \qquad [P].$$

The spaces in brackets marked *S* and *P* are to be filled in with terms indicating subject matter; the space marked *Q* is to be filled in by a quantifier and the space marked *C* by a copula:

$$(Q) \qquad\qquad (S) \qquad\qquad (C) \qquad\qquad (P)$$
Some [piano-playing bachelors] are not [fortune hunters].

2.3 TYPES OF STATEMENT IN LOGICAL ENGLISH

In the final stages of the solution of the problem that served as a model for formal treatment, two kinds of statement were involved, expressed by + and *0* on the chart or by sentences in English formed by using "is" or "is not." It is easy to see that by introducing quantifiers so as to distinguish between universal and particular class relationships the number of possible kinds of statement that can be formed within the framework of the language is increased to four. Each of the quantifiers "all" and "some" can be combined with each of the copulas "are" and "are not." The resulting possibilities (leaving the subject matter still undetermined) are:

All [   ] are [   ].
All [   ] are not [   ].   (See the following discussion.)
Some [   ] are [   ].
Some [   ] are not [   ].

This procedure seems to be simple and straightforward enough, but the fact that the quantifiers and copulas used are borrowed from the English language immediately creates difficulties. In its use of these expressions, the English language is by no means simple and straightforward; from the point of view of logic this use is even inconsistent. The difficulties arise in connection with the interpretation of "some" and the interpretation of "all" combined with "are not."

In the English language, the word "some" does not always have the same force; its exact meaning will shift from one sense to another, depending on subject matter, accent, and other considerations as well. Sometimes, "some" implicitly carries the force of *some but not all* or *only some*. Sometimes its force is weaker than that and the possibility that the corresponding universal statement might also be true is left open. What are the precise conditions on which depend the correct interpretation of any given use of "some" in ordinary language is a difficult problem for linguistic analysis. We shall not attempt to settle it in this book; it is obvious that if we wish to use this expression, borrowed from the English language, within a logical system, we must fix its meaning more exactly. In logical English, the particular quantifier "some" is not intended to carry the extra force of *but not all*. It has the same meaning as when you are told, for example, that you will pass some of your courses. If you pass all of them, that statement does not turn out to have been mistaken. Rather, it is confirmed more strongly than it need have been. It would have been proved true had you passed only one course. "Some" in this case means *at least one* (perhaps more, perhaps even all); that is the meaning it is intended to have within the logical system we are in the initial stages of developing.

A greater difficulty arises in connection with asserting a universal and negative relationship of one class to another. If the universal quantity is to be expressed by the word "all" and the negative quality by the words "are not," as they are in English, we would expect that a statement combining these two expressions as quantifier and copula respectively would assert a universal negative relationship between the classes that form the subject matter of the statement. But English, contrary to all the demands of systematic and orderly logical structure, attaches quite another interpretation to such statements. *All* [   ] *are not* [   ] (*All snakes are not poisonous*) has the same meaning as *Not all* [   ] *are* [   ] (*Not all snakes are poisonous*). The relationship expressed is particular rather than universal; it is equivalent to saying *Some snakes are not poisonous*. So in English the combination of the ordinarily universal quantifier with the negative copula has, paradoxically, the same meaning as the combination of the particular quantifier with the negative copula. In dealing with the problem that arose concerning the interpretation of "some," we could simply select one of the meanings attached to that word in ordinary English. But in this case the meaning required by strict logical system *conflicts* with the ordinary interpretation of the statement in the English language. To insist upon following the demands of a logical system would mean to sacrifice all of the advantages achieved by using a language selected from the vocabulary we ordinarily use. Consequently, we must make a concession to the usages of ordinary English and eliminate from logical English the misleading type of statement

All [   ] are not [   ].

We borrow another word that does serve this purpose in the English language—the word "no"; universal negative statements in logical English will have the form:

No [   ] are [   ].

It is important to realize that although "no" takes the position of the quantifier, it is richer in meaning than the universal quantifier "all." "No" indicates not only the universal quantity of the relationship asserted by the statement in which it occurs but also the negative quality of that relationship, a function that otherwise belongs to the copula. It is more serviceable to a common-sense interpretation and understanding of the elementary principles of logic to introduce this slight flaw in the neatness of the system than to have to be continually reminding ourselves that certain statements mean something quite different from what they might ordinarily be taken to mean.

We can summarize the types and characteristics of statements in logical English and do so in Table 2.1. Since brackets are a clumsy device for indicating that the subject matter of the statement has not yet been specified, the capital letters "*S*" and "*P*" are used to stand for subject term and predicate term respectively.[3] Furthermore, each of the four types of statement has been assigned a letter, **A, E, I,** or **O,** by which it can be conveniently designated.[4]

TABLE 2.1

Name	Quantity	Quality	Form
A	Universal	Affirmative	All *S* are *P*.
E	Universal	Negative	No *S* are *P*.
I	Particular	Affirmative	Some *S* are *P*.
O	Particular	Negative	Some *S* are not *P*.

All statements in logical English must have one of these four patterns. Compared with the rich and varied store of possibilities afforded by the English language itself, logical English would seem to be so limited as to be almost useless for the development of a logical system applicable to arguments as they are usually expressed. For the present, we shall not attempt to assess finally the extent to which this criticism has some truth. To show that it is perhaps not as overwhelming as it might superficially appear to be, it will suffice to make the observation that much of the variety afforded by the English language is of no *logical* significance at all. For instance, in logical English, we can say only, *All scientists are precise thinkers,* whereas in ordinary English we could also say, *Every scientist is a precise thinker.* Thus, in this respect, ordinary English gives a choice of at least two different forms of statement while logical English gives only one. However, it would be absurd to suggest that because of this very difference there are facts that can be expressed in ordinary English that cannot be in logical English. The two alternatives of ordinary English have exactly the same meaning; their difference is purely a matter of style. Which of the two happened to be used in formulating an argument would certainly make no difference to the logical evaluation of the argument. At most, it might

---

[3] Later on, capital letters will be used as *abbreviations* for specified terms—*L* for "lions," *T* for "tigers." The letters *S* and *P* here (and *M* in the following chapter) stand for no definite term whatsoever, that is, they stand for any term at all one wishes to specify as part of the subject matter of the statement.

[4] The traditional basis for the use of these letters is that "A" and "I" are respectively the first two vowels of the Latin word, "Affirmo" (*I affirm*), and "E" and "O" the first two vowels of "nego" (*I deny*).

make some difference in the rhetorical or literary evaluation of the way in which the argument is expressed; that is not the logician's business. He can quite comfortably content himself with a limited set of statement forms. Whether this particular set, the **A, E, I,** and **O** forms of traditional logic, is really adequate to the task of providing a systematic framework for the analysis of all the many different forms and varieties of statements that might be encountered in arguments expressed in ordinary language is a problem that will be taken up later on.[5]

2.3 EXERCISES

A. For each of the following statements that is in standard logical English form, identify its subject term, its predicate term, its quantity and quality, and the letter (**A, E, I,** or **O**) that is used to designate its form. If a statement is not in standard form, how does it deviate?
  1. No *A* are *P*.
  2. Some *S* are *P*.
  3. Some *S* are not *P*.
  4. All *S* are *P*.
  5. Some *P* are not *S*.
  6. All *P* are *S*.
  7. No *A* are *B*.
  8. Some *Y* are *X*.
  9. All *P* are not *Q*.
  10. All *P* are non-*S*.

B. Follow the same instructions for the following ten statements. Some of these could be rewritten as statements in the list in Exercise 2.3A. When the form is the same and the capital letters would be appropriate abbreviations for the terms, indicate it by identifying the pair of corresponding statements.
  1. All piemen are simpletons.
  2. Some simpletons are piemen.
  3. Some nonsimpletons are piemen.
  4. All simpletons are not piemen.
  5. No piemen are nonsimpletons.
  6. All patriotic citizens are servants of the common good.
  7. Some persons who are seeking unjustly to deprive their fellow citizens of their rights are misguided but sincere patriots.
  8. Some members of secret organizations are spies.
  9. No sincere but misguided patriots are possessors of outstanding logical capacities.
  10. Some people who are young enough to know better are xenophobes.

[5] See Chapter 6, especially Section 6.7.

2.4 VENN DIAGRAMS

The introduction of another systematic language beside logical English is not intended to increase its variety or range of expression. The new language of Venn diagrams is intended to express the same kinds of relationships between classes that are expressed by the four basic forms of statements we use in logical English. This new language is an artificial one, using marks on a geometrical pattern in order to make assertions. The diagrams introduced in this section and the marks made on them have much the same relationship to the statements of logical English as do the +'s and 0's of the chart used by Mrs. Sponsable to the corresponding statements.

Venn diagrams are constructed on the basic principle of representing the members of a class as occupying positions inside an area bounded by a circle. Membership in a class is represented graphically by a position inside the appropriate circle. To be logically outside a class is graphically represented by placing a mark outside a certain circle. The circle does not represent the class itself but the boundary between members and nonmembers of the class. However, if we just made a circle, the area outside the circle would be quite indefinite. It is convenient, therefore, to make the basic diagram for a class consist of a circle inside a rectangle. Then the geometric pattern will show a definite area bounded by a circle within a definite area bounded by a rectangle (see figure 2.1).

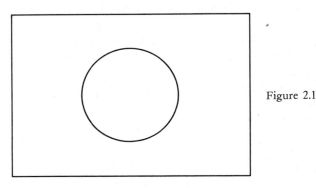

Figure 2.1

We can even attach some significance to the rectangle itself, by taking it to represent the limit or boundary of our interests in the given context. Ordinarily, the range of interest or relevance does not extend throughout the entire universe. In establishing a systematic classification of animals, for instance, one need take no account of silk hats or cabbages. If we are interested in articles of clothing, we pay no attention to walruses and so on. The range of things over which our interest extends or that are relevant to the topic we can call the "universe of discourse." The universe of discourse may be taken as the entire universe without any restriction at all, of course, but it is more likely to include a limited set of things, such as animals, articles of clothing, persons, vegetables, or objects in a room. Classes are subsets within the universe of discourse. The universe of discourse is the general range of subject matter with which we are concerned, the range from which the class or classes to which our attention is directed are *all* taken.

A circle within a rectangle divides an area geometrically into two parts, just as a universe of discourse can be divided logically into two sections: the things in that universe that belong to a certain class and the things that do not, that is to say, the things that have the distinguishing feature of the class and the things that do not. The subset of things in the universe of discourse that do not belong to a given class is referred to as the "complement" of that class in that universe of discourse. In the universe of animals, the complement of the class *sheep* will include cows, pigs, goats, and so on. It is important to note here that the members of a given class and of its complement will change as the universe of discourse changes. If the universe of discourse is *animals,* for instance, as it would be for a zoologist, all the sheep in the world will be included in the class *sheep.* Nothing that is not an animal will be included in the complement of that class, which will be made up of aardvarks, bears, civets, and so on. But if the universe of discourse is *things belonging to Farmer Brown,* the class of sheep within *this* universe will be limited to a small number in comparison with the zoologist's indefinitely large group. The complement of the class *sheep* will include not only cows and horses and other animals belonging to Farmer Brown, but his barn and plow and tractor as well. The usefulness, for purposes of logical analysis, of introducing the idea of universe of discourse will become still more apparent later on.[6]

Using the basic geometric pattern for a class within a universe of discourse that we have just illustrated, a circle within a rectangle, we are now in a position to make statements by making marks on the pattern. If, for example, we wish to say that a certain creature within the universe of discourse is a sheep, we first construct the basic pattern, label the circle *sheep,* and write the name (or an abbreviation for it) of the creature inside the circle. In figure 2.2, it is asserted that Mountain King is a sheep. The location of the letter *m* (an abbreviation for the name Mountain King)

[6] See Section 6.2.

inside the circle makes the assertion. If we wish to assert that a certain other creature is not a sheep, we write its name outside the circle. Accordingly, figure 2.2 also contains a mark asserting that Tray (*t*) is not a sheep.

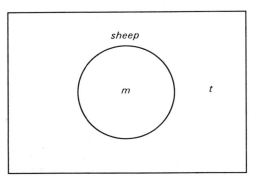

Figure 2.2

Neither of the two statements asserted in figure 2.2 could be said to correspond without qualification to any statement in logical English. The reason for this is that only one of the terms in each is a class term—the term "sheep." The other terms, "Mountain King" and "Tray," are names of individual creatures—Farmer Brown's prize-winning ram and his dog, say. The statements of logical English concern two classes and do not refer to any definite individuals. The basic idea of making statements by writing names inside or outside a circle meant to divide a universe of discourse into a class and its complement can be used to construct patterns that do correspond to the statement forms of logical English.

Our first step in developing the language of Venn diagrams, in which **A, E, I,** and **O** forms of statements are geometrically represented, is to introduce a basic pattern in which two classes appear. It is important that the basic pattern be completely neutral in its own significance—just as Mrs. Sponsable's chart was completely neutral until other marks had been made on it that finally could be judged true or false. The basic pattern must not by itself force any statement to be true or false, and it must provide for the possible truth or falsity of any statement at all. If one circle were enclosed in the other, there would be no way to say of anything that it was inside the inner class but not the outer. In effect, the diagram would say there were no things of this kind. If they did not overlap, there would be no way to say of something that it belonged to both classes. Consequently, the basic pattern must include four distinct areas, one entirely outside both circles, one in which the two overlap, and two others that are inside one and outside the other. It must look like the diagram in figure 2.3.

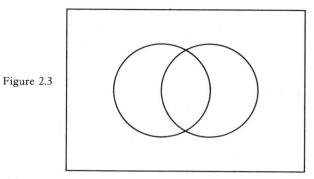

Figure 2.3

If we wish to specify a certain subject matter within a certain universe of discourse, we can attach appropriate labels to the two circles inside it. When we are not restricting our attention to specified classes in a specified universe of discourse, we can indicate the possibility of making such specifications when we wish to by labeling the one circle *S*, the other *P*. The function of the letters is exactly what it was for statements in logical English as explained in Section 2.3, except that statements in logical English do not have a clear place in which to indicate the universe of discourse.[7]

In figure 2.4, we can indicate that Mountain King is a prize winner and a sheep by writing *m* in the area where the two circles overlap.

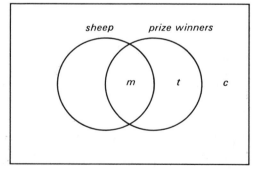

Figure 2.4. The rectangle represents the animals belonging to Farmer Brown.

We can indicate that Tray is also a prize winner but not a sheep by writing *t* in the area that is inside the circle labeled *prize winner* but outside the circle labeled *sheep*. That Farmer Brown's cat, Catiline, is neither prize winner nor sheep can be represented by writing *c* outside both circles.

Our real problem, however, is to make statements that do not concern definite individuals such as Mountain King, Tray, and Catiline. We can do so simply by introducing first of all a mark that just stands for some

[7] But see Section 6.2.

specific but unidentified thing within the universe of discourse. We can then immediately represent relationships that are particular in quantity— what these statements assert is that at least one thing that belongs to one class also belongs to the other (or does not belong to the other, depending on whether the quality of the relationship is affirmative or negative). For this purpose we use the letter "x." (In other words, used in this way, x is not an abbreviation for a specific name as are m, t, and c; it stands for someone or something in the universe of discourse. Just who or what is not further specified.) The diagrams for the **I** and the **O** relationships will then look like those in figure 2.5 (subject matter has been specified for illustrative purposes).

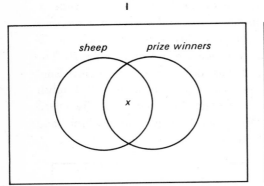

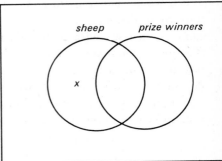

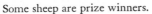

Some sheep are prize winners.   Some sheep are not prize winners.

Figure 2.5

Universal statements can be represented by the use of another device that can easily be understood in the light of what has already been presented. If all the sheep in the universe of discourse are prize winners, then the area that is to include sheep that are not prize winners will be empty. That area is the one inside the circle labeled *prize winners*. If none of the sheep in the universe of discourse are prize winners, then the area that is to include prize winning sheep will be empty. That is the area where the two circles overlap. Consequently, if we indicate that an area is empty by shading it out,[8] the **A** and **E** statements in diagram form will look like those in figure 2.6.

[8] In this respect, the parallel between the geometric pattern and the logical situation breaks down but not in a way that creates serious difficulties. The fact that a certain area on a diagram is empty (that is, contains no marks at all) does not correspond to the fact that the corresponding class is empty. The emptiness of a class must be indicated by making a definite mark on the diagram—by shading out the appropriate area

A   E

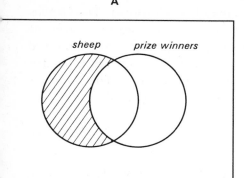
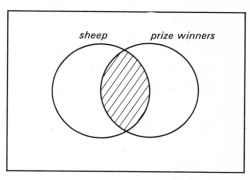

All sheep are prizewinners.   No sheep are prize winners.

Figure 2.6

The four diagram patterns that we have introduced constitute the language of Venn diagrams insofar as statements in it correspond to statements in logical English. Obviously, however, Venn diagrams really represent a somewhat richer language; by using essentially the same technique (merely increasing the number of circles in the basic pattern) statements can be made asserting that three (or four, and so on) classes all have at least one member in common, none in common, and so on. Such situations, which can be represented by just one mark on a properly constructed diagram, would require several statements in logical English.

Restricting our attention to the Venn diagrams that correspond to the four basic types of statements in logical English, we note that each one has a mark in the left-hand circle. The quantity of the relation is indicated by the nature of the mark and the quality by both the nature of the mark and its position. When the *x* is in the right-hand area (inside the circle labeled *P*), the quality is affirmative; otherwise it is negative. When the right-hand area is shaded out, the quality is negative; otherwise affirmative. Think of the *x* as a unit of positive value and of the shading as a unit of negative value. Regard a position inside the right-hand circle as a positive value and a position outside it as a negative value. Then the quality of the statement represented by a given Venn diagram follows the rule of algebraic

according to the conventions introduced here. It is only the geometric structure of the diagram, as made up of areas inside and outside the circles marked in a rectangle, that is supposed to correspond to the logical structure of classes and their complements in a universe of discourse. We cannot interpret the original appearance of the various areas in the diagram as having any significance, only the appearance of the marks that are written in them.

multiplication. **I** is represented by an *x* inside, both positive values (the product of two positive numbers is positive; **I** is affirmative). The **O** statement is represented by an *x outside* (a positive and a negative value; the product, like the quality of **O**, is negative). The **A** statement, represented by *shading outside,* calls for the product of two negatives, which is positive. The negative quality of **E**, represented by *shading inside,* is indicated by the fact that the product of a negative and a positive value is negative.

2.4   EXERCISE

Translate each of the statements (except those not in standard form) in Exercise 2.3B into the language of Venn diagrams. Use appropriately chosen capital letters as abbreviations for terms.

2.5   ALGEBRAIC NOTATION

The language that has been designated in Section 2.1 as algebraic notation can be understood best if we look at it initially as an abbreviated way of describing the four Venn diagrams we discussed in Section 2.4. In order for us to do this as neatly as possible, we must have a convenient way of designating the different areas of the Venn diagram without resorting to such relatively clumsy expressions as "the area where the two areas overlap" or "the area inside of the left-hand circle," and so forth. We can do this very easily, if we have a device for naming the "complement" of a given class. We can then use that device for designating an area outside a given circle, and the name of the class itself can be used to designate the area inside. In order to represent the complement of a class in logical Eng-

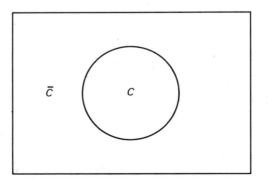

Figure 2.7

lish, we frequently use the prefix "non." The class of beings that are not householders can be referred to as the class of nonhouseholders. We shall use an even simpler notation, which is adapted to the abbreviations to be used in labeling the circles in Venn diagrams. When a certain class is designated in abbreviated form by a certain capital letter, we simply designate the complement of that class by placing a bar above the letter. In a Venn diagram involving just one class, C, in a universe of discourse, the area outside the circle labeled C will be labeled $\bar{C}$ (see figure 2.7); $\bar{C}$ is the "complement" of C. Where there are two or more circles involved, each area can be designated by combining the various letters indicating its status in relation to each circle. If there are two circles labeled S and P in the usual order, the area inside both can be labeled SP, the area outside both $\overline{SP}$, the area inside the left and outside the right $S\bar{P}$, and the remaining area $\bar{S}P$ (see figure 2.8).

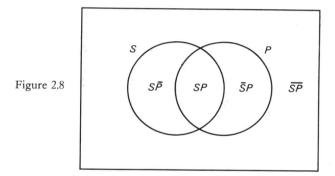

Figure 2.8

All that is needed to describe a given Venn diagram is a way of indicating which mark is in a given area of the diagram. For this purpose, we use the expressions "equal to 0" and "not equal to 0," with their obvious interpretations. An area that is shaded out is said to be equal to 0; one that contains an x is said to be unequal to 0. Thus the algebraic expression of the four basic types of statement are as they appear in Table 2.2, which combines in condensed form the essential points of this chapter.

With algebraic notation, we will notice immediately that the quantity of the statement is indicated by whether or not the equation expresses an equality or an inequality, while the quality of the relationship is indicated by this factor together with the presence or absence of a bar over the right-hand term. Thinking of equality to 0 and the presence of a bar over the right-hand term each as having negative value, the rules of algebraic multiplication give the quality of a statement in algebraic notation. The **A** statement, for instance, involves two negatives since it equals 0 and has a bar over the right-hand term; its affirmative quality is indicated by the principle that the product of two negatives is positive. Quality, however, is not as important in dealing with statements expressed in Venn diagrams or algebraic form as is quantity. It is always possible to change the position of a mark (or the presence of a bar) by changing the labels on the classes; it is never possible to change the mark itself except by appealing to a special rule that requires some kind of logical justification.

The principles and rules of inference that we will develop and apply depend on our recognition of the basic characteristics of the statements in the three languages of logic. It is essential that we become thoroughly familiar with these forms of statement and their basic logical characteristics before attempting to go on. Table 2.2 should be committed to memory

TABLE 2.2

Symbol	**A**	**E**	**I**	**O**
Quantity	Universal	Universal	Particular	Particular
Quality	Affirmative	Negative	Affirmative	Negative
Logical English	All S are P.	No S are P.	Some S are P.	Some S are not P.
Venn diagrams				
Algebraic notation	$SP = 0$	$SP = 0$	$SP \neq 0$	$S\overline{P} \neq 0$

in detail so that every item of information on it can be immediately and confidently recalled. If this is attended to, what follows will be surprisingly easy to learn.

2.5   EXERCISE

Translate each of the statements (except those not in standard form) in Exercise 2.3B into the language of algebraic notation. Use appropriately chosen abbreviations for terms.

2.6 DISTRIBUTION OF TERMS

The quantity and quality of a statement in logical English determine a significant characteristic of the terms in the statement: their "distribution" values. A term is either "distributed" or "undistributed" in relation to a statement in which it occurs. When a term is distributed in a statement, that statement tells us something about *all* the members of the class referred to by that term; if a statement *does not* tell us anything about *all* the members of the class, the term is undistributed. The subject terms of universal statements are distributed. There is no difficulty in seeing why this should be so, for universal statements are defined as those making an assertion about *all* the members of the subject class. The predicate terms of negative statements are also distributed. It is not difficult to understand why this should be so in the case of an **E** statement. The **E** statement asserts that *all* of the members of the subject class are outside of the predicate class. It can be true only if there are no individuals that belong to both classes. In this case, however, it must also be true that *all* of the members of the predicate class are outside the subject class. If *No surviving reptiles are pterodactyls,* it follows that *No pterodactyls are surviving reptiles.* The original **E** statement does tell us something implicitly concerning *all* the members of the predicate class.

The distribution of the predicate term is not so obvious in the case of an **O** statement. There is no universal statement in logical English that can be inferred from the **O** statement. There is, however, something that an **O** statement does implicitly assert of every member of its predicate class. If the **O** statement is true, every member of the predicate class must be distinct from at least one member of the subject class.

Let us consider a proposition in which the subject is not a class term but a name: Mr. O'Furioso. If Mr. O'Furioso is not a pianist, then we know of anyone who *is* a pianist that he is not Mr. O'Furioso. Then, in less definite terms but following much the same line of thought, if someone at the party is not a pianist, we can say of everyone who *is* a pianist that he is different from someone who is at the party. It is more important for our present purposes to remember accurately which terms are distributed and which terms are not than it is to understand exactly why this is so. An easy way of remembering which terms are distributed is to recall the connection of the initial vowels between *u*niversal and *su*bject and between negative and predicate. We can construct the following mnemonic device to point up this connection:

THE CROSSWORD RULE OF DISTRIBUTION

```
                        n
    s u bject         pr e dicate
       n                 g
       i                 a
       v                 t
       e                 i
       r                 v
       s                 e
       a
       l
```

Universal statements have distributed *subject* terms, and *negative* statements have distributed *predicate* terms. All others are undistributed.

Now that we have defined the distribution of terms in a statement, we can extend the concept of distribution value to apply to the complements of the terms in a statement. In relation to the same statement, a pair of complementary terms have opposite distribution values. In *No sentries are privates,* "sentries" and "privates" are both distributed terms. Although they do not appear in the statement, the complementaries of these two terms, "nonsentries" and "nonprivates," also have a distribution value determined by it. They are both undistributed.

The distribution values of terms in a statement expressed on a Venn diagram can be determined without referring back to the quantity and quality of the corresponding statement in logical English. The rule for Venn diagrams is as follows:

> A term is distributed in relation to a Venn diagram if the circle (or more generally, area) representing the term has either a single unshaded area within it or an *x* outside of it. If neither of these conditions holds, it is undistributed.

For algebraic notation, a still simpler rule of distribution value can be stated:

> Constituent terms of a class product set equal to 0 are distributed. Constituent terms of a class product set unequal to 0 are undistributed.

This rule is not inconsistent with the distinctions as they were drawn for logical English and Venn diagrams, despite the appearance that it must be.

It is only necessary to recall that complementary terms have opposite distribution values in relation to a given statement. According to the rule for algebraic notation, both of the terms in the class product set equal to 0 when an **A** statement is translated into algebraic notation are distributed. In algebraic notation, however, it is not the predicate term of the **A** statement that appears but its complement. In *All S are P*, *S* is distributed and *P* undistributed. In $S\bar{P} = 0$, S and $\bar{P}$ are both distributed. If $\bar{P}$ is distributed, however, P is undistributed. Therefore the two rules result in the same distribution values being assigned to the same terms.

2.6 EXERCISE

Determine the distribution values of terms determined by all of the standard-form statements in Exercise 2.3B. Do the same for their translations into Venn diagrams and algebraic notation called for by Exercises 2.4 and 2.5.

Chapter 3

IMMEDIATE INFERENCE

3.1 RULES OF INFERENCE

The restriction of a language to a limited set of forms that a statement may take, with definite and clearly recognizable characteristics, makes it possible for us to devise a set of rules for reasoning with such statements. We can express these rules in terms of the characteristics that the various kinds of statements have, and their application can be as mechanical as the application of the rules concerning $+$'s and 0's on the chart we discussed in Chapter 1.

During the course of the next few chapters, we will be concerned with developing such a system of rules for statements in the languages of logical English, Venn diagrams, and algebraic notation. We will construct rules of inference for these languages, rules that permit us to infer from a premise or premises with given characteristics to a conclusion with certain specified characteristics. These rules will be used mainly in justifying processes of reasoning, particularly as these become more and more complicated to the point where a common-sense evaluation of the argument's validity or invalidity ceases to be possible. In connection with the syllogism (Chapter 4), we will also take up certain rules that are not properly rules of inference at all but rules for the criticism of arguments. The difference between rules of inference in the narrow sense—the sort of rules to be emphasized here—and the traditional rules of the syllogism is that the former have a permissive function while the latter have a prohibitive one. A rule of inference tells us that if an argument is in accordance with the rule, it is valid. A rule of criticism tells us that if an argument is not in accord with the rule, it is invalid. We will see that the traditional rules of the syllogism can be taken all together as providing a permissive rule of inference. They permit us to say that if an argument does not violate any of the rules, it is valid. But, as we shall see also, to justify such a use of traditional rules of criticism, it is first necessary to establish and appeal to a rule of inference in the narrower sense.

In this portion of the text, devoted to traditional logic, the rules we will introduce into our logical system will be expected to fulfill two basic requirements. The first is a need for theoretical simplicity, keeping the number of fundamental rules of inference at a minimum. The second reflects the practical orientation in the treatment of logic in this part of the book: the rules should be in accord with our common-sense estimates of the validity of arguments, that is, they should not permit inferences that are obviously invalid from the point of view of unsystematic common sense; they should provide for the systematic justification of inferences that common sense indicates are valid. These requirements, as we shall soon see, are in a certain tension with each other. The system with the greatest degree of theoretical simplicity appears in certain cases to violate the demands of common sense. We shall consider how to meet these problems as they arise.

3.2 THE NATURE OF IMMEDIATE INFERENCE

The simplest form reasoning can take is represented by an argument in which a conclusion is derived from a single piece of information serving as premise. This has traditionally been referred to by the title of "immediate inference." Other arguments, requiring more than a single premise to support their conclusions, are not called immediate inferences. There is yet another distinction to be drawn between "direct" and "indirect" inference. Reasoning sometimes proceeds in a series of stages. A conclusion (or conclusions) drawn at one stage becomes at another stage a premise on which further conclusions are then based. The process may continue through several stages; in fact, there is no definite limit that can be imposed. If a conclusion can be drawn directly from the supporting premises without any intervening step, the inference is considered direct. If intermediate steps are necessary to reach a conclusion, it is an indirect inference. Whether a conclusion can be derived from a given set of premises directly or only indirectly will be determined by the rules of inference governing the system being used. By describing an inference as "direct," we mean to say that the conclusion is derived from one or more premises in a *single logical step;* by describing it as "immediate," we mean to say that the conclusion is derived in one or more steps *from a single logical premise.*

In the model system used in Chapter 1, we have encountered examples of both kinds of inference. The rule stating that, given a $+$ on any line, we can place a 0 on any other line in the same row or column, provides for inferences that are both direct and immediate. The $+$ represents a single piece of information, and all of the various conclusions that can be drawn from it (and it alone) within that system are drawn directly. The rule that permits us to place a $+$ in any blank space in a row or column that is otherwise occupied by 0's only provides for inferences that are equally direct. However, within the system we were using, they were not immediate; five different items of information (the five 0's) were required as premises before the rule could be applied and the conclusion drawn. The basic rules of immediate inference within a logical system determine which immediate inferences can be carried out directly and which require one or more immediate steps.

Most of the time, we shall be concerned with immediate inferences in which the premise is the affirmation of a statement, and the conclusion is the affirmation of some further statement. But this need not always be the case: the information that serves as premise may also be an assertion that a certain other statement is false, and the conclusion may be that some further statement is false. There are a variety of logical relationships that can exist between two statements. They can be identified and distinguished from each other according to the way in which information about the truth or falsity of one permits us to infer something about the truth or falsity of the other.

Before examining particular examples of such relationships on what is called the "square of opposition," we will first describe the different kinds of relationships we might expect to encounter.

If, when we know the first statement to be true, we can infer that the second is true, and when we know the first to be false we can infer the second to be false, then the relationship is one of "logical equivalence."

	When the first is:	*The second is:.*
Logical	*T*	*T*
Equivalence	*F*	*F*

All three of the following statements are equivalent to each other. They are either all of them true or all of them false. The equivalence between the first and second statement can be construed in terms of a logical principle, the "principle of conversion," which we shall discuss in Section 3.4. That the first and the third statements are equivalent depends on the fact that their subject terms and their predicate terms, although verbally different, have the same meaning.

1. No sows are hogs that lie.
2. No hogs that tell lies are sows.
3. No adult female hogs are lying hogs.

If, when we know the first statement to be true, we can infer the second to be false, and when we know the first to be false, we can infer the second to be true, then the relation is one of "contradiction."

	When the first is:	*The second is:*
Contradiction	*T*	*F*
	F	*T*

No boars are liars and *Some boars are liars* are contradictory statements. They have opposite truth values. In the illustrative square of opposition on p. 48, they are at the ends of the diagonal running from lower left to upper right. The statements at the ends of the other diagonal constitute another pair of contradictory statements.

If knowing the first statement to be true or knowing it to be false does not permit any inference to be drawn about the second, the two propositions are "logically independent."

	When the first is:	*The second is:*
Independence	*T*	?[1]
	F	?

---

[1] The symbol "?" does not mean a special truth value different from both *T* and *F* but is used only to indicate that neither *T* nor *F* can be inferred.

All boars are liars and *All sows are liars* have the relation of independence. Any combination of truth values is possible. (How many combinations are there if each of the two can be either true or false, no matter what truth value the other has? See the discussion of truth tables on p. 216.)

The other relationships to be considered can all be regarded as combining one of the features of either equivalence or contradiction with one of the features of independence. They are (in abbreviated form):

	When the first is:	*The second is:*
Implication	T	T
	F	?

The examples of equivalent statements we have just discussed can be said to imply one another; equivalence could be regarded as two-way implication. Here we have to do with simple implication, running in just one direction. *All boars are liars* implies *Some boars are liars* but is not itself implied by the latter. This example appears on the left-hand side of the square of opposition. There is another example on the right-hand side. In connection with this relationship and all of those that follow, see Section 3.7.

	When the first is:	*The second is:*
Subimplication	T	?
	F	F

The same statements we cited in illustrating implication can be cited in illustrating "subimplication," but the relationship runs in the other direction. From the falsity of *Some boars are liars* we can infer the falsity of *All boars are liars*. That is subimplication. The relationship appears on the square of opposition along the two vertical sides, as indicated by the arrows pointing from bottom to top.

	When the first is:	*The second is:*
Contrariety	T	F
	F	?

No boars are liars and *All boars are liars* cannot both be true but can both be false. They are, therefore, "contraries." On the square of opposition, they are at the two ends of the line across the top.

	When the first is:	*The second is:*
Subcontrariety	T	?
	F	T

Some boars are liars and *Some boars are not liars* can both be true but cannot both be false. The relationship of "subcontrariety" that they illustrate is indicated along the horizontal line at the bottom of the square of opposition.

The relationships distinguished as implication and subimplication are sometimes combined under the title "subalternation"; it is more desirable for us to refer to them by distinct names, for they are distinct patterns of logical relationships.

3.3 THE TRADITIONAL SQUARE OF OPPOSITION

We can represent a direct inference by letting a horizontal line separate premises and conclusion, with the premises above the line and the conclusion below. If the inference is an immediate inference, there will be one statement above and one statement below the line. If both statements are written in logical English, the basic structure of the inference will look like this:

$$( ) \underline{\hspace{2cm}} [\quad\quad] \underline{\hspace{2cm}} [\quad\quad]$$
$$( ) \underline{\hspace{2cm}} [\quad\quad] \underline{\hspace{2cm}} [\quad\quad]$$

As before, we intend the bracketed spaces to be occupied by terms and the underlined spaces to be occupied by quantifiers and copulas indicating the form of the respective statements. The parentheses to the left of the premise and the conclusion have been added to the basic statement structure to accommodate a mark that serves to deny the statement— ∼ or *It is false that*. Since we are considering relationships in which the denial rather than the affirmation of a statement may be involved, such a mark will be called for on occasion.

The square of opposition is traditionally used to summarize, in diagrammatic form, the relationships between the four types of statement in logical English. We can see a somewhat modified version of the traditional square in figure 3.1.

The square of opposition sets forth twelve relationships, the possible combinations that emerge when we take each of the four statements of logical English as the first statement in a relationship and then pair it with each

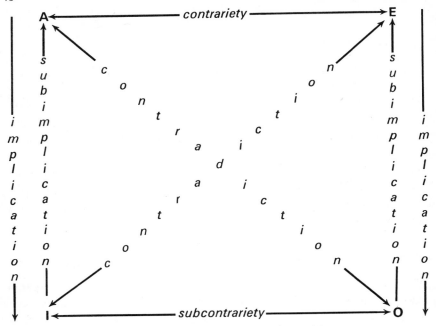

Figure 3.1. The traditional square of opposition.

of the three remaining ones in turn. In each pair, we must determine the inference that can be drawn (if any) when the first is known to be true and the inference that can be drawn if it is known to be false. It is essential to realize that the relationships do not hold between *any* two statements of the given forms. They hold only within a very stringent restriction as to subject matter.

It is obvious to our common-sense appreciation of logical relationships that from information concerning one subject matter, a conclusion concerning an entirely different subject matter cannot be drawn. There must be at least some resemblance between the subject matter of the premise or premises and that of the conclusion. Resemblance is not even sufficient to form the basis of a possible deductive inference. Arguments from analogy, arguments based on resemblances between one kind of thing and another, confer a certain degree of probability on their conclusions; they do not represent logically necessary reasoning. That is to say, they are inductive arguments and not deductive ones.[2]

The relationships presented on the traditional square of opposition observe this restriction in its most stringent form. Not only does the con-

---

[2] This is true without exception in the system of logical English. There are exceptions in other systems, in a sense. See the principle of simple addition in Section 4.9, and the principles of addition and absorption in Section 10.2.

clusion refer to basically the same subject matter as the premise, but it also has exactly the same terms as the premise in exactly the same positions. In other words, on the square of opposition, we consider relationships between propositions that differ only in their logical form, since they both have exactly the same subject term and predicate term. As far as the relationships summarized in the square of opposition are concerned, we can think of the terms of both premise and conclusion as fixed on the basic structure of immediate inference according to the following pattern:

$$\frac{(\ \ ) \ \text{———} \ [S] \ \text{———} \ [P]}{(\ \ ) \ \text{———} \ [S] \ \text{———} \ [P]}$$

What differences there are between premise and conclusion will involve the presence or absence of a mark indicating denial, and quantity or quality, never the terms that specify subject matter.

The relationship of contradiction will conveniently serve us as an example. If it is true that *No sane panthers are pink panthers,* the particular affirmative (**I**) statement with the same terms—*Some sane panthers are pink panthers*—must be false. And if it is false that *No sane panthers are pink panthers,* then it must be true that *Some sane panthers are pink panthers.* Turn to the relationship of contrariety (which holds between **E** and **A** statements on the square of opposition). If it is true that *All Siamese cats are playful pets,* then the corresponding **E** statement—*No Siamese cats are playful pets*—is false. If the former statement, the **A** statement, is false, the latter may or may not be true.

There is an interesting development if we next consider the relationships in the light of the Venn diagrams. By stating two principles concerning the marks to be made on the diagrams, we can reach the same results. The relationships along the diagonals of the square (**A** and **O**, and **E** and **I** are contradictory pairs) are established by the principle that the same area cannot contain both marks—that is, an area cannot be shaded out and also contain an *x*. The relationships across the top and bottom and along the sides require an additional principle: The circle on the left must have an *x* in it somewhere. (Remember, all this means is that the class does have at least one member. The *x* is not supposed to name anything.) The first principle is just a restatement (in terms of marks on the diagram) of the common-sense rule that the same proposition cannot be both true and false. The second is a reflection of the fact that we do not ordinarily use the universal forms in logical English to make literal and factual statements about classes of nonexistent things.[3]

[3] See Section 3.7 for a discussion of this point. LIBRARY - SEMINARY OF ST. VINCENT DE PAUL BOYNTON BEACH, FLA.

If these two principles are applied to the diagrammatic statement of the truth or falsity of the four basic types of propositions, the same results called for by the traditional square of opposition are produced in the language of the diagrams. However, the fact that only two principles are needed suggests that the various relationships are not exactly independent of each other. We can get along just as well with only two of them. The only difference will be that some of the immediate inferences that are also direct inferences when justified by appealing to the traditional square become indirect when their ultimate basis is reduced to a pair of rules. The inferences that remain direct are those involved in implication and contradiction. All of the rest can be derived indirectly by applying these two. Fundamentally, then, the system of immediate inferences presented on the traditional square of opposition is the direct or indirect product of two basic rules. One of them permits us to infer from the truth or falsity of any proposition the opposite truth value for another proposition that has the same terms but opposite quantity and opposite quality. We can call this the "principle of contradiction." The other permits us to infer the truth of a particular statement from the truth of a universal with the same terms and quality. This we can call the "principle of limitation." The inference permitted on the square from the truth of **A** to the falsity of **E** can be derived indirectly by first moving from the truth of **A** to the truth of **I**, by applying the principle of limitation (LIM) and then moving from the truth of **I** to the falsity of **E**, by applying the principle of contradiction (CONTRAD).

Indirect inferences carried out according to a definite set of principles of inference are also called "formal proofs." We shall follow a regular or standard pattern for carrying them out. Each statement, given as an original premise or derived, is assigned a number that serves as a convenient way of reference whenever necessary in subsequent stages of the proof. The first time a statement appears, if it is not among the original premises, the way in which it has been derived must be indicated. For this purpose, we write, first, the premise or premises from which it has been derived and, second, the principle that justifies the derivation of this statement from those premises. The informal example of the sane panthers would be set up in this way:

1. All *S* are *P*.   Premise
2. Some *S* are *P*.   1, LIM
3. It is false that no *S* are *P*.   2, CONTRAD

LIBRARY · SEMINARY OF
ST. VINCENT DE PAUL
BOYNTON BEACH, FLA.

See if you can work out for yourself the routes needed for some of the other inferences permitted by the square of opposition, such as subimplication—from the falsity of **O** to the falsity of **E**, for example.

3.3 EXERCISES

A. Reconstruct from memory the traditional square of opposition. Check the result by turning back to p. 48 and correct any mistakes.

B. Write each of the following statements in its appropriate place on a square of opposition, using appropriate abbreviations when it is convenient to do so. Write in the other statements that belong on the same square of opposition in their places. What, if anything, can be inferred about them if the original statement is known to be true? What can be inferred if it is known to be false? What information concerning other statements on the square would permit one to *infer* that it is true? To *infer* that it is false?

1. Some *A* are *B*.
2. No *X* are *Y*.
3. All *R* are *W*.
4. Some *M* are not *N*.
5. All villains are mustache twirlers.
6. Some giants are cowards.
7. Some sheepdogs are not pets.
8. No psychologists are neurotics.
9. All prima donnas are sensation seekers.
10. No rodents are aleurophiles.

3.4 CONVERSION

Another set of valid immediate inferences could be obtained if we were able to change the terms of a statement without fundamentally altering the subject matter with which it is concerned. This becomes possible when we realize that the restriction within which the square of opposition is developed—that the subject and predicate terms of the two propositions concerned must be exactly the same—is actually more confining than it need be. There are two ways in which either the subject or predicate terms of a statement, or both, can change without introducing any entirely new subject matter. We can, for instance, simply reverse them. The second way involves the relationship between a class and its complement. When we introduced the idea of a class, we pointed out that identifying a class always involves the implicit identification of its complement; a universe is divided into two mutually exclusive and exhaustive subsets. To turn our attention from the class to its complement will not fundamentally alter the basic distinction with which we are concerned, and it will certainly not alter any of the facts in the universe that is so divided. The logical status of Miss Ellenee within a universe of human beings who are either married or unmarried is the same whether we describe her as *among those who are unmarried* or *outside the class of those who are married*. In a sense, then, replacing a class by its complement represents an acceptable way of changing the terms of a statement without introducing any new subject matter (new class distinction) or introducing new factual assumptions. We can say that either procedure is essentially in conformity with the common-sense rule that conclusions cannot be inferred from premises that provide no information about the subject matter of the conclusion.

Of course, this does not mean that we can, without restriction, validly infer a conclusion from a premise by just reversing the order of the terms as originally given or by replacing a term with its complement. The one procedure is restricted by the form of the proposition given as premise, and the other is restricted according to the position of the term to be replaced. The procedure of reversing the order of the terms to arrive at a new proposition is called "conversion" (CONV). It can be applied only to **E** and **I** statements. Why this is so can be understood by reflecting on some examples of the various kinds of statement in the light of common sense, and we can understand them still more clearly by considering the process of conversion in terms of Venn diagrams. Reversing the order of terms in a verbally formulated proposition corresponds to turning a diagram around, since the subject term is represented by the diagram's left-hand circle and the predicate term by the circle on the right. The diagrams for the **E** and the **I** propositions are symmetrical, so that when they are reversed they look exactly the same (or almost the same, see figure 3.2). However, when the **A** or the **O** diagram is reversed (figure 3.2), the result is not one of the four basic patterns at all. We are forced to say that by reversing the order of terms in an **A** or an **O** statement, we do not derive any statement within the language, so far as it corresponds to logical English.

Although only **E** and **I** statements can validly be "converted," there is a similar procedure that is applicable to **A** and **O** statements. A valid inference can be drawn from an **A** or an **O** statement by reversing the terms *and replacing them with their complements*. We will call this procedure "complement conversion" (CC), although its traditional designation is "contraposition." The relationship between the two procedures is

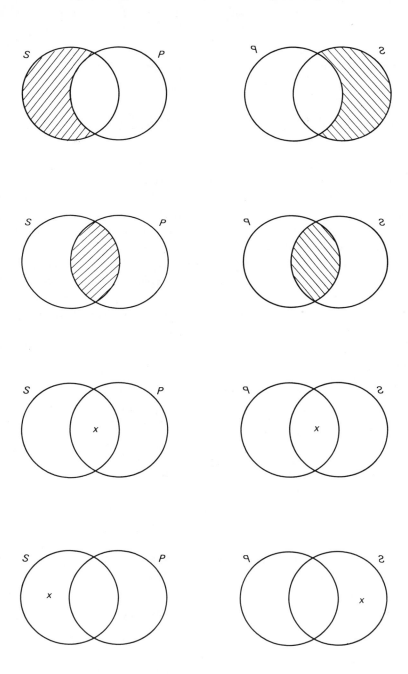

Figure 3.2

plain in the schematic representations of the valid inferences they respectively provide for.

Conversion	*Complement conversion*
No S are P.	All S are P.
No P are S.	All $\overline{P}$ are $\overline{S}$.
Some S are P.	Some S are not P.
Some P are S.	Some $\overline{P}$ are not $\overline{S}$.

Actually, complement conversion is not an independent procedure at all. We could derive the same conclusions from the **A** or the **O** premise by applying the principle of conversion *and* the principle of obversion, to be introduced in the next section, in an indirect inference. It is only for the sake of convenience, then, that we incorporate into the system of rules not only the principle of conversion, permitting the reversal of terms in an **E** or an **I** statement, but the principle of complement conversion, permitting the terms of an **A** or an **O** statement to be replaced by their complements and reversed.

Along with simple conversion and simple contraposition (complement conversion), the traditional logic also recognized as valid principles of immediate inference, "conversion by limitation" and "contraposition by limitation." These are represented in the following diagram.

Conversion by limitation	*Contraposition by limitation*
All S are P.	No S are P.
Some P are S.	Some $\overline{P}$ are not $\overline{S}$.

In each case in which the universal statement does not permit the terms to be reversed, as in simple conversion, or their complements to be reversed, as in simple complement conversion, that procedure becomes permissible if the quantity of the statement is reduced to the particular. We can arrive at the same outcome by indirect inference, using the principles in their simple forms after the principle of limitation has been applied to the original universal premise. The indirect inferences required are indicated in these formal proofs:

1. All S are P.	1. No S are P.	
2. Some S are P. 1, LIM	2. Some S are not P. 1, LIM	
3. Some P are S. 2, CONV	3. Some $\overline{P}$ are not $\overline{S}$. 2, CC	

In these cases, we shall not introduce still another redundant rule, as we did complement conversion, for the sake of symmetry and convenience. Instead, we shall make use of the indirect inferences indicated if the need should arise.

3.5 OBVERSION

We have already seen that a class and its complement divide a universe into two mutually exclusive and exhaustive subsets. The members of a class have a certain distinguishing characteristic, and the members of its complement do not have it. Either of the two can be taken as the primary focus of attention. Consequently, in turning our attention from a class to its complement, we are not really introducing anything new but rather changing the point of view toward a distinction that has already been made in specifying the original class.

This logical relationship between a class and its complement allows for another form of immediate inference, a procedure called "obversion" (OBV). Its common-sense justification is so obvious as to seem trivial. The point is that whatever is inside a given class is outside its complement and vice versa. In a statement in logical English, it is the copula that determines the quality of the relationship asserted—whether it is an affirmative relationship (inside) or a negative one (outside). The predicate term indicates the class to which some or all of the members of the subject class have this relationship. Obviously, if we replace the predicate term by its complement, the character of the relationship is going to be reversed. What was inside the original class will now be outside its complement, and what was outside the original will be inside the complement. This applies to any statement whatsoever. We can, therefore, state as a general principle that from a given premise we can infer a conclusion with the same quantity and opposite quality if the predicate term is replaced by its complement. For example, from the statement *Some guests are married,* we can infer *Some guests are not unmarried.* From *No contestants who finished in third place or above are winners of less than four games,* it follows that *All contestants who finished in third place or above are winners of four games or more.* This is the "principle of obversion." It is to be emphatically noted that this rule does not permit us to replace the *subject* term by *its* complement, because the common-sense principle appealed to in justifying the rule does not apply in the same way to members of the subject term and members of its complement. Such a procedure we might be tempted to call "subversion"; in any case, it is a fallacious form of reasoning as can be established easily by an example. We cannot validly infer from *All cows are herbivorous* the conclusion that *No noncows are herbivorous.*

When we introduce the principle of complement conversion (contraposition) in Section 3.4, we made the observation that it was not really needed as an independent principle of inference, since the same result could be obtained by using conversion and obversion in an indirect inference. The formal proof that shows this to be the case for an inference with the **A** statement as premise has the following form:

1. All S are P.
2. No S are $\overline{P}$.   1, OBV
3. No $\overline{P}$ are S.   2, CONV
4. All $\overline{P}$ are $\overline{S}$.   3, OBV

The introduction of the principle of obversion completes the set of rules of immediate inference for this system of logic. There are four basic principles: contradiction, limitation, conversion, and obversion. There is also the subsidiary and expendable principle of complement conversion. The application of these rules, in direct and indirect inferences, will provide us with a method for the systematic demonstration of every valid immediate inference in the system.

3.5   EXERCISE

Write the converse, or complement converse, and the obverse of each of the statements in Exercise 2.3A and B.

3.6   PRINCIPLES OF IMMEDIATE INFERENCE IN THE LANGUAGE OF VENN DIAGRAMS AND ALGEBRAIC NOTATION

The emphasis in the preceding discussion has been on statements in logical English, which are subject to a common-sense interpretation. However, the four basic rules that we have introduced can be formulated appropriately for any of the three languages. In fact, as we have seen in connection with the discussion of conversion, the Venn diagram language provides a neat mechanical way of establishing the validity of simple conversion. The following list includes the abbreviations that will be used for the identification of each of the principles as well as a statement of each of them in terms appropriate to logical English, Venn diagrams, and algebraic notation.

The Principle of Contradiction (CONTRAD)

LOGICAL ENGLISH   From the truth or falsity of a given statement, the opposite truth value can be inferred for another statement with the same terms, opposite quantity, and opposite quality. Changing both quantity and quality changes truth value.

VENN DIAGRAMS   An x and *shading* exclude each other. Changing the mark changes the truth value.

ALGEBRAIC NOTATION An equality and an inequality with the same terms cannot both be true nor both be false. Changing the equation sign ($= 0$ to $\neq 0$ or vice versa) changes the truth value.

The Principle of Limitation (LIM)

LOGICAL ENGLISH   The universal quantifier can be replaced with the particular quantifier.

VENN DIAGRAMS   The left-hand circle must not be entirely shaded out; that is, it must contain an x somewhere inside it.

ALGEBRAIC NOTATION A bar can be taken from the right-hand term and applied to the equality sign. (See Section 3.7.)

The Principle of Conversion (CONV)

LOGICAL ENGLISH   The terms of an **E** or an **I** statement may be reversed.[4]

VENN DIAGRAMS   Any diagram may be reversed.

ALGEBRAIC NOTATION The terms of any equality or inequality may exchange positions.

The Principle of Obversion (OBV)

LOGICAL ENGLISH   The quality of any statement may be changed and the predicate term replaced by its complement.

VENN DIAGRAMS   A circle may be relabeled to represent the complementary class if the marks inside it are moved outside and those outside moved inside.

ALGEBRAIC NOTATION An even number of bars may be added to any term.[5]

---

[4] To compensate for the restriction on the applicability of the principle of conversion in logical English to **E** and **I** statements, it is useful to add, for application to **A** and **O** statements, the principle of complement conversion, which provides for the reversal of complementary terms.

[5] Actually, the rule of obversion given here for algebraic notation is just a case of a general rule of double negation, which permits us to add or subtract an even number of bars to or from any term, no matter what language is being used. It is listed as a

Some interesting comparisons can be made among the ways in which these rules apply within the framework of the different languages. Perhaps it has already been noticed that the rules formulated for algebraic notation have a particularly "mechanical" character to them. Notice, too, that while the rules we have formulated for each language are all roughly equivalent, they do not have *exactly* the same force in each. For example, there is no restriction on the application of CONV in the languages of Venn diagrams and algebraic notation. This rule can be applied directly, for example, to an **O** diagram or to an inequality but not to an **O** statement. There is no inconsistency here, however; the result of applying the rule to the diagram or the inequality does not correspond to the result of reversing the terms of an **O** statement, which would violate the restriction on the rule for logical English.

Another difference can be seen in the fact that the principle of limitation, as stated for algebraic notation, cannot be applied directly to an equality of the basic **E** form ($SP = 0$). The principle of obversion (essentially double negation) must first be applied to produce $S\bar{\bar{P}} = 0$ to which **LIM** is then applied to reach $S\bar{P} \neq 0$. With this exception, however, we can say that these four rules provide for the direct inferences represented by the relations of implication and contradiction on the square of opposition and for obversion and conversion. The inferences involved in subimplication, in contrariety, and subcontrariety on the square, in conversion by limitation, and in certain other immediate inferences of traditional logic can be justified only indirectly by applying two or more rules in succession.

Complement conversion (contraposition) is just such an example. The complement converse can be derived indirectly in logical English by a series of three steps: obversion, conversion, and obversion. In algebraic notation, the corresponding inference would require only two steps, as in the following formal proof.

1. $S\bar{P} \neq 0$.
2. $\bar{P}S \neq 0$.   1, CONV
3. $\bar{P}\bar{S} \neq 0$.   2, OBV

---

rule of obversion for algebraic notation only for the sake of uniformity. It would be more accurate to say that the process of obversion can be justified in algebraic notation by appeal to a rule of double negation that has general applicability to all languages. In some cases, there is no transformation in algebraic notation corresponding to an obversion in one of the other languages. For example, *All A are B* and *No A are $\bar{B}$* would both be written as $A\bar{B} = 0$ in algebraic notation. The need to use a principle of double negation arises for such cases as the one corresponding to the transition in logical English from *No A are B* to *All A are $\bar{B}$*, written respectively as $AB = 0$ and $A\bar{\bar{B}} = 0$ in algebraic notation.

This possibility arises from the fact that in the algebraic notation there is no restriction on the applicability of CONV as there is in logical English. The intermediate step $\overline{PS} \neq 0$ corresponds only to *Some $\overline{P}$ are S* in logical English; this cannot be derived *directly* from *Some S are not P* by the rules of that language. In most cases, however, the procedure will be the same, whichever language is used.

In order to transform a given statement into one with terms that are either complementary to the original terms or in the opposite order (or both), the first point we must consider is what differences must be provided for. The steps we need to infer from an **O** statement what its complement converse is, for example, and the order in which they must be taken, are immediately indicated if we follow the illustrated procedure. There are three changes that must be made in the original statement:

1. P must be replaced by $\overline{P}$.
2. S must be replaced by $\overline{S}$.
3. The terms must be reversed.

Only one, the first one, of these changes can be made by a direct immediate inference, by applying the principle of obversion. Of the two changes remaining, again only one can be accomplished directly: the terms can be reversed by applying the principle of conversion, a procedure that has become possible because the result of the first step was to produce an **E** statement. The remaining change, the replacement of S by $\overline{S}$, can be accomplished directly by application of obversion once more, since now it is S rather than P that has the predicate position. With that step, the desired result is obtained: *Some $\overline{P}$ are not $\overline{S}$.*

3.7 THE PROBLEM OF EXISTENTIAL IMPORT

The introduction of the principle of limitation brings us directly to grips with the problem of the *existential import* of universal propostions, and the possibility of using this principle in indirect inferences complicates the situation. The problem is concerned with the proper interpretation of the universal statements **A** and **E**. Fundamentally, the issue is this: When such a proposition is asserted to be true, are we to assume that the classes that enter into it actually have members? If *All A are B* is true, does this fact have existential import—does it mean that there are A's or B's or both? The simplest interpretation is that it does not, that only particular statements involve a commitment to the existence of anything. Yet this interpretation comes into direct conflict with what common sense judges to be the systematic logical relationships and valid inferences concerning such statements.

For example, if we do not attach any kind of existential significance at all to universal statements but regard them purely as denials—an interpretation obviously suiting the Venn diagrams and the algebraic notation —both the **A** and **E** statements become true when the subject class has no members. Further, the relationships of contrariety on the square of opposition collapses and so do the relationships of subcontrariety, implication, and subimplication as well. If there are no unicorns, then (on this interpretation) both *All unicorns are spotted* and *No unicorns are spotted* are true; one denies that there are spotted unicorns, and the other denies that there are spotless ones. Worse still, by obversion we can infer from *No unicorns are spotted* that *All unicorns are spotless.* Then we have a situation in which the two statements, *All unicorns are spotted* and *All unicorns are spotless,* are both true at the same time. Clearly, the simple interpretation of universal statements as being entirely without existential import will not do. If we want our logical system to have not only the utmost simplicity and economy in its basic principles but also conformity to the dictates of common-sense reasoning, we will have to explore matters further.

An obvious solution to the problems that arise in connection with this interpretation is to say that what the universal statements mean includes the existence of members in at least the subject class. If that is so, then when there are no members of the class, both universal statements are false. If there are no unicorns, and yet the existence of unicorns is part of the very meaning of saying either *All unicorns are spotted* or *No unicorns are spotted,* both of these statements must be false. This may seem to solve the problem, until we reflect that common-sense reasoning conforms to the principle of contradiction. When we are told that the statement, *All unicorns are spotted,* is false, we are likely to infer from this assertion that its contradictory, *Some unicorns are not spotted,* is true. However, if there are no unicorns at all, neither particular statement can be true.

The problems that arise in interpreting universal statements are: (1) If we do not include the existence of the members of the classes involved as part of the meaning, it becomes logically possible for them both to be true, in violation of common sense. (2) If we do interpret them as including the existence of members of their classes as part of their meaning, the principle of contradiction (and with it common sense) is violated.

Exactly how to deal with these problems has long been a subject of dispute among logicians. The answer partly depends on what one wishes from a logical system. Logicians who are interested mainly in systematic values as such—simplicity, economy, the utmost explicitness—and in the technical applications of logic as a foundation for mathematics, or as an instrument to be used by the sciences, generally prefer to adopt the simple interpretation of universal statements. They are indifferent to whether any of the classes mentioned have any members. Logicians who are interested in using a logical system to formalize and clarify the reasoning processes that are carried out with the guidance of common-sense judgment but without any very clear and explicit conception of the underlying controlling principles cannot operate with the simple interpretation.

Neither of these alternatives provides a satisfactory solution for a logical system with conformity to common sense as one of its controlling objectives. Such a system must preserve *all* of the relationships set forth in the square of opposition; it can afford to sacrifice neither the relationship of contrariety nor that of contradiction. The introduction of a special rule of inference, the principle of limitation, into the system represents an attempt to preserve both relationships. What we have done, essentially, is to avoid a definite commitment as to exactly what an **A** or an **E** statement *means* and to direct our attention instead to the truly *logical* problem of what can be inferred from such a statement. We do not look for the justification of the principle of limitation in the meaning of the statements but rather in the inferences it provides for.

If we are to provide a justification for the principle at all—apart from the inferences it provides for—it would be best to look to the factors controlling the *use* of statements in the forms *All S are P* and *No S are P* in ordinary English. Whatever we say about the meaning contained in such statements, we can say that when the English language is used normally, neither one of them is asserted when there are no members of the subject class. We might contrast the function of *No S are P* with *There are no SP's* in ordinary English in this respect. It would not be appropriate, given the rules according to which we normally use the English language, to say *No red patches on this page are square;* it would be appropriate to say, *There are no square red patches on this page.* To convey the difference, we do not have to say that *No red patches on this page are square* includes the existence of red patches on this page as part of its meaning and is therefore false. We can just leave it as a matter of a restriction on the circumstances in which the use of that expression is an appropriate way of denying red square patches on the page, a restriction that does not apply to the use of the other expression for the same purpose. The justification for the principle of limitation can then be stated in this way: In ordinary

English, we do not normally use statements of the **A** and **E** forms when there are no members of their subject classes, even if they would be true if used in such contexts. Therefore, anyone who makes such a statement, observing the conditions that normally determine its use, is committed to permitting inferences that depend on the existence of members of the subject class. By using logical English as the framework for the development of logical principles, we can take advantage of our familiarity with the sentences it borrows from ordinary English and the inferences we make on the basis of such sentences without having any conception of the principles underlying them. It is just for this reason that we must maintain the same inferences the sentences permit in ordinary usage, whatever justification we may give for them in logical English.

The same justification, however, cannot be given for the use of a principle of limitation in the other two languages. They are entirely artificial, and the marks by which assertions are made in them are not subject to any already established rules of usage. It makes no difference whether or not we recognize a principle of limitation within the system of Venn diagrams or algebraic notation, as long as we consider them as not having any relevance to ordinary ways of expressing logical relationships in everyday language. If we wish to regard these systems as the exact counterparts of the system of logical English, we must impose such a principle on them. However, if we regard their universal assertions as counterparts of statements in English in the form *There are no . . .* , then there is no basis for incorporating such a principle into the system; such statements in English are not subject to the same restriction on usage as are the statements borrowed for use in logical English. Even when the principle of limitation *is* incorporated into a system, absolute theoretical precision would require that it be applied with some restriction in order to prevent the possibility of inferences that are not acceptable to common-sense judgment.

Some rather odd immediate inferences are permitted in some systems, the so-called partial and full inverses. In the partial inverse, the subject term has indirectly been replaced by its complement, and yet the order of terms is the same as when they were originally given. In the full inverse, both terms have been replaced by their complements, and the order is as originally given. In either case, the quantity of the original statement must be reduced from universal to particular. As with the contrapositives, the full inverse has the same quality as the premise from which it is derived; the partial inverse has an opposite quality. The derivation of the full inverse of an **E** statement, for example, would look like this:

1. No S are P.   Premise
2. No P are S.   1, CONV
3. All P are $\overline{S}$.   2, OBV
4. Some P are $\overline{S}$.   3, LIM
5. Some $\overline{S}$ are P.   4, CONV
6. Some $\overline{S}$ are not $\overline{P}$.   5, OBV

In terms of a more graphic example, from the truth of the statement *All bachelors are happy,* we would be justified in inferring that *Some married men are nonhappy* or that *Some married men are not happy,* the full and the partial inverse respectively. That this should be a permissible inference on purely logical grounds seems odd. If, as seems logically possible at least, all men were happy, the conclusion would be false while the premise was true. A logical system that judges such an inference to be valid according to the rules, while a common-sense interpretation shows that it could not be valid unless it were logically impossible for all men to be happy, cannot be said to be in accord with common-sense reasoning. While common sense might tell us that it is *psychologically* impossible for all men to be happy at once, it certainly regards this utopian social situation as *logically* possible; common sense would probably reject any systematic theoretical interpretation of logical possibility according to which it was *not* logically possible. The inferences involved in arriving at the partial or the full inverse are consequently contrary to common-sense reasoning. It would be well to eliminate them from any system of logic that pretends to provide a framework of interpretation and extension of our common-sense judgments as to the validity and invalidity of arguments.

There are various ways in which this can be accomplished. One way is to be more careful in specifying the universe of discourse and complementary terms. If the universe of discourse for *All bachelors are happy* is taken to be wider than men, then the complement of *bachelors* cannot be expressed as *married men;* there will be things in such a universe that are neither bachelors nor married men. However, this way of guarding against unwelcome inferences creates awkwardness in some of the statements without really getting to the heart of the difficulty. A better method is to impose a restriction upon the principle of limitation by requiring that it be applied only at the first opportunity and not thereafter. In our derivation of the full inverse of the **E** statement, this restriction was not followed; the transition from step 3 to 4 by applying limitation did not represent the *first* opportunity to do so. What this means is that only the subject classes of our original statements are to be regarded as nonempty classes. In terms of the example we have been considering, it means that while no one would ordinarily say *All bachelors are happy* unless he believed that bachelors existed, he might make such a statement without wishing to commit himself to believing in the existence of men who are not happy. He might also say *No bachelors are happy* without meaning to indicate any belief concerning the existence of men who are happy. When this restriction is imposed, it no longer becomes possible to derive the partial or full inverse from an **A** or an **E** proposition; in both cases, the derivation requires that the rule of limitation be applied *after* the first opportunity has passed.

3.8   A GENERAL METHOD FOR DETERMINING LOGICAL RELATIONSHIPS

All of the relationships in which the truth or falsity of one statement determines something about the truth or falsity of another are represented on the square of opposition. This is not the case for logical equivalence. Two statements are logically equivalent if we can validly infer from the truth value of one, whether truth or falsity, the same truth value of the other. If we admit the relationship of a statement to itself into our consideration of logical relationships, we can say that even logical equivalence is represented on the square, for certainly each of the four statements is equivalent to itself.

Although every variety of positive logical relationship is represented on the square of opposition, it would be far from true to say that every example of logical relationship can be so represented. It must be repeated that the relationships on the square of opposition are limited to statements that have the same subject term and the same predicate term. The square of opposition will indicate the relation between *All A are B* and *No A are B,* but it does not indicate what positive relationship, if any, holds between *All A are B* and *All B are $\overline{A}$*. It is in fact the same relationship, contrariety; that fact cannot be read from any square of opposition restricted to statements with the same subject and the same predicate terms.

We have already observed that if two statements are to have some positive logical relationship (that is, if they are not to be logically independent), there must be a fundamental identity in their subject matter. The one cannot contain a term (not even its complement) that does not occur in the other.[6] Within the system, therefore, assuming problems of interpretation to have been resolved so that synonymous terms are all represented by the same letter respectively with and without a bar over it (complementary terms), the first test of logical relationship will be to compare the two statements in order to see whether or not the same capital letter appears in each one as terms. If not, the two statements are logically independent: the truth or falsity of the one will determine nothing concerning the truth or falsity of the other.

If the same two letters do occur in each statement, there will be some positive logical relationship between the statements. The truth or falsity, or perhaps both, of the one will permit us to make some inference about the truth or falsity of the other. The inference will be immediate in the sense we have defined: the premise from which it issues is a single statement; the inference need not be direct. Within the system defined by our rules of immediate inference, of the relationships on the same square of opposition, only implication and contradiction can be established by direct inference. A single rule applied once (LIM or CONTRAD) secures the positive inference in each case. As we have seen, the other relationships, such as contrariety, are demonstrated by indirect inference.

Although the inferences involved in the various relationships on the square of opposition do not all have the same status in relation to the basic rules of immediate inference, some being direct and others indirect, for our present purposes, we can treat the logical relationships as given.

---

[6] This is true without qualification only if we restrict our attention to formal patterns in which a term is represented by a single capital letter and its complement by the same letter with a bar over it. Outside this restriction, we can assert logical relationships that hold by virtue of meanings of the terms, although they are distinct terms. The fact that Mr. Allardyce is a confirmed bachelor is not logically independent of the fact that he is unmarried; in the relevant universe of discourse, the two predicate terms would be distinct, however.

We would also have to take account of relationships based on the fact that two terms, while not precisely complementary, represent what might be called contrary opposites. The fact that something is black is not logically unrelated to the fact that it is not white. Asserting that someone is happy is not logically unrelated to another statement asserting that he is unhappy. Yet, in neither case are the two terms complementaries. The relation of complementary classes is like that of contradictory statements: A given item in the universe can neither be inside both classes nor outside both classes. The relation of classes that are contrary opposites is like that of contrary statements: Nothing can belong to both classes, but it is possible for something to be within the universe of discourse and yet belong to neither. The division of a universe into complementary classes is both exclusive and exhaustive. Contrary classes are mutually exclusive but do not exhaust their universe. Without a special mark, like the bar, to represent their relationship, we cannot express purely formal rules for the resulting valid inferences.

The problem we face is to extend what we know about the relationships on the same square to others between statements that do not belong on the same square because they have different subject terms, or different predicate terms, or both. The key to meeting this problem is to be found in the "rule of replacement":

> *The Rule of Replacement*
>   Any statement can be replaced by a statement logically equivalent to it in any logical context.

The logical contexts referred to in the rule are the statements in the system and the relationships and inferences between statements.

We can easily understand the justification of the rule of replacement. Two statements are logically equivalent if they must have the same truth value, that is, if, from the truth value of the one, the same truth value can be validly inferred for the other. The valid inferences that define and distinguish the various logical relationships we have enumerated fall under the general definition of validity—a definition that is formulated in terms of the possibility of combining the truth of the premise(s) with the falsehood of the conclusion. The replacement of a statement by another statement that must have the same truth value will not affect any relationship that is defined in terms of possible combinations of truth value, hence the rule of replacement.

In order to apply the principle of replacement, it is necessary that we be able to recognize examples of logical equivalence other than the trivial case of a statement's equivalence to itself. The result of applying CONTRAD to a statement offers an obvious example: A statement is equivalent to the negation of its contradictory. In applying CONTRAD, we first change both the quantity and the quality of the statement, forming the contradictory of the original statement. Its truth value is the opposite of the truth value of the original, whether it is true or false. We then produce, by negation, a statement with a truth value that is the opposite of the contradictory's truth value. The truth value of this last statement must be the same as that of the original.

> All sentries are privates.

is contradictory to

> Some sentries are not privates.

but it is equivalent to

> ~ (Some sentries are not privates).

Even this case of equivalence, however, does not take us beyond the realm of relationships between statements with the same subject and predicate terms. For that, we must have a more general test of equivalence than the principle that a statement is equivalent to the negation of its contradictory.

As a general test of equivalence between two statements, we shall use the following criterion:

> Two statements are equivalent if they have the same quantity and determine the same distribution values for all terms.

Any pair of statements that fulfill this condition can be exchanged, one for the other, according to the rule of replacement.

With a general test of equivalence available, we are in a position to determine the logical relationship between any two statements in logical English. If one or both of the two statements is preceded by a negation sign, it can be replaced by an equivalent statement according to the principle of contradiction—a statement is equivalent to the negation of its contradictory. The new pair of statements, neither one negated, will have the same logical relationship as the original pair.

The relationship between two unnegated statements with the same subject and the same predicate terms is indicated on the square of opposition. The relationship between two statements that belong on different squares of opposition is determined by applying the equivalence test so as to determine whether one of them has an equivalent on the same square of opposition as the other. The two equivalent statements have the same logical relationship to any third statement.

The procedure to follow, then, is to construct a square of opposition for each of the two statements and proceed to search for an equivalent of either of them on the other one's square. Let us suppose, for example, that we are to ascertain the relationship between the statements below:

> It is false that some persons who do not manufacture sausages are pork butchers.
> Some pork butchers are not sausage manufacturers.

Introducing appropriate abbreviations, we can rewrite these statements as:

> $\sim$ (Some $\overline{S}$ are P).
> Some P are not S.

We can replace the negated statement by an equivalent unnegated statement, transforming the problem into the determination of the logical relation between:

> No $\overline{S}$ are P.   and   Some P are not S.

The squares of opposition for each are constructed next:

All $\overline{S}$ are P	No $\overline{S}$ are P	All P are S	No P are S
Some $\overline{S}$ are P	Some $\overline{S}$ are not P	Some P are S	*Some P are not S*

The statements in which we are interested are in italics. Each of them has an equivalent on the other square of opposition. The equivalent of *No $\overline{S}$ are P* is *All P are S*. The two statements have the same quantity and the distribution of terms in relation to each of them is the same: S is undistributed and $\overline{S}$ distributed; P is distributed and $\overline{P}$ undistributed. They will have the same relationship to any third statement. Since *All P are S* is, on the same square of opposition, the contradictory of *Some P are not S*, the relation of *No $\overline{S}$ are P* to *Some P are not S* must also be contradiction.

The procedure we just completed will identify the relationship between any two statements. If neither of the two statements has an equivalent on the same square of opposition as the other statement, they are independent. *All A are B* and *No $\overline{A}$ are B,* for example, are an independent pair. No inferences can be drawn from the truth or falsity of the one to the truth or falsity of the other.

We have applied, in carrying out this procedure, a test of equivalence. How a statement can be transformed into an equivalent statement has not, however, been discussed, except in reference to the relevance of CONTRAD. In fact, the application of the principles of conversion (including complement conversion) and obversion produces a new statement equivalent to the original. Since the pattern of distributed and undistributed terms is symmetrical in an **E** and an **I** statement—both terms are distributed or both undistributed—reversing the order of the terms affects neither the quantity of the statement nor the distribution value of any term. Reversing the terms in an **A** or an **O** statement does change their distribution values; when each one is replaced by its complement, the distribution values are reversed back to the original. To change the quality of a statement also changes the distribution value of its predicate term, but replacing the predicate term by its complement reverses the values again. The application of these principles produces a new statement equivalent to the original. We can therefore add to the content of the rule of replacement:

> Any statement can be replaced in any relationship by a statement produced from it by applying CONTRAD, CONV, CC, or OBV.

Notice that the principle of limitation does *not* produce an equivalent to the original statement. If the original universal statement is false, it is still possible for the particular statement resulting from applying LIM to be true.

To the determination of logical relation, we are now in a position to add a way of proving, by direct or indirect inference, any of the valid inferences that define the relationship. In our previous example, we established that the relationship of contradiction held between

$$\sim (\text{Some } \overline{S} \text{ are } P). \quad \text{and} \quad \text{Some } P \text{ are not } S.$$

This means that we are able to infer from either truth value of the one the opposite truth value for the other. Here is an example of such a proof:

1.	$\sim$ (Some $\overline{S}$ are P).	Premise
2.	No $\overline{S}$ are P.	1, CONTRAD
3.	No P are $\overline{S}$.	2, CONV
4.	All P are S.	3, OBV
5.	$\sim$ (Some P are not S).	4, CONTRAD

The other inferences involved in the relation of contradictory statements are all demonstrable in terms of the basic principles of immediate inference.

We have now completed the study of immediate inference within the system of logical English and its associated languages. There are four basic rules that govern reasoning of this extremely simple type: the principles of contradiction, limitation, conversion, and obversion. We have shown that by using them, we can determine the logical relationship between any two statements within the systematic scope of these languages. Our next step will be to determine what additional rules are required in order to make possible more complex types of reasoning in which the restriction to a single premise is abandoned. In the next few chapters, we will be shown that one such additional rule is sufficient; by using it together with the rules of immediate inference presented in this chapter, we can give a justification for any valid inference that can occur in this system.

3.8 EXERCISES

The Iowa hogs referred to in Exercise 1.5A can be divided into two groups, those who were liars and those who were not. They could also be divided according to gender, those who were boars and those who were not. How many statements can be made in logical English using a vocabulary limited to these two pairs of complementary terms (L, $\overline{L}$, B, $\overline{B}$), not including statements in which both members of the same pair of complementary terms occur in the same statement?

A. Suppose it to be true that all of the nonboars are liars (All $\overline{B}$ are L). What, if anything, can be inferred concerning the truth or falsity of each of the following?

1. No B are L.
2. Some $\overline{B}$ are not L.
3. Some $\overline{B}$ are $\overline{L}$.
4. All L are B.
5. Some L are B.
6. Some $\overline{L}$ are B.
7. All $\overline{L}$ are B.
8. No $\overline{L}$ are $\overline{B}$.
9. No $\overline{B}$ are L.
10. Some B are not L.

B. What can be inferred if $\sim$ (All $\overline{B}$ are L)?

C. What is the name of the logical relationship in each case?

Chapter 4

THE SYLLOGISM

4.1 STRUCTURE OF THE SYLLOGISM

The discussion in Section 3.8 dealt with immediate inference, that is, inference from a single premise. Syllogistic inference, with which this chapter is concerned, is inference from a pair of premises to a conclusion that could not be deduced from either one of them alone. A "syllogism," therefore, is composed of three statements, two of them premises and the third a conclusion that is supposed to follow from these premises.

In ordinary English, an argument including two premises and a conclusion can be stated in any order. The conclusion may be stated first, followed by the supporting premises, or the premises may be stated first and then the conclusion, or the conclusion may be sandwiched in between the two premises. However, the mere order in which the constituents of an argument are stated will make no difference to its validity or invalidity. Order may have stylistic or rhetorical significance—one sequence may provide for more graceful expression or more persuasive effect, for example —but it has no logical significance. Consequently, we can restrict the order in which a syllogism is presented to one standard form, and we can still give a systematic account of the factors affecting the validity of an argument. The sequence we shall use has the premises first and then the conclu-

sion. In order to reinforce the distinction between premises and conclusion
(which is already indicated by order according to this convention), we also
separate the premises from the conclusion by a horizontal line. The basic
pattern for a syllogism will then be:

By filling in the brackets, we can indicate the subject matter of the argument; by filling in the underlined spaces with quantifiers and copulas, we
can indicate the logical form of each of its three constituents. As in previous discussions, we shall concentrate our attention on the latter aspects
of the argument; it is on them rather than on the subject matter that
validity or invalidity will depend. Even so, there are two requirements
that the terms of a syllogism must fulfill if the argument is to function as
an example of syllogistic inference. No valid inference can be drawn if
the premises are irrelevant to the conclusion, that is, if the conclusion concerns subject matter to which no reference has been made in the premises.
Obviously, then, each of the terms in the conclusion must appear somewhere in the premises. There must also be some effective connection between the premises so that they can function together in implying the
conclusion. This connection is provided for by the presence of one term
that occurs in both premises.

As a consequence of these two requirements, there will be three terms
(in the brackets) in the basic structure, each of them occurring twice. In
the present treatment of the subject, therefore, the number of terms is one
of the defining conditions of a genuine syllogism to which the rules of
validity for syllogisms are applicable. For the traditional treatment, the
rule of three terms was introduced as a rule of validity itself. One way in
which a syllogism could go astray was by committing the "fallacy of four
terms." Here we shall treat arguments that violate this condition as incompletely formulated cases of more complex types of reasoning. (See
the discussion of enthymemes and sorites in Sections 5.5 and 5.6.)

There are definite risks involved in treating the number of terms in a
syllogism as a rule of validity rather than as a condition of being an argument in standard form and therefore subject to other rules of validity.
These dangers are illustrated in A. E. Taylor's edition of DeMorgan's
treatise on formal logic. DeMorgan had written the following reproof,
aimed at "the affirmation of logical form applied to that which wants it,
a very common thing among us."

A little time ago, either the editor or a large-type correspondent (I forget which) of a newspaper imputed to the clergy the maintenance of the "logic" of the following as "consecutive and without flaw." This was hard on the clergy (particularly the Oxonians) for there was no middle term, neither of the concluding terms was in the premises, and one negative premise gave a positive conclusion. It ran thus,

Episcopacy is of Scripture origin.

The church of England is the only episcopal church in England,

Ergo, the church established is the church that should be supported.

To this passage in DeMorgan's text, however, the editor added a footnote:

DeMorgan's example is unfortunate. The argument was not meant to be a syllogism but a train of reasoning with certain suppressed premises. The reasoning is valid, *if the implied premises are granted.* The argument might be expressed more fully thus:

(1) The form of Church Government which existed in apostolic times is the right form of Church Government. (As we see from the Scriptures), the form of Church Government which existed in apostolic times was Episcopacy. Episcopacy is the right form of Church Government.

(2) The Church with the right form of Government is the Church that ought to be supported.

The Anglican Church is the Church with the right form of Government (by the conclusion of syllogism 1).

The Anglican Church is the Church that ought to be supported. The reasoning is "consecutive and without flaw;" the only question is whether the implied premises are, in point of fact, true.[1]

The fact that a syllogism includes three terms, each occurring twice, provides us with a basis for further restriction on sequence by allowing us to make a general distinction between the two premises. The predicate term of the *conclusion* is called the "major term," and the subject term is called the "minor term." The premise in which the major term occurs we can then call the "major premise" and that in which the minor term occurs, the "minor premise." To our specification of one standard form, we can now add the provision that the premises must be in the order of major premise first and minor premise second. The term that occurs in both premises is called the "middle term." When we are using capital letters in place of brackets, we shall use the letter M for the middle term and S and

[1] Augustus DeMorgan, *Formal Logic* (1847), A. E. Taylor, ed. (London 1926), p. 311.

P for the minor and major terms respectively. The basic structure for the syllogism in standard form will then be:

Major Premise ——— [ ] ——— [ ] (Brackets contain M and P)

Minor Premise ——— [ ] ——— [ ] (Brackets contain M and S)

Conclusion ——— [S] ——— [P]

4.2 SIGNIFICANT LOGICAL CHARACTERISTICS OF THE SYLLOGISM

In the basic structure of the syllogism, the positions of S and P are the only fixed ones, and this is only because we arbitrarily chose to use those letters to represent respectively the subject and predicate terms of the conclusion. The position taken by the terms in the premises—whatever subject matter they may represent—is a significant logical characteristic of the argument. That is one of the characteristics on which its validity depends. The positions taken by the terms in relation to each other determines the "figure" of the syllogism. There are four possible figures that can be distinguished on the basic structure, and they are traditionally distinguished by a number. In the "first figure," the terms have the same positions in the premises that they occupy in the conclusion: the major term is predicate of the major premise as well as of the conclusion, and the minor term is subject of the minor premise as well as of the conclusion. In the "second figure," the positions of the terms in the major premise are reversed while those of the terms in the minor premise remain the same. In the "third figure," the position of the major term is the same as in the conclusion, but the position of the minor term in the minor premise is reversed. In the "fourth figure," the role of each term in the premise is the reverse of its role in the conclusion.

	1		2		3		4
M	P	P	M	M	P	P	M
S	M	S	M	M	S	M	S
S	P	S	P	S	P	S	P

When the argument is in standard order—major premise, minor premise, conclusion—a line drawn through the middle term will have a characteristic position and orientation. We can use a horizontal foot on the line when it is vertical to indicate the location of the other terms (see figure 4.1).

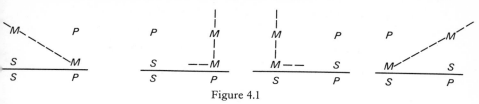

Figure 4.1

The four figures can be easily symbolized and remembered in terms of the patterns in figure 4.2.

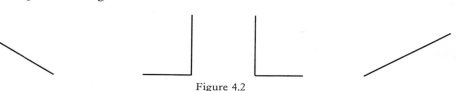

Figure 4.2

When the figure of the syllogism has been determined by fixing the positions of its terms in the brackets provided in the basic structure, there remains only one further significant characteristic to be determined: the logical forms of the constituent statements. These forms are specified by filling in the underlined spaces in the basic structure (p. 72) with quantifiers and copulas. It should be clear, now, that when the logical character of the premises and the conclusion is determined in this way, it will be a factor on which the validity of the syllogism will depend. The specification of the logical form of the constituent statements defines the "mood" of the syllogism. The letters that name the form of each statement in the standard order serve to identify the mood. Thus, a syllogism with the mood **AEE** has a major premise of the **A** form, a minor premise of the **E** form, and a conclusion of the **E** form.

Once figure and mood have been specified, the syllogism has been made perfectly definite as far as its significant logical characteristics are concerned. The only further specifications that could be made on it would be to replace the letters representing as yet unspecified terms by words or letters standing for some definite subject matter. This, as has been observed before, is irrelevant to the purposes of a general logic. The structural, or formal, characteristics represented by figure and mood permit the construction of 256 different patterns of syllogistic reasoning, each one valid or invalid depending on its form, that is, its figure and mood.

4.2   EXERCISE

Identify the figure and the mood of each of the following syllogisms. (Which of them are not in standard order?)

A. All B are L.
   No S are B.
   —————————
   No S are L.

B. Some M are not W.
   Some O are W.
   —————————
   Some M are O.

C. All M are W.
   No S are M.
   —————————
   No S are W.

D. All A are P.
   Some R are P.
   —————————
   Some A are R.

E. All F are S.
   Some S are not L.
   —————————
   Some L are not F.

F. No B are L.
   Some B are not S.
   —————————
   Some S are not L.

G. Some P are V.
   All V are H.
   —————————
   All H are P.

H. All A are R.
   All R are P.
   —————————
   All A are P.

I. Some F are not W.
   All F are S.
   —————————
   Some S are not W.

J. All C are M.
   All T are M.
   —————————
   No T are C.

4.3 RULES OF THE SYLLOGISM

The usual method of determining the validity or invalidity of a syllogism (apart from appeal to common-sense judgment) is to apply a set of rules of criticism. A syllogism that violates any one of these rules is thereby proved to be invalid. Validity is accordingly demonstrated indirectly by showing that a syllogism does not violate any of these rules. In order for this method to be effective, we must have a sufficient and complete set of rules of criticism. If the set does not include all of the conditions of validity a syllogism must fulfill, some syllogisms that pass all of the rules will nevertheless be invalid by other tests, such as appeals to common sense. In this section, we will consider the traditional rules by which syllogisms are logically criticized; in Section 4.4, we will discuss the method of testing syllogisms for validity by the use of Venn diagrams. In the following sections, we will turn our attention to the problem of discovering a rule or rules of inference, as distinguished from rules of criticism, by which we can positively justify valid cases of syllogistic reasoning.

The rules of the syllogism we will use are four in number. Two of them concern the quality of the constituent statements, and the other two concern the distribution of terms. One rule of each pair can be applied by considering the premises alone, and the other requires a comparison between the premises and the conclusion. In the list that follows, the rules concerned with the premises alone are given as the *first* rules and the others as the *second;* the abbreviations by which they are designated we construct accordingly.

The Rules of Quality

FIRST RULE OF QUALITY (Q1)   There can be only one negative premise.

SECOND RULE OF QUALITY (Q2)   If there is a negative premise, the conclusion must be negative; if there is a negative conclusion, one premise must be negative.

The Rules of Distribution[2]

FIRST RULE OF DISTRIBUTION (D1)   The middle term must be distributed at least once.

SECOND RULE OF DISTRIBUTION (D2)   If a term is distributed in the conclusion, it must be distributed in the premise in which it occurs.[3]

It is important to acquire the habit of applying these four rules systematically when criticizing syllogisms so that their use becomes reflex action. The order in which they have been presented here is as good as any.

4.3   EXERCISE

Check the syllogisms in Exercise 4.2 for validity by applying the rules of quality and distribution. Indicate whether the syllogism is valid or invalid; if it is invalid, indicate which rule is violated.

[2] There are two common errors in applying the rules of distribution that must be avoided. The first rule of distribution does not prohibit the middle term from being distributed in both of its occurrences; it only requires that it be distributed at least once.

The second rule of distribution does not prohibit terms from being undistributed in the conclusion that were distributed in the premises. Unlike the second rule of quality, it operates only in one direction.

[3] The second rule of distribution is responsible for the restriction on conversion in logical English. **E** and **I** statements have terms that are respectively both distributed and undistributed. Reversing the order of the terms will consequently not alter the distribution of either one. In **A** and **O** statements, however, one term is distributed and the other is not; reversing their order moves one term from a position in which it is undistributed to a position in which it is distributed, violating the second rule of distribution. (Although the second rule of distribution is given as a rule for the criticisms of syllogisms, its application is perfectly general. Its common-sense justification is that we cannot make a valid inference from a premise telling something about only at least one member of a class to a conclusion that asserts something about every member of that class.)

4.4 THE VENN DIAGRAM TEST

There is at least one objection to criticizing syllogisms by applying the rules of quality and distribution: there is no clear reason why these particular rules should effectively distinguish between valid and invalid syllogisms. That they do we will demonstrate in the next chapter. In this section, we will turn to another method of testing validity that gives us a more direct and obvious result. The Venn diagrams, as we have observed, are adaptable in principle to dealing with any number of classes, although their practical usefulness is limited to three in number. The basic Venn diagram pattern for three classes is shown in figure 4.3.

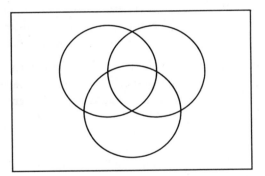

Figure 4.3

The area within the rectangle provides space for representing every possible item in the universe of discourse, whether it belongs to all three classes, to none of them, to only one, to only two, and so on. This is the basic requirement that must be fulfilled by a pattern if we are to use it for making statements in the language of Venn diagrams.

Although the diagram on which the statements of a syllogism will be represented must contain three interlocking circles instead of the two overlapping circles on which single statements are represented, it is not necessary to introduce any new method of using the basic diagrammatic statement patterns. Each statement of a syllogism involves just two classes and can be represented by an appropriate pattern on two of the three circles in the diagram. When *No S are M* is represented on a diagram for a single statement, the pattern is as the one in figure 4.4.

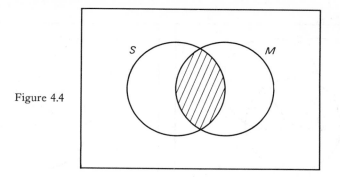

Figure 4.4

When the same statement is represented on a diagram containing three circles, it will have exactly the same pattern as the one in figure 4.5. Although the orientation of the overlapping circles S and M may have changed, the pattern by which the **E** statement with these as its terms is represented is not affected.

What the three circles introduce is not a need for a new way of representing statements but a need for care in applying the familiar method. A statement with two terms will be expressed by an appropriate pattern involving two overlapping circles, as S and M in figure 4.5. In the basic diagram, however, the third circle P cuts through both S and M. That circle must not be permitted to have any significance in the representation of a statement that does not involve the term that identifies it. It cannot be a boundary demarcating a shaded area from an unshaded one. Only the circles representing terms involved in the statement expressed on the diagram can play that role. Neither of the diagrams in figure 4.6 would by itself constitute an adequate expression of the statement *No S are M*.

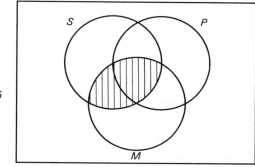

Figure 4.5

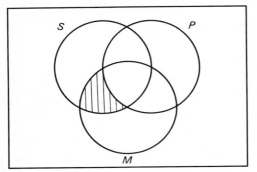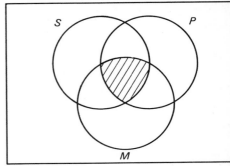

Figure 4.6

When a particular statement is expressed by making an *x* in the appropriate portion of the diagram, it is equally important that the third circle that stands for a term *not* involved in the statement play no significant role. This means that we cannot place the *x* either inside or outside the irrelevant circle; we must place it on the boundary. Figure 4.7 correctly represents the statement *Some P are M*. Each of the two diagrams in figure 4.8 is an incorrect representation of *Some P are M*.

The diagram on the left indicates that there is something inside the class represented by the circle labeled *S* and the one on the right indicates that there is something outside *S*. Neither assertion is warranted by the statement that *Some P are M*, which says nothing at all about *S*.

In using the Venn diagrams as a test of validity for syllogisms, it is best to have a fixed basic pattern with which to work (just as we have a standard order for writing premises and conclusion in logical English). The

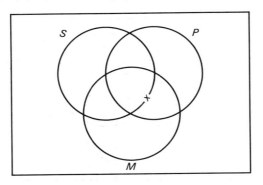

Figure 4.7

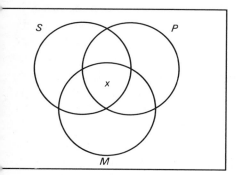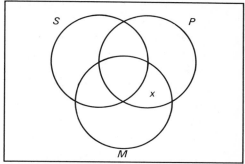

Figure 4.8

standard Venn diagram pattern for a syllogism will be in the form of
three overlapping circles (figure 4.9). The minor term is represented by
the circle on the left and the major term by the one on the right. The
middle term is represented by the circle below and in the middle of the
rectangle.

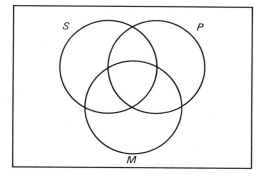

Figure 4.9

In our use of the Venn diagram to test validity, it is enough to place
just the premises of the syllogism on the diagram. If the syllogism is valid,
the conclusion will appear on the diagram. If it is invalid, it will still be
possible to make a mark representing the conclusion to be false. This can
be done without violating the basic rules controlling Venn diagrams: the
same area cannot both contain an *x* and be shaded out, and areas representing subject classes must contain an *x* somewhere. If you recall the definition
of validity—an argument is valid if it is impossible for the premises to be

true and the conclusion false—it is easy to understand how the diagram serves as an effective test. The rules of the diagram determine what is possible and what is not. If the conclusion of the syllogism already appears on the diagram once the premises have been written onto it, then it becomes impossible for any mark to be made on the diagram that would represent the conclusion as false. Only by violating one of the rules could the premises be represented as true and the conclusion as false. Consequently, if it is possible to make such a mark even after the marks representing the truth of the premises have been written in, the syllogism must be invalid.

For practical reasons, when writing the premises of a syllogism containing a particular premise onto a Venn diagram it is desirable to hold off writing in the x for that premise even if it occurs first when the syllogism is written in standard form. The reason for this is that when one part of an area is shaded out, we are justified in placing an x wholly in the other part of the area, if an x is called for at all. The point of having an x straddle a line is to leave open the possibility that it might just as well fall to one side of the line as to the other. However, when the area to one side has already been shaded out, that possibility no longer remains; if the x is to be in the area at all, it must be within the unshaded part of it. Shading out an area as called for by a universal premise will often restrict the possibilities for the placement of the x called for by a particular premise. For example, in diagraming a syllogism in the third figure, mood **OAO** (3-**OAO**) (figure 4.10), it would be necessary to have the x for the major premise straddle the line ab. This line belongs to the S circle, and the major premise says nothing at all about S. However, if the minor premise is diagramed first, there is no point in considering the possibility that the x should be outside the S circle; that possibility has been effectively excluded by the shading. The syllogism turns out to be valid; there is now at least one thing (represented by the x) that is inside the class S and outside P—the conditions for truth of the **O** statement relating S and P.

Of course, we cannot always expect this to occur. Frequently even after the universal premise has been diagramed, it will still be necessary to have an x for a particular premise straddling a line. And when both premises are particular, there is no possibility of taking advantage of the shading called for by a universal premise. When both premises are universal, it makes no difference which one is written in first. As a matter of technique, when two universal premises both call for the same space to be shaded out, it is undesirable to shade out only the previously unshaded part. It is

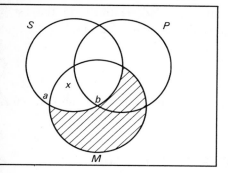
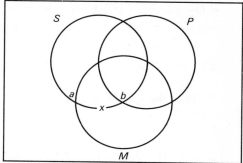

Figure 4.10

better[4] to duplicate shading of the one part and to preserve the same pattern of shading for a universal statement every time one is written onto a diagram (see figure 4.11, 4-**EAE**).

Figure 4.11
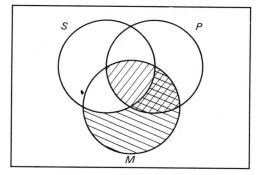

The student is advised to note that in a logical system not using the rule of limitation—the rule that permits inference from a universal premise to a particular conclusion—there will be fewer valid syllogisms than will be included in the system being developed here. Such a system will require still another rule of criticism for syllogisms: If a syllogism has two universal premises, it must have a universal conclusion. The addition of such a rule here would result in inconsistencies, for we are already committed to the acceptance of syllogisms that have universal premises and a particular conclusion. We are committed by our acceptance of the relationships around the sides of the square of opposition and of conversion by limitation as at

[4] This is purely a practical consideration. It has no theoretical significance.

least indirectly justifiable immediate inferences. Nevertheless, we shall single out such syllogisms for special attention and treatment in the list of valid forms of the syllogism developed in the following sections.

4.4 EXERCISE

Check the syllogisms in Exercise 4.2 for validity by using the Venn diagram method.

4.5 THE VALID FORMS OF THE SYLLOGISM

The rules presented in Section 4.3 are rules of criticism, and no one of them alone indicates what conclusion we can draw from a given set of premises. Each merely prohibits us from drawing certain conclusions under conditions stated in the rules. For this reason, they cannot directly provide the justification for any valid syllogistic inference. They could do so indirectly if we show that the rules of quality and distribution are sufficient by themselves to distinguish valid from invalid syllogisms. We would then be in a position to say that any syllogism not violating any of the rules is valid. At present, however, this is merely an assumption, one that so far has had no support.

We could support the assumption by appealing to the Venn diagrams, for they do give a positive justification of syllogistic reasoning when it is valid. To follow this procedure, we would have to apply to each of the possible forms of the syllogism first the rules of quality and distribution and then the Venn diagram test. If, in each case, the result was the same— if failure to violate any of the rules always corresponded to the positive proof of validity given by the diagram—then we would have good reason for accepting the four rules as sufficient for justifying validity. There are, however, fully 256 distinct forms the syllogism can take. The prospect of dealing with each one individually is indeed a dreary one (although the tedious task could be carried out easily enough by a machine designed for the purpose).

In establishing a positive test of validity, we will use an alternative method. The mechanical procedures made possible by the formal and systematic character of the rules will be used, but we will not apply them one by one to each of the possible forms of the syllogism. What we will do first is determine, using some short cuts, which of the forms *do* pass the test provided by the four rules; we shall find that there are only twenty-four of them. The task of testing each of these by the diagram method is considerably less staggering than the task of testing the original 256, and it has been reduced to reasonable dimensions.

Instead of resorting to the diagrams, however, we shall continue to shrink the dimensions of the problem still further. We can show that four of these twenty-four, if we accept the principles of immediate inference introduced in Chapter 3, are sufficient to provide justification for all the rest. Finally, we will see that these four can all be justified in terms of one basic principle, which we will then identify as the "principle of the syllogism" and add it to the list of basic rules of inference.

4.6 PAIRS OF PREMISES

We begin by identifying the twenty-four forms of the syllogism that do not violate any of the rules of quality and distribution. This task is divided into two stages. In the first stage, we consider only the premises of the various forms of the syllogism, without regard to the conclusion attached to them or to the figure. The possible combinations of the four basic types of statement into pairs serving as premises of a syllogism can be arranged systematically, as in Table 4.1. The type of statement serving as major premise is indicated by the first letter and the type of statement serving as minor premise is indicated by the second letter in each pair.

We can take each of the pairs in Table 4.1 to represent sixteen distinct forms of the syllogism, for each one can have attached to it any of four possible statement forms as conclusion and can be specified to have any of the four figures. It is easy to see that at least in some cases there is no possibility of constructing a valid syllogism, no matter what the figure or the conclusion

TABLE 4.1

1	2	3	4
AA	EA	IA	OA
AE	EE	IE	OE
AI	EI	II	OI
AO	EO	IO	OO

might be. We can begin with the most obvious cases. The first rule of quality concerns the quality of the premises only. It requires us to eliminate the four cases in which both premises are negative, since they directly violate this rule: the **EE** and **EO** forms in column 2 and the **OE** and **OO** in column 4.

The first rule of distribution also concerns the premises only, although it cannot be applied as directly as the first rule of quality. But at least one pair of premises can be seen to involve a violation of the first rule of distribution: **II** in column 3. Since **I** statements contain no distributed terms, there is no place in which the middle term can be distributed.

None of the other pairs can be eliminated by the application of a single rule, but there are three more that can be shown to violate two or more of the rules. Which rules are violated will depend on the figure and the conclusion that completes the specification of the syllogism, or both. However, it is not necessary to take up specific cases separately to indicate this. It is enough merely to consider the rules and the premises involved. The first two we will discuss contain particular premises of opposite quality: **IO** in column 3 and **OI** in column 4. In both pairs of premises, only one term is distributed, the predicate of the **O** statement. However, one of these premises is negative and so, by the second rule of quality, the conclusion must likewise be negative. In that case, the predicate term in the conclusion is a distributed term. By the second rule of distribution, it must have been distributed in the premises as well. Thus we find that if the two second rules are both to be fulfilled, the major term must be distributed in the major premise. By the first rule of distribution, the middle term must be distributed at least once; only one term can be distributed in the premises. It can be either the middle term or the major term, but it is impossible for both of them to be distributed at the same time. Consequently, depending on what specifications as to figure and conclusion are made, *either* the first rule of distribution will be violated (because the middle term is undistributed) *or* the second rule of quality will be violated (by having an affirmative conclusion with a negative premise) *or* the second rule of distribution will be violated (by having the major term distributed in the conclusion but not in the premises). In some cases, more than one of these flaws will be found, but in no case will all three be absent.

It is worth while to consider a somewhat more formalized presentation of the line of argument that we have just given. What we are interested in knowing is whether the following statements 1, 2, and 3 can all be true together. The line of argument proves that they cannot by showing that

the implications of two of them contradict the third. Such a set of statements is called an "inconsistent triad," and the method of proof is called
"reductio ad absurdum," *reduction to absurdity*. We shall encounter reductio ad absurdum in Section 4.8 and in demonstrating the validity of
certain forms of the syllogism (Sections 4.8 and 4.10).

Reductio ad Absurdum
1. The rules of quality and distribution are fulfilled.
2. One premise is negative.
3. There is only one distributed
   term.
4. The middle term is distributed.   D1
5. The conclusion is negative.   2, Q2
6. The major term is distributed   5, Definition of distributed
   in the conclusion.   terms
7. The major term is distributed
   in the premises.   6, D2

But the major term and the middle term are two different terms, making
statements 4 and 7 inconsistent with statement 3. Therefore there can be
no syllogism that fulfills the rules and has a negative premise but only one
distributed term.

Finally, by a line of reasoning quite similar to this but without need-
ing to take the first rule of distribution into account, we can show that **IE**
(in the third column of Table 4.1) cannot be used as a pair of premises in
any valid syllogism. The minor premise is negative, and the second rule of
distribution requires that the conclusion be negative. In that case, its predicate term is distributed and must be distributed in the premises as well.
But the predicate term of the conclusion appears in the major premise, the
one listed first. Since this is an **I** statement, it contains no distributed
term. Therefore, a syllogism with such a pair of premises cannot avoid
violating either the second rule of quality or the second rule of distribution.
With the elimination of this last pair of premises, we have reduced by half
the number of forms of the syllogism to be included in our further investigations. Eight out of the sixteen possible combinations of premises
will give no valid form of the syllogism no matter what figure may be
specified nor what conclusion attached to them. All valid forms must be

constructed from the eight remaining pairs, by appropriate choice of conclusion and figure.

4.7 DERIVATIVE RULES FOR EACH FIGURE

As a preliminary to the final determination of the valid forms, we consider the special significance the rules of quality and distribution have when applied to a specified figure of the syllogism. The four basic rules are perfectly general—they apply, that is, to any syllogism in standard form, prior to any specifications of mood or figure. Once the figure of a syllogism has been specified, however, these general rules permit us to lay down more special ones. These are not *new* rules, only the consequences in certain circumstances of the four rules. We could get along without them entirely if we wished. Just as the restriction of our attention to pairs of premises without regard to figure or conclusion helped to guide us systematically in the direction of our present goal—the list of valid forms of the syllogism— so a consideration of the special implications of the general rules for each of the four figures will assist in much the same way. By combining the conclusions reached about pairs of premises in the last section with the results that will be achieved in this section by investigating special requirements for each figure, we will be able to identify all of the valid forms.

For each of the first three figures, two special rules can be derived; for the fourth figure, there are three. We begin with the first figure and not because we have arbitrarily placed it first. For reasons that will become apparent later on, the special rules governing syllogisms in the first figure are especially significant:

  1. The major premise must be universal.
  2. The minor premise must be affirmative.

The proof that the minor premise must be affirmative is the simpler, and we will begin with it. For convenience, we will repeat the pattern of the first figure.

$$
\begin{array}{ll}
M & P \\
S & M \\
\hline
S & P
\end{array}
$$

We will try to show that if the minor premise is not affirmative, then it is impossible to avoid violating at least one of the primary rules of quality and distribution. We will start, then, with the supposition that the special rule has been violated.

1.	The minor premise is not affirmative.	Supposition
2.	The conclusion is negative.	1, Q2
3.	The major term is distributed in the conclusion.	2, Definition of distributed terms
4.	The major term must be distributed in the premises.	3, D2
5.	The major premise must be negative.	4, Definition of distributed terms

We have now arrived at a point where 1 and 5 together represent a violation of the first rule of quality. The only way of avoiding this result is by either violating one of the other rules appealed to in the steps leading from 1 to 5 or by making the minor premise affirmative and preventing the argument from getting started. In other words, it is impossible for any syllogism to fulfill all of the following three conditions: (1) it is in the first figure, (2) it has a negative minor premise, and (3) it fulfills the rules of quality and distribution.

The rule we have just demonstrated can now be used to assist in demonstrating another special requirement for the first figure: the major premise must be universal. We begin again with a supposition, that the major premise is not universal, and then show that it is impossible on that assumption to avoid violating at least one of the general rules of quality and distribution.

1.	The major premise is not universal.	Supposition
2.	The middle term is not distributed in the major premise.	1, Definition of distributed terms
3.	The middle term must be distributed in the minor premise.	2, D1
4.	The minor premise must be negative.	3, Definition of distributed terms

Since the argument would simply continue along the lines used in proving that the minor premise cannot be negative, it is unnecessary to repeat them. They will involve applications of Q2 and D2 and will lead to the conclusion that the major premise must be negative, which represents a violation of Q2. Therefore, in proving that the major premise of a first-figure syllogism must be universal, all of the basic rules of quality and distribution are involved. At least one of them is bound to be violated if the major premise is particular. Which one will depend on the other unspecified factors.

The two rules especially applicable to the first figure are now established.

1. The major premise must be universal.
2. The minor premise must be affirmative.

Applying these special rules to the eight pairs of premises that remain for further consideration in Table 4.1, we find that only four of them qualify. In the first figure, a syllogism can be valid only if it has premises that are **AA, AI, EA,** or **EI.** The second rule of quality restricts the conclusion to an affirmative statement when the premises are **AA** or **AI** and to negative statements when the premises are **EA** or **EI.** It can also be shown that no valid syllogism in any figure can have a universal conclusion if it has a particular premise. (Once again, this is not a new and independent rule but a consequence of the four basic rules. The proof is very much like the proof used in Section 4.6 to show that no valid syllogism can have two particular premises.) Taking this further restriction on the conclusion into account, six forms remain: 1-**AAA**, 1-**AAI**, 1-**AII**, 1-**EAE**, 1-**EAO**, and 1-**EIO.**

There are two special rules for the second figure:

1. The premises must be opposite in quality, one negative, one positive.
2. The major premise must be universal.

They are considerably easier to prove than those for the first figure. For easy reference, we repeat the pattern of the second figure.

$$
\begin{array}{cc}
P & M \\
S & M \\
\hline
S & P
\end{array}
$$

For the first of the two rules, the proof follows directly from applying **D1** to the pattern of terms in the second figure and combining the result with the general prohibition against two negative premises. For the second rule, we begin by realizing that, from the first rule, the conclusion must be negative. From this, it follows that the major term must be distributed in the major premise. In the second figure, that means that the major premise must be a universal statement. Taking these special rules into account, and the restrictions on the conclusion noted in the discussion of the first figure, there are again six forms of the syllogism that survive: 2-**AEE**, 2-**AEO**, 2-**AOO**, 2-**EAE**, 2-**EAO**, and 2-**EIO**.

Of the two special rules for the third figure, one is the same as one rule for the first:

 1. The minor premise must be affirmative.
 2. The conclusion must be particular.

The pattern for the third figure is:

$$\begin{array}{cc} M & P \\ M & S \\ \hline S & P \end{array}$$

Proof for rule 1 is the same as for the corresponding rule in the first figure. Proof for the second rule begins with the condition imposed by the first rule, taking into account the requirements imposed by D2. The list of forms that we arrive at by using the same method already employed in connection with the first and second figures is: 3-**AAI**, 3-**AII**, 3-**IAI**, 3-**EAO**, 3-**EIO**, 3-**OAO**.

There are three special rules for the fourth figure, but instead of stating a categorical, that is, unconditional principle, each one states a hypothetical one:

 1. If the major premise is affirmative, the minor premise must be universal.
 2. If either premise is negative, the major premise must be universal.
 3. If the major premise is affirmative, the conclusion must be particular.

We can see that the proofs for these three rules are relatively straightforward and simple upon inspection of the characteristic pattern of terms of the fourth figure:

$$\begin{array}{cc} P & M \\ M & S \\ \hline S & P \end{array}$$

The valid forms that emerge after application of the now familiar procedure are: 4-**AAI**, 4-**AEE**, 4-**IAI**, 4-**AEO**, 4-**EAO**, and 4-**EIO**.

The entire list of valid forms is given in Table 4.2 for reference and comparison. It is not desirable to attempt to memorize the list since it is more important to know the four general rules of quality and distribution on which it ultimately depends and the way in which the rules are applied in order to reach these results.

TABLE 4.2

First figure	Second figure	Third figure	Fourth figure
AAA	AEE	AAI	AAI
AAI	AEO	AII	AEE
AII	AOO	IAI	IAI
EAE	EAE	EAO	AEO
EAO	EAO	EIO	EAO
EIO	EIO	OAO	EIO

These twenty-four forms of the syllogism include all of the candidates for acceptance as valid forms. They *are* the valid forms, if the four rules of quality and distribution alone are sufficient to distinguish between valid and invalid syllogisms; these twenty-four are the complete set of forms of the syllogism that do not violate the rules. (Even this statement is somewhat stronger than would be justified by the procedure we have used. It should really read: These twenty-four are the forms that do not violate the basic rules, if there are no special rules applicable to any of the figures other than those that were actually used in preparing the list.)

4.8 THE PRINCIPLE OF SYLLOGISTIC INFERENCE

What is required now is some positive test of validity by which the presumptive status of these twenty-four forms, established by the fact that they do not violate a set of rules assumed without proof to be sufficient, can be definitely confirmed. One possibility is to appeal to the diagrammatic representation of each of them. It was shown (in Section 4.4) that in the diagrams we have a positive criterion of validity—if a syllogism is valid, then once the premises have been recorded on the diagram, the conclusion can be read off directly; there is no need to make any further marks. This is not the case with arguments expressed in logical English or in algebraic notation. Whether the syllogism is valid or invalid, in those languages the conclusion is represented by a separate statement distinct from the premises.

There is another possibility, and a somewhat more systematic one. It is to attempt to discover some underlying principle (or principles) of syllogistic reasoning comparable to the four principles that were introduced in Chapter 3 for immediate inference. In this section, we will consider the use of such a principle for arguments in logical English; in Section 4.9 we will approach the same problem in terms of algebraic notation. In each case, we will find that a limited number of additional principles (one for logical English and two for algebraic notation), all capable of common-sense justification, are sufficient to provide for all valid forms of syllogistic reasoning.

The principle of syllogistic reasoning that will be used in logical English will be stated first in terms that can best be understood and appreciated from the point of view of common sense; we will restate them in an equivalent form that is more directly and mechanically applicable to the statements of logical English. In its common-sense form, the principle is:

> If something is known about *all* the members of a given class, and it is also known that a second class is *included* (wholly or in part) in it, then what is known about the former class can be drawn as a conclusion about (all or part of) the latter class.

In a still more simple form, we can say that

> what we know about all the members of a class, we can validly assert about the members of any group known to fall inside of that class.

The more complex statement brings out an important feature of the principle: its application depends on two pieces of information (therefore it is a principle of *syllogistic* reasoning and not of immediate inference). One piece of information concerns *all* the members of a given class, the other asserts a relation of inclusion of all or some of the members of one class within another. In other words, the information is respectively of the kind given by a universal statement on the one hand and an affirmative statement on the other. If we refer back to the special rules we applied to the first figure, we note that they restrict the two premises of a first-figure syllogism to statements expressing precisely two such pieces of information. Furthermore, the position of the middle term is such that in the first premise it refers to the class that is the subject of the universal premise;

we know something about *all* the members of that class. In the second premise, the middle term is the predicate; it stands for the class within which all or some of the members of its subject class are *included*. Therefore, the valid first-figure syllogisms are perfectly fitted to the application of the principle that has been stated. The major premise tells us something about all the members of a class, and the minor premise tells us that all or some of the members of another class are included in it. The conclusion then asserts of these individuals what was known about the entire class within which they are included.

For example, in one of the stock examples of valid syllogistic reasoning

> All animals are mortal; all men are animals; therefore all men are mortals.

(1-**AAA** in form), the major premise tells us something about all animals; the minor premise tells us that all men are included in the class of animals; and the conclusion then goes on to state of all men what was known of all animals, namely that they are mortal. Every other example of valid syllogistic reasoning in the first figure can be analyzed in substantially the same way.

We can now reformulate the common-sense principle with which we began so it conforms more neatly to the characteristics we have learned to recognize in statements expressed in logical English and give it a formal name.

> *Principle of the Syllogism* (SYL)
>
> In the first figure, when the major premise is universal and the minor premise is affirmative, a conclusion can be drawn that has the quantity of the minor premise and the quality of the major premise.

This principle, together with the principles of immediate inference introduced earlier, is sufficient to justify all cases of syllogistic reasoning, whether they are originally stated in the first figure or not.

There are even two cases of valid syllogisms in the first figure that do not exactly conform to this principle: 1-**AAI** and 1-**EAO.** In these two cases, the quantity of the minor premise is universal while it is particular in the conclusion. All that is necessary in order to bring these cases within the scope of the principle of the syllogism is to apply the rule of limitation as well. By first applying LIM to the minor premise, we reduce its quantity to a particular statement; then, by applying SYL, we produce the particular conclusion. What this means is that while SYL does not permit the conclusions of 1-**AAI** and 1-**EAO** to be drawn as direct inferences, we can demonstrate the validity of these forms of argument by showing that the same conclusion can be derived by an indirect route from these premises. Therefore, we can take the four remaining valid forms of the syllogism in the first figure as the basic direct forms of syllogistic reasoning and reduce all other forms to indirect inferences combining one of these four with one or more applications of immediate inference.

The indirect proof of the example drawn from the first figure itself can be set up in abbreviated and formal terms.

1. All *M* are *P*.	Premise		
2. All *S* are *M*.	Premise	To prove: Some *S* are *P*.	
3. Some *S* are *M*.	2, LIM		
4. Some *S* are *P*.	1, 3, SYL		

When we turn to the consideration of valid forms of argument that are not in the first figure, appeal must be made to conversion and, sometimes, obversion in order to construct an indirect derivation of the conclusion. This procedure is referred to as "reduction to the first figure." It is easiest when the premises of the syllogism are simply convertible. One of the most elementary cases is represented by a syllogism in the form 2-**EAE**. The demonstration of the validity of this form by reducing it to the first figure and applying the principle of the syllogism would be as follows:

1. No *P* are *M*.	Premise		
2. All *S* are *M*.	Premise	To prove: No *S* are *P*.	
3. No *M* are *P*.	1, CONV		
4. No *S* are *P*.	3, 2, SYL		

A somewhat more complicated problem is presented by a syllogism in the form 3-**IAI**. In this case, to convert the minor premise would put the terms in the desired first-figure arrangement. However, since the minor premise is an **A** statement, it cannot be converted simply but would first have to pass through a limitation that would reduce its quantity to particular. If that were done, we would have two **I** statements as premises and no syllogistic conclusion could be drawn. Therefore the following procedure becomes necessary.

1. Some *M* are *P*.	Premise		
2. All *M* are *S*.	Premise	To prove: Some *S* are *P*.	
3. Some *P* are *M*.	1, CONV		
4. Some *P* are *S*.	2, 3, SYL		
5. Some *S* are *P*.	4, CONV		

When neither premise can be converted, the problem is obviously still more difficult. In our system, such a problem can be met by the use of obversion. For example, in proving the validity of 2-**AOO,** we could proceed in this way:

1. All P are M.	Premise	
2. Some S are not M.	Premise	To prove: Some S are not P.
3. No P are $\overline{M}$.	1, OBV	
4. Some S are $\overline{M}$.	2, OBV	
5. No $\overline{M}$ are P.	3, CONV	
6. Some S are not P.	5, 4, SYL	

In classical logic, there was a different procedure for dealing with cases like this last one. This method, called "reductio ad absurdum," was used to escape the difficulties involved in a situation where neither premise is convertible without having to resort to obversion. Essentially, it represents the same kind of demonstration that was used to prove the special rules for the first figure. By applying the rules of immediate inference (excluding obversion) and the principle of the syllogism, it is possible for us to show that there is an implicit contradiction or absurdity in assuming that, to take another example, 3-**OAO** is invalid. If it were invalid, it would be possible for the premises to be true and the conclusion false. If we can show that this is *impossible,* we shall have shown that the argument is valid. The argument would run:

1. Some M are not P.	Assumed
2. All M are S.	Assumed
3. Some S are not P is false.	Assumed
4. All S are P.	3, CONTRAD
5. All M are P.	4, 2, SYL
6. Some M are not P is false.	5, CONTRAD

Statement 6 is inconsistent with 1. Therefore, 1, 2, and 3 form an inconsistent triad. It is impossible for the premises of 3-**AOA** to be true and the conclusion false (see Section 4.10).

What we have shown, not completely, to be sure, but by example, is that the principle of the syllogism is all that is needed in addition to the principles of immediate inference, introduced in Chapter 3, to justify all cases of valid syllogistic reasoning. In fact, as we shall see in the next few chapters, these are all the principles we will need to justify any valid argument, as long as it falls within the system of logical English. To the extent that other arguments can be translated into this system, these rules are sufficient for dealing with them as well.

4.8 EXERCISES

Construct an example of each of the following forms of the syllogism. Prove validity by showing that the conclusion can be derived from the premises by using the principles of immediate inference and of the syllogism.

A. 2-**EIO**   B. 3-**IAI**   C. 2-**AEE**   D. 3-**OAO**   E. 4-**IAI**

F. 4-**AAI**   G. 1-**EAO**   H. 2-**EAE**   I. 3-**AII**   J. 2-**AOO**

4.9 RULES OF INFERENCE FOR SYLLOGISTIC REASONING IN ALGEBRAIC NOTATION

We have already seen, in connection with immediate inference, that the Venn diagrams and algebraic notation have a somewhat greater flexibility than does logical English. The rule of conversion is limited to **E** and **I** statements in logical English but applies without restriction in the other languages. The same holds true in connection with syllogistic reasoning. We have seen that its treatment in terms of Venn diagrams requires not a new principle but another method; when valid syllogisms are formulated in the diagrammatic language, the conclusion need not be stated separately once the premises have been recorded. In algebraic notation this is not true; even if the argument is valid, the conclusion remains a separate statement from the premises. Consequently, we need to make explicit the principles by which we move from the premises to a new and distinct statement inferred from them.

There was a single principle of the syllogism for logical English, but its direct application was restricted to syllogisms in the first figure. For algebraic notation, two principles of syllogistic reasoning are needed; the difference is more apparent than real. It exists only because inferences that are condensed into one complex rule for logical English are treated under separate and relatively more simple rules in algebraic notation.

We shall also wish to make use of two additional principles of immediate inference, for which there are no counterparts in logical English. The need for such additional principles does not arise because of a weakness in the system of algebraic notation, but rather out of its relatively greater strength and flexibility. There is no provision in the system of logical English, as we have developed it so far, for statements with fewer or more than two terms. For logical purposes in that system, each term functions as a simple unit, a logical atom, even if it may have a very complex logical structure itself. There must be two of them. There is no such restriction on algebraic notation, although so far we have encountered only such statements in algebraic notation as correspond to statements in logical English; they are implicitly subject to its restrictions. In algebraic notation, we can construct statements of the form $S = 0$ and $S \neq 0$ corresponding to statements such as *There are no unicorns* or *There are unicorns* in ordinary English. There are no adequate counterparts in logical English—a problem that we shall take up later (see Chapter 6).

Within a universe of discourse, for example, human beings, we may distinguish various classes by citing just one distinguishing characteristic: those who are tall, those who are intelligent, those who have red hair. We can also form classes by combining two or more distinguishing characteristics. The class formed in this way is the class of individuals who belong to both of the classes distinguished by the simple characteristics respectively. Such a class is called the "class product" of the two classes on which it is based. The class of tall, intelligent human beings is the class product of the first two classes mentioned in our list of examples. We can continue forming such classes indefinitely—the class of tall, intelligent human beings with red hair. The classes represented by areas where two or more circles overlap are class products of the classes represented by the circles themselves. So, for that matter, is any area on a Venn diagram with more than one circle on it; the area inside one circle and outside another is a class product formed out of the class represented by one circle and the complement of the class represented by the other. On the basic Venn diagram for a single statement involving two classes, there are four areas representing class products. We have already designated them in terms of the classes on which they are based: SP, $\bar{S}P$, $S\bar{P}$, and $\overline{SP}$. The areas on the Venn diagram for syllogisms represent still more complex class products: SPM, $S\bar{P}M$, $\bar{S}PM$, and so on.

The fact that statements in algebraic notation may have fewer or more than two terms indicates the possibility of stating two new principles of immediate inference. The first, which permits us to add terms (indefinitely) to an equality, is the "principle of simple addition" (SA). The other permits us to eliminate terms (indefinitely) from an inequality that contains more than one term: the "principle of simple elimination" (SE). Common sense justifies the principle of simple addition by taking account of the fact that if there are no members of a class at all, then there are no individuals that belong to that class and some other class as well, no matter what the other class may be. If there are no unicorns, then there are no spotted unicorns (if $U = 0$, then $SU = 0$). The principle of simple elimination is justified by the fact that if there are things that belong to each of two classes, then there must be things that belong to each class by itself. If there were spotted unicorns, it would follow from this fact both that there are spotted things and that there are unicorns (if $SU \neq O$, then $S \neq 0$ and $U \neq 0$).

There is still another principle of immediate inference we could add for the sake of completeness, although it is not essential for the account of syllogistic reasoning that follows: the "principle of association" (ASSOC). A class product involving more than two terms can be regarded either as a product of as many terms as there are or as a product of a fewer number of terms, some of which are already internally complex. For example, the class product SMP can be regarded as the product of S and M and P; it can also be regarded as the product of S and MP (which is itself the product of M and P). In the latter case, it would be better to use parentheses in order to indicate the intended grouping: $S(MP)$. The principle of association permits us to vary the grouping of terms in such a complex class product at will by shifting the parentheses. For certain technical purposes, it is desirable to impose strict limitations on the application of rules of inference in such a way that regrouping the terms in a class product becomes an essential part of the procedure.

The principle of association, like the principles of simple addition and elimination, provides for forms of argument that are obviously valid when expressed in ordinary or logical English but for which it is difficult to state a rule without having to include inconvenient restrictions. Association permits us, for example, to infer from $(SM)P = 0$ to $S(MP) = 0$. If we let S stand for tall men, M for red-headed men, and P for intelligent men, such an inference, reformulated into logical English, would be the inference from *No tall, red-headed men are intelligent* to *No tall men are both red-headed and intelligent*. The rules of immediate inference for logical English, since they take no account of the internal complexity of terms, make no provision for this kind of inference.

We are now ready to introduce the two principles directly justifying syllogistic reasoning in the system of algebraic notation. Combined with the principles of immediate inference we have just introduced, these new principles will provide a systematic basis for every valid case of syllogistic reasoning in that system—those corresponding to the twenty-four cases already considered in logical English. The first principle provides a basis for syllogisms that have equalities (universal statements) as their conclusions: the "principle of complementary elimination" (CE) permits us to eliminate a pair of complementary terms from two equalities that would otherwise include the same terms. It is an easy principle to justify by appeal to common sense: if there are no members of a certain class either inside or outside some other class, then there are no members of that class at all. If there are no spotted unicorns and no spotless unicorns either, it must be that there simply are no unicorns at all.

The second principle, the "principle of complementary addition" (CA), provides a basis for syllogistic arguments with inequalities (particular statements) as their conclusions. It states that to a term set unequal to 0, we may add the complementary of any term that in class product with the original term is set equal to 0. The common-sense justification of this principle is easier to understand than the principle itself: if there are members of a certain class and yet there are no members of it within some other class, then there must be members of it that are outside that other class. If there were unicorns but no spotted unicorns, then it would follow that there were spotless unicorns. If there are S's but none inside P, there must be S's outside P.

The five principles, three for immediate inference and two for syllogistic reasoning, are listed below with their abbreviations:

Principle of Simple Addition (SA)
   Any term can be added to a term (or terms) set equal to 0.

$$\frac{S = 0}{SP = 0}$$

Principle of Simple Elimination (SE)
   Any term can be eliminated from a group of terms set unequal to 0.

$$\frac{SP \neq 0}{S \neq 0}$$

Principle of Association (ASSOC)
   The position of parentheses indicating grouping in a class product may be changed in any way desired.

Principle of Complementary Elimination (CE)
   A complementary pair of terms can be eliminated from two sets of terms, both equal to 0, which otherwise include exactly the same term.

$$SP = 0$$
$$\frac{S\bar{P} = 0}{S = 0}$$

Principle of Complementary Addition (CA)

When a term set unequal to 0 is equal to 0 in class product with a second term, the complementary of that second term may be added to the inequality.

$$SP = 0$$
$$\frac{S \neq 0}{S\bar{P} \neq 0}$$

With these principles, we are in a position to give a systematic justification to any of the valid forms of the syllogism when they are reformulated in algebraic notation. We shall use 1-**AAA** as our initial example of the method of proof.[1]

1. $M\bar{P}\ \ = 0$ Premise
2. $S\bar{M}\ \ = 0$ Premise   To prove: $S\bar{P} = 0$
3. $M\bar{P}S = 0$ 1, SA
4. $S\bar{M}P = 0$ 2, SA
5. $S\bar{P}\ \ = 0$ 3, 4, CE, eliminating the pair M and $\bar{M}$

This proof would become considerably more rigorous and available to us as a basis for purely mechanical treatment by imposing the requirement that application of CE must exhibit precisely the pattern of the exemplary case that was used when it was introduced. This would require manipulation (appealing to CONV and ASSOC) that would produce from the original premises the two premises $(S\bar{P})M = 0$ and $(S\bar{P})\bar{M} = 0$. These technicalities are irrelevant to the understanding of the essential point involved in applying CE. For nonmechanical treatment, it might just as well take the less rigorous form in which it is applied in our proof.

We shall use 3-**EIO** as an example of a syllogism that yields a particular conclusion. Its justification would take the following course:

---

[1] Although the language that has been designated as algebraic notation is the language of what has come to be known as Boolean Algebra (but not quite in the form in which Boole introduced it), the rules for syllogistic reasoning that have been developed in this section are taken from the logical system developed very briefly by Franz Brentano in the first edition (1874) of his *Psychologie vom empirischen Standpunkt.*

1. $MP = 0$ Premise
2. $MS \neq 0$ Premise   To prove: $S\bar{P} \neq 0$
3. $MPS = 0$ 1, SA
4. $MS\bar{P} \neq 0$ 2, 3, CA
5. $S\bar{P} \quad \neq 0$ 4, SE

Once again, a more rigorously mechanical treatment would require transformations on the premises until they exhibited exactly the standard pattern for complementary addition.

4.9 EXERCISE

Translate the syllogism in Exercise 4.8 into algebraic notation and prove their validity by applying the principles of inference for that language.

4.10 FURTHER APPLICATION OF THE PRINCIPLE OF THE SYLLOGISM

The application of the method of reductio ad absurdum[2] is not restricted to those cases in which neither premise can be converted. In fact, by extending its use to other cases, we can dispense with the rule of conversion as a separate and independent rule of inference in the system. Obversion can be only partly dispensed with so that we must reduce the basic rules of the system to the principles of obversion, contradiction, limitation, and syllogism.

We can achieve indirectly the same results we achieved directly by applying the rule of conversion to an **E** statement by the following procedure (essentially a type of reductio ad absurdum):

1. No B are A.   Assumed
2. It is false that No A are B.   Assumed
3. All A are A.   Necessary truth
4. Some A are B.   CONTRAD
5. Some A are not A.   1, 4, SYL
6. It is false that All A are A.   5, CONTRAD

The last statement, since it contradicts 3, a necessary truth, is absurd; the assumption (1 and 2), *No B are A* can be true, while its converse is

2 See Section 4.8.

false, involves us in an absurdity. Therefore the inference from *No B are A* to *No A are B* must be valid.

In this proof, a statement that is necessarily true was introduced. This procedure has no effect on the validity of the argument as it was originally stated. Logically, or necessarily true statements are exceptions to the general rule that logic does not provide information about the truth or falsity of single statements but only about relationships between statements. A statement that is affirmative and has identical subject and predicate terms is logically true, and a negative statement in which the terms are complementary to each other is also a necessary truth. Affirmative statements with complementary terms and negative statements with identical terms are logically false.

Logically true	*Logically false*
All A are A.	All A are $\overline{A}$.
Some A are A.	Some A are $\overline{A}$.
No A are $\overline{A}$.	No A are A.
Some A are not $\overline{A}$.	Some A are not A.

In Chapter 6, statements that are true by definition or "by the meaning of the terms" will be mentioned. In a broader sense, such statements are also logically true. Whether there are any necessarily true statements that are not logically true either by the formal test stated here or by virtue of the meaning of the terms is an important problem in the theory of knowledge but we will not discuss it here.

Another method by which we can derive the principle of conversion proceeds by using reductio ad absurdum to establish the validity of a certain syllogism and then using this syllogism in order to derive the converse of the statement in question. This procedure is illustrated below with the derivation of the converse of an **I** statement:

A. Prove the validity of 3-**AII** by reductio ad absurdum.

1.	All M are P.	Assumed
2.	Some M are S.	Assumed
3.	It is false that Some S are P.	Assumed
4.	No S are P.	3, CONTRAD
5.	Some M are not P.	4, 2, SYL
6.	It is false that All M are P.	5, CONTRAD

Statement 6 contradicts 1 and, therefore, it cannot be the case that both premises are true and the conclusion is false. The argument is valid.

B. Derive the converse of **I**.

1. Some A are B.   Premise
2. All A are A.   Necessary truth
3. Some B are A.   2, 1, 3-**AII**—validity proved above

Another necessarily true statement, *No A are $\overline{A}$,* can be used to derive obverses indirectly, using the principle of the syllogism.

1. All B are A.   Premise   To prove: No B are $\overline{A}$.
2. No A are $\overline{A}$.   Necessary truth
3. No B are $\overline{A}$.   2, 1, SYL

Not all obverses can be derived in an equally simple way by using appropriate forms of the syllogism. When the process of obversion calls for inferring an affirmative statement as a conclusion, there will obviously be no method like the one above; the syllogism would have a negative premise and an affirmative conclusion, in violation of the second rule of quality.

4.10   EXERCISES

Determine whether each of the following syllogisms is valid or invalid. For those that are valid, give a formal proof of validity by using the principles of immediate inference and syllogism to derive the conclusion from the premises. Identify figure and mood for each syllogism.

A. No illogical persons are geniuses.
   No illogical persons are authors of textbooks on logic.
   _____
   All authors of textbooks on logic are geniuses.
B. Some students of logic are not mental defectives.
   All students of logic are persons who are capable of making mistakes.
   _____
   Some persons who are capable of making mistakes are not mental defectives.
C. Some teachers of logic are authors of textbooks on logic.
   No authors of textbooks on logic are students of logic.
   _____
   Some students of logic are not teachers of logic.
D. No employees of the University are mental defectives.
   Some employees of the University are students of logic.
   _____
   Some students of logic are not mental defectives.
E. All teachers of logic are employees of a university.
   Some illogical persons are not employees of a university.
   _____
   Some illogical persons are not teachers of logic.
F. Some employees of the University are geniuses.
   All teachers of logic are employees of the University.
   _____
   Some teachers of logic are geniuses.

G. All students of logic are critical thinkers.
All geniuses are critical thinkers.

All students of logic are geniuses.

H. No illogical persons are critical thinkers.
All lovers are illogical persons.

No lovers are critical thinkers.

I. Some students of logic are not lovers.
Some lovers are not geniuses.

Some students of logic are not geniuses.

J. No lovers are critical thinkers.
All students of logic are critical thinkers.

Some students of logic are not lovers.

Chapter 5

GENERAL APPLICATION

The principles of immediate inference and the syllogisms plus the rules of quality and distribution provide us with all the systematic tools we need for the critical evaluation of arguments and the derivation of the conclusion in the case of a valid argument. However, our development of these rules was subject to rather stringent restrictions; before we can apply these tools more generally, we will have to increase the limited range that they have so far been able to illuminate. Some of the restrictions have to do with the argument taken as a whole.

Below is an example of an argument that violates this restriction:

> No syllogisms that are not in standard form are valid arguments, and no invalid arguments are persuasive arguments, so all persuasive arguments are syllogisms in standard form.

The argument is a syllogism, and it is expressed in logical English. It is not, however, in standard form. When its terms are abbreviated by S (for syllogisms in standard form), V (for valid arguments) and P (for persuasive arguments), its structure can be rendered as:

No $\overline{S}$ are V.
No $\overline{V}$ are P.
All P are S.

Instead of a middle term, there is a pair of complementary terms. Further-more, it is not the predicate of the conclusion that appears in the major premise but its complement. We have not yet developed a systematic way of determining whether such an argument is valid or not. (It is valid, but not sound. The argument itself provides a counter example showing the falsity of its first premise. Its second premise is surely false also.)

Other restrictions that have limited the range of our system so far have to do with the statements that make up an argument. The following ex-ample violates those restrictions; its premises and conclusion are not ex-pressed in logical English.

> Only syllogisms in standard form are valid, and an invalid argu-ment is not persuasive. Hence, an argument is not persuasive unless it is a syllogism in standard form.

In this chapter, we shall break through the restrictions that limit the ap-plicability of the system to arguments in standard form. We will not do so for those restrictions that limit it to statements expressed in one of the three standard languages. We shall develop a way of dealing with the first of the two examples above but not with the second. That task will be left for Chapter 6.

The restrictions defining when an argument is in standard form have concerned (1) sequence, (2) number of constituent statements, and (3) number of terms. Obviously, none of these restrictions has any justification other than that of convenience; we can expect to encounter arguments that do not fulfill any of them. Arguments not limited by them can and do occur in realistic rhetorical contexts. We need no new rules for dealing with them, however. Any deductive argument that we are able to express in logical English or one of its counterparts can be subjected to critical evaluation and proved valid (when it *is* valid) by referring back to the basic principles and rules. All direct deductive reasoning within the three systems of logical languages will be either an immediate inference or a syllo-gistic inference in standard form. All other reasoning will be indirect, using immediate and syllogistic inferences as direct steps. This holds true no matter in what order its constituents are stated nor how many of them there are.

5.1 VARIATIONS IN ORDER

We shall take up first those arguments that do not conform to the condi-tions that standard form imposes on the sequence in which the con-stituents of an argument are to be stated. This is, in fact, the most trivial of the different variations from standard form we need to consider; even when it is violated, we can still directly apply the principle of syllogistic reasoning in justifying the basic syllogistic arguments of the first figure. This principle requires that the argument be in the first figure and that its major and minor premises have certain characteristics—in any first-figure syllogism, if the major premise is universal and the minor premise is affirmative, a conclusion can be drawn with the quality of the major premise and the quantity of the minor. Sequence, however, does not define the major and minor premises; when the argument is put into standard form, order is determined by first establishing which is the major premise and which is the minor. Since we can identify the major and minor premises independently of the order in which they are stated, the rule can be applied without reference to the order. It is, of course, more convenient to be able to identify each premise merely by referring to its position.

The order in which the premises appear does, however, relate significantly to the conclusion. We can reverse the order of the major and minor premises and neither change the character of the argument in any way nor change the respective roles of the premises as major and minor (for those roles are defined independently of order). We cannot alter the relation of the statements to the line that separates premises from conclusion in standard form without altering the entire character of the argument. We *must* be able to determine which statements are the premises and which statement is the conclusion before we can even say what the argument is to which we intend to apply our logical principles. If we cannot rely on order and a horizontal line, as we can with arguments in standard form, we must rely on something else to indicate the direction of the process of reasoning.

In ordinary English, which is not governed by the requirements of what we have defined as standard form, this purpose is served by words. Order is not at all a necessary indication; it is possible to state the conclusion of a syllogistic argument in any position relative to its premises, if we are governed only by the ordinary rules of the English language. The conclusion may be first, it may be last, it may even be sandwiched between two premises. (For the present, we are restricting our attention to syllogistic reasoning; arguments with more than two premises will be discussed later, in Section 5.5.) The words indicating which statement is the conclusion of an argument not in standard form can point in either direction. Some words indicate that the statement preceding is the conclusion and the statement or statements following the supporting reason: "inasmuch as," "since," "because," "for," "in view of the fact that," and so on. Others proclaim the statements preceding as reasons advanced in support of the statement following: "therefore," "hence," "consequently," "thus," "it follows that," and so on. Our first step in the analysis of any argument not known to be in standard order is, of course, to ascertain what are the premises and what is the conclusion. We can take the cue from the "direction indicators" discussed above and from other words serving the same functions. Anyone who has a familiarity with the English language can readily recognize these words and expressions and the direction that any particular one indicates.

There are complications, however. They arise from the fact that in English we use some of these words to indicate causal relationship ("because" and "consequently" are good examples). When they are used for this purpose, the result is not an argument but a causal explanation. Compare *The streets are wet because it was raining* with *It was raining, because the streets are wet.* The first sentence gives an explanation of why it is that the streets are wet. The second cites the wetness of the streets as a reason for judging that it was raining. Only the latter is an argument; (it is an inductive rather than a deductive one, because it would be possible for the streets to be wet without any rain having fallen). With these examples, it is possible to tell one from another on the basis of the facts involved. We would never advance the wetness of the streets as an *explanation* of the fact that it had rained. Sometimes, however, it is impossible to tell without further information about the situation. For example, the statement *He died because he was poisoned* could be used to give an explanation if we already knew that *he died* is true. If we did know that the person referred to had been poisoned but had no direct knowledge of his death, we might conclude, from the information we possessed, that he had died. In that case, the statement would express an argument (again, an inductive one). There is, then, no hard and fast rule by which we can recognize an argument as distinguished from the statement of a causal explanation just by noting the occurrence of the words that frequently serve as direction indicators in arguments. Still, it helps us to know what to look for; in most cases, the context and our general store of factual information will suffice to make the meaning clear.

5.2 VARIATIONS IN THE NUMBER OF TERMS

The next variation from standard form that needs to be considered concerns the number of terms in an argument. A standard-form syllogism contains just three terms, but there is obviously no such restriction on the structure of arguments in ordinary contexts. Consequently, we must look for some way to deal with arguments that do not meet this condition, although they are truly deductive arguments and subject indirectly to the principles that have been set down in the preceding chapters.

We can divide variations from standard form of this type into two quite different cases. The distinction arises between two different ways of counting the number of terms in an argument. One way neglects the difference between a *term* and its *complement;*[1] it takes account only of the letters themselves. If there are pairs of complementary terms in an argument, the number of terms arrived at by this method of counting will be less than the actual number of distinct terms. This latter number must be arrived at by counting each member of a pair of complementary terms as a separate unit. Despite their logical relationship, C and $\overline{C}$ are literally distinct terms. One important point about such a pair is that their logical relationship makes it possible for arguments to be constructed in which one appears in the premises and the other in the conclusion. This point has been already discussed in connection with obversion as an immediate inference. Because of this fact, we have seen that some immediate inferences have just two distinct terms; conversion gives us examples of immediate inferences of this type. But others, exemplified by obversion and complement conversion, exhibit three or even four distinct terms. The obverse has a new predicate term, so that there are three in all when we compare it with the premise from which it is derived. When complement conversion is used, deriving *All $\overline{P}$ are $\overline{S}$* from *All S are P,* for example, there are four distinct terms involved. Even in this extreme case, there are actually two *pairs* of terms or two terms if you are counting only the letters. This is true of all immediate inferences: counting complementary pairs as one instead of two, there are two terms in the argument. As long as we can presuppose that we are using letters as abbreviations for terms, we can say, more accurately, two letters. In the case of complement conversion, while there are four distinct terms involved, there are only two letters meaning that the members of the two pairs of terms are related to each other as complements.

As a general rule, applicable to every deductive argument except the direct use of the principles of obversion and complement conversion, the argument must contain the same number of statements as it does distinct terms. When the number of distinct terms exceeds the number of statements in any argument with two or more premises, we must reformulate it so that terms and statements agree in number; only then can we apply

[1] After all, the two together involve just *one* division of the universe. On the primitive Venn diagram, *one* circle is responsible for the two distinct areas.

rules to it. We can do this either by reducing the number of terms in the argument or by increasing the number of statements. The first possibility only arises when the occurrence of complementary pairs of terms is responsible for the excess. Where there are more letters than statements, so that even when complementary pairs of terms are counted as one there remains an excess of terms over statements, the argument must be treated as incomplete. We begin our consideration of arguments in which there are more terms than statements with the case in which it is possible to reduce the number of terms. We will consider the second type in Section 5.4.

5.3 EQUIVALENT ARGUMENTS

For every argument that is not in standard form because it includes pairs of complementary terms, there is an equivalent argument that is in standard form. By equivalent arguments, we mean arguments with constituents that are logically equivalent to each other. The concept of logical equivalence becomes the key concept to the understanding of how we deal with the problem posed by this particular variation from standard form. Two statements are logically equivalent if they always have the same truth value, whatever the circumstances. If one is true, the other is likewise true; if one is false, so is the other. This concept was introduced earlier in our general survey of logical relationships (see Section 3.2). In fact, the application of the principles of obversion and conversion give statements that are equivalent to the original statements. This is not true of the results of applying the principle of limitation. It is possible for a universal statement to be false even though the corresponding particular statement, with the same terms, is true. It is not possible for any statement to be false even though its obverse (or converse, if it has one directly) is true or to be true when its obverse (or converse) is false.

The correct application of obversion or conversion results in a statement equivalent to the original; by applying these principles to the constituents of an argument, we can transform one argument into another equivalent to it. The significance of this possibility is that, if two arguments are equivalent, they must have the same "validity value." If one is valid, the other must be also; if one is invalid, so must be the other. Validity and invalidity in equivalent arguments are like truth and falsity in equivalent statements. Where equivalence exists, the relevant characteristics must be the same. It is no accident, of course, that this is the case. Validity is defined in terms of possible combinations of truth values; if the possible combinations of truth values of premises and conclusion are not altered by a change in the argument, its validity or lack of it will not be affected. (Recall the Rule of Replacement introduced in Section 3.8.) The replacement of one or more of the constituents of the argument by an equivalent statement or statements will not alter the possible combinations of truth values, since equivalent statements must have the same truth-value. Therefore, the principle that equivalent arguments have the same characteristic as to validity is really a direct consequence of the relationship between equivalent statements.

We can take advantage of the identical validity values of equivalent arguments so as to determine the validity or invalidity of arguments including pairs of complementary terms. By applying conversion and obversion to their constituents we produce an equivalent argument that is in standard form. We can then directly apply the rules of criticism for syllogisms to an argument in standard form; the result of the test—valid or invalid—will apply to the original argument not given in standard form. It is important to remember, now that we are considering a wider range of arguments, that the rules of the syllogism apply directly only to syllogisms that *are in standard form*. We could not say that a syllogism of the form:

$$\text{No } M \text{ are } P.$$
$$\underline{\text{No } S \text{ are } \overline{M}.}$$
$$\text{No } S \text{ are } P.$$

is invalid because of what appears to be a violation of the first rule of quality. This rule applies only to syllogisms in standard form. This example is not in standard form because it includes a pair of complementary terms: M and $\overline{M}$. Instead, we must first construct an equivalent version of the argument in standard form. We can easily do this by replacing the second premise with its obverse: *All S are M.* Immediately, we can recognize the form of the equivalent version as 1-**EAE**, one of the basic cases of valid syllogistic reasoning.

To take a case of a different kind, we could not say that a syllogism in the form:

$$\text{All } M \text{ are } \overline{P}.$$
$$\underline{\text{All } S \text{ are } M.}$$
$$\text{All } S \text{ are } P.$$

is valid. We cannot apply any rules until we have constructed an equivalent version in standard form, which we do by replacing the first premise with its obverse. We can say of this syllogism that it is invalid because it violates the second rule of quality. For the reasons that have been given above, we are justified in saying that the original argument of which this is an equivalent is also invalid. Note that we would not be justified in saying that the original violates the second rule of quality. It cannot be said to violate, or to conform to, any of the rules; their proper sphere of applicability is restricted to arguments in standard form. All we can say of the original argument is that *it has an equivalent that violates the second rule of quality*. This is sufficient to demonstrate its invalidity. In fact, there will be a number of different equivalents that can be constructed. One might violate one rule and one another, but each will violate *some* rule. For example, all of the following syllogisms are equivalent and all but the first are in standard form, yet the rule violated is different in each case in standard form.

No M are $\overline{P}$.	All M are P.	All $\overline{P}$ are $\overline{M}$.	No M are $\overline{P}$.
No M are S.	No M are S.	All S are $\overline{M}$.	No M are S.
No S are P.	No S are P.	All S are $\overline{P}$.	All S are $\overline{P}$.

If our objective is to give a proof of validity by applying positive rules of inference, instead of simply testing validity by the rules of quality and distribution, the essential procedure we must follow is much the same as it was for the mere validity test. First, we draw the immediate inferences necessary to transform the original premises into an equivalent syllogism in standard form. Now we can draw the appropriate syllogistic conclusion. Finally, if necessary, the immediate inferences needed to transform that conclusion into the conclusion of the original argument are made. The following proof will serve as an illustration:

1. All $\overline{P}$ are $\overline{M}$.	Premise	
2. Some M are S.	Premise	To Prove: Some S are P.
3. No $\overline{P}$ are M.	1, OBV	
4. No M are $\overline{P}$.	3, CONV	
5. All M are P.	4, OBV	
6. Some S are M.	2, CONV	
7. Some S are P.	5, 6, SYL	

Steps 3, 4, and 5 can be condensed to an application of Complement Conversion, and step 6 is needed only if we insist not only on constructing an equivalent standard form syllogism but also on reducing it to the first figure. From now on, we shall not regard this step as an essential procedure, and we will accept an appeal to the principle of the syllogism for any case in which the two premises and the conclusion conform to the rules of quality and distribution. It has already been demonstrated (in Chapter 4) that any syllogism that fulfills those four rules can be either directly (if it is one of the four basic first figure forms) or indirectly (if it is not one of them) justified by the principle. In order to simplify proofs, we can take this fact for granted and only actually go through the procedure of reducing valid syllogisms in standard form to the first figure if there is some special reason to do so.

The results of this section are summed up in the following discussion. In order to test the validity of a syllogism containing pairs of complementary terms (but only three distinct letters), we must transform the argument into an equivalent syllogism in standard form. We do this by replacing the constituents with statements that can be derived from the original constituents by obversion or some combination of obversion and conversion. We can then apply the usual rules of criticism to the result. In order to construct a proof of validity for such an argument, we first transform the premises (by obversion and conversion) into the premises of an equivalent standard-form syllogism, draw the correct syllogistic conclusion from those premises, and then (if necessary) transform the conclusion into the original conclusion by application of obversion and conversion or both.

5.3 EXERCISES

Determine the validity or invalidity of each of the following arguments by constructing an equivalent argument in standard form and applying to it the rules of quality and distribution.

A. All $\overline{P}$ are $\overline{M}$.
   All M are $\overline{S}$.
   ———————
   No $\overline{S}$ are P.

B. No $\overline{P}$ are M.
   All $\overline{M}$ are $\overline{S}$.
   ———————
   All S are P.

C. Some M are not $\overline{P}$.
   All M are S.
   ———————
   Some S are not P.

D. No M are P.
   All $\overline{M}$ are $\overline{S}$.
   ———————
   All S are $\overline{P}$.

E. Some $\overline{P}$ are not M.
   All $\overline{M}$ are S.
   ———————
   Some $\overline{S}$ are not P.

F. Some P are $\overline{M}$.
   No S are M.
   ———————
   Some $\overline{S}$ are not $\overline{P}$.

G. No serpents with human heads are pythons, for all pythons are natural creatures, and all serpents with human heads are unnatural creatures.

H. Since no natural creatures are monsters, no creatures incapable of flying in the air are monsters, for no creatures capable of flying in the air are natural creatures.

I. No creatures that are not monsters are winged serpents, but some monsters are incapable of flying through the air, so some winged serpents are not capable of flying through the air.

J. It is true that some monsters are winged serpents, since no winged serpents are rational creatures, and some irrational creatures are not monsters.

5.4 THE ENTHYMEME

When the number of terms in an argument with just two premises exceeds the three terms of the standard-form syllogism because there are more than three different letters involved (not because there is at least one pair of complementary terms), we are confronted with a completely new problem. Such an argument must be invalid, either because a term appears in the conclusion that does not appear in the premises or because there is no middle term by which the premises are linked together so that jointly they imply a conclusion that neither one implies by itself.

There is, however, another way of looking at such an argument. Frequently, when arguments are offered in the course of the give-and-take of an ordinary discussion, they are left incomplete. Instead of arguing that *All men are mortal and Socrates is a man, therefore Socrates is mortal,* we could argue that *Socrates is a man, and so he is mortal.* It is doubtful whether it would be appropriate to say that these represent two different arguments. It would be better to say that they are two different ways of expressing what is at bottom the same argument. The significant difference is the fact that in the first case, all of the argument's logical elements are explicitly included; in the other, one of them is omitted.

Usually, when an argument is not made fully explicit, it is a premise that is omitted, possibly because both parties to the discussion can be assumed to take generally accepted or obvious facts for granted. Sometimes, however, the conclusion itself is thought to follow so obviously from the premises that once they have been given, it is no longer thought necessary to continue with an explicit statement of the conclusion.

We can easily make a general test for the completeness of an argument as explicitly formulated. We need only make a comparison between the number of statements it includes and the number of fundamentally distinct terms involved in those statements; for terms abbreviated by capital letters, if the number of terms exceeds the number of statements in the argument, it must be regarded as incomplete. The question can then be raised as to whether there is any additional statement that could be added to the argument to make it complete and valid. If there is, what statement would it have to be?

This rule governing the completeness of an argument is perfectly general: an immediate inference can involve only two fundamentally distinct terms; a syllogism can involve only three; and, as the number of constituent statements increases, so does the number of terms that can be accommodated.[2] In this section, we shall be concerned with the syllogism. When one or the other of the three constituents of a standard-form syllogism is left unstated, the result is called an "enthymeme." We can recognize this type of argument by applying the rule for completeness: we will see that it includes three terms but only two statements, usually a single premise and a conclusion. The enthymematic version of the traditional illustration establishing Socrates' mortality serves as an example. As stated, it is made up of a premise and a conclusion. However, between the two statements it contains three terms: Socrates, men, mortals. This marks it as an enthymeme. In order for it to be formulated as a fully explicit syllogism, one more statement would have to be added (without increasing the number of terms, of course).

It was suggested earlier that it is usually some obviously true statement that is omitted from the explicit formulation of an argument; this, however, need not always be the case. A somewhat dishonest debater may well choose to leave unstated a very dubious premise of his argument, hoping that no one will think to expose his implicit assumption and criticize it. Whether or not an unstated factual assumption of an incomplete argument is obviously true, or more probably, false is beyond the power of logical principles to ascertain. We can, however, use the rules of the syllogism to determine what such an incomplete argument *must* have added to it, if it is to be completely explicit *and* valid. The truth value or degree of probability of the required addition can then be determined by appropriate factual investigation. In order for an argument to prove its conclusion, it must be valid and its premises must be true. The additional premise introduced to complete the explicit argument must fulfill the conditions imposed by these two requirements. Logic determines what is required of it to fulfill the one; the facts determine whether it fulfills the other.

The procedure we are to follow in determining the implicit premise that turns an enthymeme into a standard-form valid syllogism, if it can be

[2] See the example at the end of Section 5.6.

done, is to apply the rules of quality and distribution. We are then able to ascertain all of the conditions the added statement must fulfill. For example, if the major premise is given and is negative, the first rule of quality tells us that only by adding an affirmative minor premise can we hope to produce a valid standard-form syllogism. Once we have ascertained the conditions of quality and distribution of terms, we can decide what kind of statement, if any, will fulfill them.

Here is an illustrative example, in which the major premise has been left unstated:

All missionaries are servants of the Lord.	All M are S.
Some servants of the Lord are not Protestants.	Some S are not P.

The first rule of quality has already been fulfilled, since the stated minor premise is affirmative; it imposes no conditions on the major premise. The second rule of quality, since the stated conclusion is negative, requires that the premise to be added shall be negative. The first rule of distribution is fulfilled (M being distributed in the stated premise), but the second rule of distribution requires that P must be distributed in the major premise. The conditions imposed on the major premise, if the syllogism is to be valid, are two: it must be a negative statement and P must be a distributed term. These two conditions will be fulfilled either by an **E** statement, with its terms in either order, or an **O** statement, with P as the predicate term. What we are looking for, however, is the *minimum* requirement that must be fulfilled for the argument to be valid; it is the **O** statement that fulfills the conditions *but nothing else*. It is not necessary for S to be distributed also, as it would have to be in an **E** statement. If we add *Some M are not P,* the result is a valid argument:

(Some M are not P.)
All M are S.
Some S are not P.

This is a sufficient answer to the original question. It would be improper for us to claim that someone advancing the argument in its original enthymematic form is making any stronger assumption than that.

Sometimes, the rules indicate that it will be impossible to add any statement to obtain a valid syllogism. For example, these arguments cannot be completed as valid syllogisms:

All S are M.	All M are P.
All P are M.	( )
( )	No S are P.

In the one case, the first rule of distribution has already been violated and in the other, the second rule of distribution has been broken. There are no repairs that could be made simply by introducing a properly selected conclusion for the one and a minor premise for the other.

When the rules of quality seem already to have been violated, the possibility of constructing a valid argument cannot be absolutely excluded, however. The reason for this is that when not all of the constituents of the argument are stated, we are left free to complete the argument by introducing an additional component that, while it does not yet produce a standard-form syllogism, does produce one that is valid and that can be shown to be valid by the method discussed in Section 5.3. There is nothing to prevent the introduction of an additional premise that has a term forming a complementary pair with one of the terms already given. In the equivalent standard-form syllogism, the rule of quality may not be violated:

$$(\qquad)$$
$$\underline{\text{Some } S \text{ are not } M.}$$
$$\text{Some } S \text{ are } P.$$

An argument of this type would seem to have violated the second rule of quality, so that no valid syllogism could be produced merely by adding another premise. If the additional premise were limited to the terms M and P, this assumption would be correct. Once the possibility of working with complementary terms is recognized, we realize that this is not so. If either of the statements given in the enthymeme were to be replaced by its obverse, the resulting pair of statements would be equivalent to the original pair. They would no longer appear to violate the second rule of quality, and there would no longer be any immediate reason to question the possibility of adding a major premise (with appropriate terms and form) to produce a valid syllogism. In other words, we can change the original problem into a new one. For example, what additional premise is required to produce a valid syllogism from the following enthymeme?

$$(\qquad)$$
$$\underline{\text{Some } S \text{ are } \overline{M}.}$$
$$\text{Some } S \text{ are } P.$$

We can determine the answer in the same way we did for the previous example. The first rule of quality is already fulfilled, and the second rule of quality requires that the major premise be affirmative. The first rule of distribution requires that $\overline{M}$ be distributed in the major premise. The second rule of distribution imposes no conditions, for neither term of the conclusion is distributed. The major premise must be affirmative and include $\overline{M}$ as a distributed term. The only statement, then, that fulfills these two conditions is: *All $\overline{M}$ are P*. When it is added to the original enthymeme the result, while not a standard-form syllogism, is a valid syllogism; it does have a valid standard-form syllogism as its equivalent:

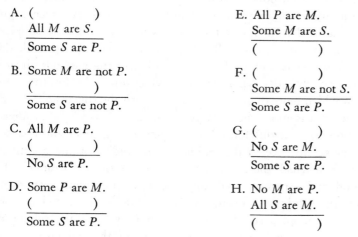

$$\begin{array}{l}(\text{All } \overline{M} \text{ are } P.) \\ \underline{\text{Some } S \text{ are not } M.} \\ \text{Some } S \text{ are } P.\end{array} \quad \text{is equivalent to} \quad \begin{array}{l}(\text{All } \overline{M} \text{ are } P.) \\ \underline{\text{Some } S \text{ are } \overline{M}.} \\ \text{Some } S \text{ are } P.\end{array}$$

The method of procedure in this case can be stated generally: where an enthymeme appears to violate either of the rules of quality, transform it (by obverting one of its constituents) into an equivalent enthymeme in which the rules of quality are not violated; proceed in the usual way from that point.

5.4 EXERCISES

Complete the syllogisms below so that they are valid; if that is not possible, indicate why it is not.

A. (   )
   All *M* are *S*.
   Some *S* are *P*.

B. Some *M* are not *P*.
   (   )
   Some *S* are not *P*.

C. All *M* are *P*.
   (   )
   No *S* are *P*.

D. Some *P* are *M*.
   (   )
   Some *S* are *P*.

E. All *P* are *M*.
   Some *M* are *S*.
   (   )

F. (   )
   Some *M* are not *S*.
   Some *S* are *P*.

G. (   )
   No *S* are *M*.
   Some *S* are *P*.

H. No *M* are *P*.
   All *S* are *M*.
   (   )

I. All felines are halibut lovers, so some halibut lovers are mousers.

J. No felines are swimmers, for all swimmers are water lovers.

5.5   THE SORITES

An argument made up of three statements but containing four basically distinct terms is also incomplete. We can see that it is by applying the test introduced in Section 5.2. We can complete it by adding one more statement, so that the argument will have the same number of statements as it has terms. The result of completing it, however, does not produce an argument in any of the forms we have considered previously—the three premises and a conclusion do not fit the pattern of either immediate or syllogistic inference. Therefore, before we can begin to consider the way to deal with the incomplete form of such an argument, we must develop a way of dealing with the new complete form.

Arguments like this are called "sorites" (the singular and plural forms of this word are identical: one sorites or two sorites).

> Socrates is a man, all men are created beings and all created beings are mortals, therefore Socrates is mortal

offers an example of a relatively simple sorites. Instead of two premises as in the syllogism, it has three statements preceding the *therefore*. It is not so complicated that its validity is not obvious without resort to the explicit principles of a logical system (although the truth of one or more of its premises might be challenged). We shall need to provide for the systematic treatment of such arguments and for more complex ones.

We do not need to introduce any new principles of direct inference in order to handle arguments with more than two premises. All such arguments can be analyzed from indirect inferences in which (in the simplest kind of case) the direct steps are all syllogistic inferences. In general, the treatment of the sorites is nothing but an extension of the methods already used in connection with the syllogism. The syllogism is the limiting case of reasoning in which more than one premise supports the conclusion.

As in syllogistic reasoning, the constituents of a sorites can be arranged in a variety of orders. The difference between one arrangement and another is of no greater significance to the validity or invalidity of the argument than is the order in which the constituents of a syllogism are arranged. To avoid confusion and errors in analyzing the more numerous statements and in proving the validity (or invalidity) of a sorites, it is somewhat more important that we adopt a standard order than it was for the syllogism. For this reason, we generalize the standard form of the syllogism as far as order is concerned and apply it to the sorites. We shall expect a sorites in standard order to have its conclusion at the bottom, separated from the premises by a horizontal line; and its premises arranged so that the one with the subject term of the conclusion is last, and each successive pair of premises shares a common term. The arrangement of the syllogism is a special limiting case of this arrangement—there is only one pair of premises and so only one middle term. In the sorites, there must be as many "middle terms" as there are adjoining pairs of premises.

Another condition of standard form for the sorites, as for the syllogism, is the absence of any complementary pairs of terms. Standard form for all arguments, except those expressing immediate inferences, must meet the following conditions:

> 1. All constituents must be in a standard-form language.
> 2. There must be exactly as many pairs of identical terms as there are constituents of the argument, and there must be no pairs of complementary terms.
> 3. The constituents of the argument must be arranged with the conclusion last, immediately preceded by the premise that includes its subject term, and the members of each successive pair of premises must have one term in common.

When these conditions are fulfilled, the rules of quality and distribution for syllogisms can be extended to cover the sorites. We must, however, be careful in stating the rules for sorites. When we state the first rule of quality for syllogisms, it makes no difference whether it requires the argument to have at least one affirmative premise or that it have no more than one negative premise. When there are only two premises, either way of expressing the requirement comes to the same thing. When there are more than two premises, we cannot be as arbitrary. Only the latter way of formulating the rule will be appropriate for the criticism of sorites.

> Q1: Arguments in standard form, no matter how many premises they may include, can have no more than one negative premise.

The first rule of distribution must be stated so that it is impossible to speak of *the* middle term when we are criticizing a sorites. It is easily generalized, however, by requiring that each of the terms shared by adjoining pairs of premises must be distributed at least once. If we can think of each of these shared terms as a middle term, all that is called for is the replacement of *the* by *each* in the original formulation of the rule:

> D1: Each middle term must be distributed at least once.

The two remaining rules, the second rule of quality and the second rule of distribution, can be applied without any change at all when we shift attention from the special case of the syllogism to nonimmediate inference in general.

Q2: If there is a negative premise, the conclusion must be negative (and vice versa).

D2: If a term is distributed in the conclusion, it must be distributed in the premises (but not vice versa).

The criticism of sorites in standard form can follow the same systematic procedure originally introduced in criticizing syllogisms: the successive application of each of the four rules of criticism.

When we must prove the validity of a sorites, our procedure is to break the argument down into a series of syllogisms. Once the sorites has been arranged in standard form, the two premises at the top can be regarded as the constituents of an enthymeme in which the conclusion has been omitted. From these two premises, we can derive the strongest possible conclusion permitted by the rules (in other words, we always try to draw a universal conclusion), justifying the step by appeal to the principle of syllogistic reasoning. The resulting conclusion is then combined with the next premise, and the procedure is repeated until finally a conclusion has been reached that represents the combined force of all of the premises. This last conclusion will be the conclusion of the entire sorites. The procedure in the following example would be:

1. All A are B.   Premise
2. All B are C.   Premise
3. No C are D.   Premise   To prove: No D are A.
4. All A are C.   1, 2, SYL
5. No D are A.   4, 3, SYL

Since each pair of premises is regarded as an enthymeme, which is to be taken as the major premise and which the minor is not fixed. Common practice is to take them in the order in which they appear, once in standard form, introducing each new premise as the minor premise of the syllogism at that stage. However, when this would mean the difference between drawing a universal conclusion rather than a particular one, we can deviate from that sequence. When there are two **A** premises, with the middle term the subject of one and the predicate of the other, the choice between a first-figure and a fourth-figure syllogism must be made in favor of the first figure; it permits a universal conclusion to be drawn. The principle of the syllogism, by itself, does not justify drawing a particular conclusion from two universal premises. We can derive the particular conclusion only indirectly from the universal premise, by first applying LIM to one of them and *then* applying SYL.

5.5 EXERCISES

Determine the validity or invalidity of each of the arguments below by applying the rules of quality and distribution. In the case of arguments that are valid, give a positive proof of validity by deriving the conclusion from the premises.

A. Some P are R.
   All P are Q.
   All R are S.
   _____
   Some S are Q.

B. All A are B.
   No C are D.
   All B are D.
   _____
   No A are C.

C. All X are Y.
   Some W are not Y.
   All Z are X.
   _____
   Some Z are not W.

D. All L are T.
   All W are M.
   All T are M.
   _____
   All W are L.

E. Some Q are not T.
   All Q are W.
   All W are V.
   All Y are T.
   _____
   Some V are not Y.

5.6 COMPLEX VARIATIONS FROM STANDARD FORM

We have now considered separately several ways in which arguments can deviate from the forms to which the rules of quality and distribution and the principles of immediate inference and the syllogism directly apply, even when all the constituents are stated in a standard-form language. We have seen these variations in order, the occurrence of complementary terms, incompleteness, and the number of premises. There is no reason at all that could lead us to believe that such variations would always occur in isolation from each other. In fact, the more terms and premises an argument includes, the more likely it is that there will be a pair of complementary terms, and that at least one of the premises that ought to be included in a fully explicit formulation of the argument has been omitted.

The most effective way to approach an argument that combines two or more of these variations is to deal with the deviations in the sequence in which we have discussed them separately. Initially, we must determine the conclusion the argument is intended to support (unless the argument is incomplete and the conclusion is omitted). Once this is known, we can set up the argument in standard form as far as order is concerned (although this is less significant than it is convenient). Then we eliminate complementary pairs of terms by using immediate inference. If the resulting argument is an enthymeme, we must complete it. We can determine the conditions the added premise must fulfill by applying the rules of quality and distribution. We must break it down into a series of syllogisms by the same procedure.

There is another and more important class of arguments that require further detailed consideration. What if the argument is enthymematic, incompletely expressed, and a sorites? We shall divide this class of arguments into two subclasses, depending on whether one of the premises or the conclusion has been left unstated. In the case of the first type, we are able to arrange the premises in standard order, with a gap somewhere along the line. We do this by adding to our requirement for standard order the further provision that the premise including the predicate of the conclusion must stand at the head, just as the premise including the subject term of the conclusion must stand at the foot of the list of premises. To determine the premise that must be added if the argument as a whole is to be valid, it is enough for us to apply the rules of quality and distribution in their generalized forms. The procedure is only an extension of the one used in the simpler case of the enthymeme.

The following example, an enthymematic sorites of the first type, looks back to the problem of chess and taxes in Exercise 1.5D and ahead to the discussion of translation into logical English in Chapter 6. The argument is:

> No contestant who improved his score had a name beginning with a consonant and no contestant who failed to improve his score had a final score of more than five points; therefore, no contestant with a name beginning with a consonant won.

In standard form, it would have to have more than two premises; one premise has been omitted.

The universe of discourse for this argument is the group of chessplayers who were contestants in the invitational tournament. There are five classes mentioned in the two premises and the conclusion. They are listed below, with appropriate abbreviations:

> C: those with names beginning with a consonant.
> I: those who improved their scores.
> $\bar{I}$: those who failed to improve their scores.
> M: those who had a final score of more than five points.
> W: those who won (a class with only one member).

The first thing we notice is that although there are five classes mentioned, there are only four independent distinctions, since two of the classes are complementaries (I and $\bar{I}$). We are able, therefore, to reduce the number of classes involved in the argument to four, using the procedures described in Section 5.5. We are, however, still left with four classes, none of them complementary to any other, and only three statements composing the argument—two premises and the conclusion. A complete argument would have to have three premises.

In logical English, using the abbreviations defined above, the argument has the form:

No I are C.		No $\bar{I}$ are M.
No $\bar{I}$ are M.	or	No I are C.
No C are W.		No C are W.

An equivalent argument, without any complementary pairs of terms, would be:

No $\bar{I}$ are M.
All C are $\bar{I}$.   (By what procedure?)
No C are W.

An additional premise, with M and W as its terms, is required if the argument is to be valid. It must be affirmative (by what rule?), and W must be distributed (by what rule?). The additional premise must therefore be *All W are M*. Only that statement will satisfy the rules of quality and distribution. Adding it to the original premises, we can construct a formal proof in which the conclusion is derived by indirect inference:

1. No I are C.	Premise
2. No $\bar{I}$ are M.	Premise
3. All W are M.	Added Premise[3]
4. No C are I.	1, CONV
5. All C are $\bar{I}$.	4, OBV
6. No C are M.	2, 5, SYL
7. No M are C.	6, CONV

[3] Can you prove the truth of the added premise from the information given in the problem, using common sense and arithmetic rather than explicitly formulated principles of inference? That is, can you prove that the winner had more than five points? Since we are told that only Aleking and Euwin improved their scores, one of the premises given is already known. What about the premise that no one who failed to improve his score had more than five points? This becomes a matter of simple arithmetic if you can prove that no one had more than two and one-half points in the first round? Can you prove that?

8. No W are C.   7, 3, SYL
9. No C are W.   8, CONV

When it is the conclusion that has been omitted from an argument (or if we want to ascertain what conclusion can be derived from a given set of premises), it is impossible to set the premises up in standard-form order. We determine that by reference to the position of the terms in the conclusion. Since order is significant only as a convenience, this is not a serious problem. It will be possible, if nothing but the conclusion is missing, to pick out the two terms that have only one occurrence in the argument. The rules of quality and distribution will determine what conclusion with these two terms can validly be inferred, if any.

When more than one constituent of an argument has been omitted, there can be no purely systematic way of determining what should be added. Without understanding something about the subject matter involved and the context of the argument, it will not be clear which of the terms occurring singly should be assigned to the conclusion and which to the premises. The decision will usually have to rest on the purpose the argument is intended to serve in the context in which it occurs. The answer to what relationships between which terms one would ordinarily be expected to assume or to know under the circumstances in which this argument is being used also affects the decision. No purely formal answer can be given; even the most obvious cases depend on the interpretation of the terms involved, the facts, and our own knowledge.

5.6   EXERCISES

Determine the validity or invalidity of each of the arguments below. Give a formal proof of validity for the valid arguments.

A. Some A are $\overline{B}$.
   All C are B.
   No D are $\overline{C}$.
   _____
   Some A are not D.

B. No Q are $\overline{R}$.
   No S are T.
   All R are T.
   _____
   No S are $\overline{Q}$.

C. All O are S.
   Some B are not $\overline{O}$.
   No S are U.
   _____
   Some B are not U.

D. No E are $\overline{C}$.
   Some L are B.
   No C are B.
   _____
   Some $\overline{L}$ are not E.

E. No B are S.
   No $\overline{L}$ are O.
   (What premise is needed?)
   _____
   Some L are $\overline{B}$.

F. All A are M.
   No F are $\overline{S}$.
   No M are S.
   _____
   (What conclusion can be
   drawn?)

G. All U are W.
   No $\overline{E}$ are W.
   No F are G.
   All M are U.
   All E are G.
   All M are $\overline{F}$.

H. No D are I.
   All M are P.
   No H are K.
   All C are D.
   No $\overline{K}$ are $\overline{I}$.
   All $\overline{M}$ are H.
   _____
   (What conclusion can be
   drawn?)

I. Some true statements are not statements that are self-evident, and all statements that are not self-evident are statements that require justification. Therefore, some true statements are not useful as ultimate philosophical premises, for all statements that require justification are useless as ultimate philosophical premises.

J. All advocates of States' Rights are critics of the Federal Government, and all Congressmen from Alabama are advocates of States' Rights, so some Congressmen from Alabama are not Democrats. (What premise needs to be added?)

Chapter 6

TRANSLATION INTO
LOGICAL ENGLISH

In the preceding chapters, we have shown that it is possible to bring any argument that is formulated in the language of logical English within the scope of a relatively small set of systematic rules. By the substitution of equivalent statements, we are able to determine the validity of any argument by applying the rules of quality and distribution. Indirect inference makes it possible for us to derive the conclusion of any valid argument by applying the principles of immediate inference and the syllogism. In order to extend the scope of this system of rules and principles still further, we must now consider how we may go about applying it to arguments composed of statements not formulated in logical English or in either of the artificial languages of Venn diagrams and algebraic notation.

6.1 THE PURPOSE OF TRANSLATION

Although it may seem peculiar to speak of *translating* statements already in the English language into a language that is only an artificially restricted version of English, there is some justification for the use of this word in referring to what we are to take up in the present chapter. The point underlying the extension of our system to include such arguments is the same one that was involved in extending the scope of the rules to include arguments not in standard form because of occurrence of pairs of complementary terms: the replacement of a statement by one that is equivalent to it could not affect the validity of the argument. The validity of the argument:

> No contestant who improved his score had a name beginning with a consonant, and no contestant who failed to improve his score had a final score of more than five points; therefore no contestant with a name beginning with a consonant won

is not affected when

> No contestant who failed to improve his score had a final score of more than five points

is replaced by

> No contestants who failed to improve their scores are contestants who had final scores of more than five points

nor when the latter is replaced, according to abbreviations specified, with *No I are M.*

To eliminate pairs of complementary terms and construct statements in logically equivalent standard-form arguments, we appealed to the rules of obversion and conversion for justification. The technique it served—the substitution of equivalent statements—is not applicable to the arguments we will be working with here. Now, we will substitute equivalent statements written in logical English for statements that are not. The appeal to obversion and conversion, or any other formal principle, is impossible because one of the equivalent statements is not in logical English. Consequently, it lies outside of the range of applicability of the rules. The equivalences must be supported by our *understanding* of the statements concerned and by an appeal to their *meanings.*

We have been implicitly assuming this from the very beginning. Whenever we replaced a statement written out in English with one that makes use of abbreviations for the class terms, the identity of meaning depends on the arbitrarily determined abbreviations. In this chapter, we shall be concerned with different forms of statement in ordinary usage that convey the same meaning.

Previously, we argued that if each of the two statements can be inferred from the other, they must be logically equivalent; the one could be substituted for the other without affecting the validity of an argument. Now we must argue that if two statements *mean* the same thing, they are equivalent; the one can be substituted for the other without affecting the argument's validity. Since the replacement of one statement by another, on the grounds that they have the same meaning, is precisely what is done in translating from one language to another, it is appropriate to apply the same word to the aspect of logical analysis to be considered in this chapter. Consequently, we will be dealing with the replacement of a statement not in logical English by one that is, not on the grounds of the formal principles, but on the grounds that the two statements have the same meaning.

We have already seen that logical English and the rules and principles applicable to it have a much wider scope than we might initially have suspected. The possibilities to be introduced in this chapter will extend its scope even farther. It would be an exaggeration, however, to say that ultimately *any* argument can be brought within the range of applicability, direct or indirect, of this system. That would be true only if there was an exact equivalent in logical English for every statement in unrestricted English. This, however, is not the case. There are many types of statements for which it is possible to establish such exact equivalents;[1] for others, logical English can capture only a part of their meaning. There are some statements for which it is impossible to give even an imperfect equivalent.

It would be impractical for us to attempt to consider every one of the enormous variety of forms of statements available to us in ordinary English. It is impossible, in the nature of the case, for us to give a reasonably small set of sufficiently broad general rules to cover all forms implicitly, owing to the many quirks and peculiarities of the language. (Recall what was said in Section 2.3 about combining the universal quantifier and the negative copula.) In translation, there is finally no substitute for a sensitive understanding of the language itself.

What we can do to promote such an understanding is to consider some representative kinds of translation. We shall begin with statements that, while differing in one way or another from the form of a statement in logical English, can be perfectly translated into a single such statement. We shall then consider examples of statements that can be perfectly trans-

---

[1] It can be argued that no two statements ever have *exactly* the same meaning, but the issues involved here are too technical to warrant treatment in an introductory textbook. A difficulty of more practical importance arises from the fact that it is not always clear what a statement is intended to mean. In fact, the speaker himself may not be entirely clear as to precisely what he means. In the present discussion, such problems are being ignored. However, some aspects of them are taken up in the next chapter.

lated but only by a *combination* of two or more statements in logical English. Next, we shall take up statements that can be only imperfectly translated, that is, only with some loss of significant meaning. Finally, we shall examine some statements that cannot be translated into logical English at all.

6.2 THE UNIVERSE OF DISCOURSE
AND THE INTERNAL STRUCTURE OF TERMS

To prepare ourselves for the study of translation into logical English, we should begin by considering what might be called the "internal structure of terms." Until now, we have considered the terms of a statement "externally," that is, as units in the structures of **A, E, I,** and **O** statements. In determining the correct translation of a statement that is not in logical English, much difficulty can be avoided if we can make clear what the terms *ought* to be. How we are to decide on the appropriate terms becomes easier once we understand the internal complexity that can be discovered in the term, even if it is not there explicitly.

The function of a term is to designate some class that has been selected from some universe of discourse. This function is accomplished if we can say (1) what the universe of discourse is and (2) what the distinguishing feature or features of the class within that universe of discourse are. The terms of a statement in logical English, if they were set down in full, would give explicit indications on each of these points. There would be a factor common to both terms. Consider the statement *No single men are happy men.* "Men" is common to both terms and indicates the universe of discourse. Each term would then indicate what distinguishes the class it singles out within the common universe of discourse. In the example, this function is carried out by the adjectives "single" and "happy."

Where there are a number of statements constituting one argument, the universe of discourse must be the same for all. Each term, no matter how many there are, must have a common factor that denotes the universe of discourse. In practice, it is unnecessary and painfully repetitive to indicate the universe of discourse in every term. What is important for our purposes is to be able to recognize what the universe of discourse is and to be able to think of each distinct term as singling out some class within that universe of discourse. This is done sometimes by naming it with a general noun and sometimes by referring to a distinguishing characteristic or set of characteristics. Abbreviations for terms should then be selected so as to suggest as strongly as possible the name or distinguishing characteristic of the terms they stand for.

The most common way in which a statement in ordinary English diverges from the strict requirements of logical English concerns the explicit mentioning of the universe of discourse, especially in the predicate term. The result of this is likely to be a grammatical predicate that is not truly a predicate *term* but merely an adjective that indicates the distinguishing characteristic of some class. For example, the statement *All felines are carnivorous* is not precisely in the standard form for an **A** statement; the predicate is an adjective rather than a general noun or its equivalent. We can easily remedy the situation by providing an explicit indication of the universe of discourse for the adjective to qualify. In this case, *creatures* or *animals* would be appropriate: *All felines are carnivorous animals*. With terms appropriately abbreviated, the statement would read: *All F are C,* where *F* represents animals distinguished as feline, and *C* represents animals distinguished as carnivorous.

6.3 SOME BASIC VARIATIONS IN QUANTIFIER, COPULA, AND TERMS

The form of a statement in logical English is determined by its quantifier and its copula. Variations from the four forms will most often depend on some sort of change involving quantifier or copula: there are cases in which alternatives are used, cases in which the quantifier or copula is displaced from its standard position, and cases in which one or the other is omitted. It is possible, of course, for more than one of these variations to occur within the same statement.

The universal affirmative function, represented in logical English by the **A** statement, can be formulated in various other ways. The example *All doctors are wealthy men* can be expressed otherwise by using an alternative quantifier, *Every doctor is a wealthy man;* by displacing the quantifier, *Doctors are all wealthy men;* by omitting the quantifier altogether, *Doctors are wealthy men*. The four statements, the standard-form **A** statement of logical English and the three examples of variants permitted in ordinary English, do not significantly differ from each other in meaning. They can, therefore, be regarded as equivalent and be mutually substituted whenever one of them occurs as part of an argument. The fact that one of the variant forms is given as a premise or the conclusion is no obstacle to determining the argument's validity by application of the rules governing logical English, if substitution of equivalent statements based on identity of meaning is permitted as well as substitution of equivalents based on the formal rules of obversion and conversion.

In the example of *wealthy doctors,* the deviations from standard form occurred as a consequence of variation, displacement, or omission of the quantifier. By omitting the reference to *men,* the divergence that was first mentioned—abbreviation of the predicate term by leaving out explicit reference to the universe of discourse qualified by the predicate adjective—could also have been exemplified. Sometimes something of the same sort occurs in connection with omission of the usual copula. The grammatical predicate may be formed with a verb other than the appropriate form of the verb *to be.* In such cases, the verb helps determine the predicate class. For example, in the statement *All lions eat meat,* we can recognize two classes: *lions* and *creatures that eat meat,* or *meat eaters.* If either of these expressions were to be used as a predicate term in combination with the usual copula, we would have a statement of identical meaning in standard form: *All lions are meat eaters.* Generally a statement of this sort can be readily translated into a standard-form statement by inserting between the subject term and the verb the formula *are (   ) that,* with an appropriate universe of discourse to be specified in the space reserved by the parentheses. The result in the example would be *All lions are creatures that eat meat.* Where there is a corresponding noun, such as *meat eaters* or *carnivores,* it is a convenience; it is not at all necessary for an adequate translation into standard form.

The subject term can be indicated just as readily as the predicate term can be, if we resort to a pattern of expression like the one introduced above. *All creatures that eat meat are mammals* is in standard form, although it happens to be false. Such expressions lend themselves to displacement in the English language so that the order of terms can be reversed from what it would be in standard form. This reversal is likely to occur when special emphasis is desired. It can occur in combination with other divergences from standard form as well. *Any man is truly wise who fully knows himself* would correctly be translated into standard logical English by making *men who know themselves* the subject, not the predicate term: *All men who fully know themselves are truly wise men.* In fact, the word "truly" might well be omitted entirely on the ground that it contributes more to the rhetorical effect than to the logical significance of the statement. We can see a more complicated example in *It is a wise child who knows his own father.* This does not mean that all wise children know their own fathers, but that all children who know their own fathers are wise. The expression *who knows his own father* is a displaced subject term. More precisely, it stands for the distinguishing feature that determines the subject class within the universe of discourse.

6.4 MORE COMPLEX VARIATIONS: "ONLY" AND "THE ONLY"

Enough has been said about the possibilities of variation, displacement, and omission in connection with the basic elements of a standard-form sentence of logical English to illustrate the flexibility of language even at relatively simple levels. In the examples that we have been considering, while there were various patterns of expression to be interpreted, each one could be brought within a rule of interpretation. To that extent, the flexibility was systematic. Language is by no means always so systematic and, as we have seen in other contexts, often presents us with surprises. Instead of attempting to describe the variety and elusiveness of our ordinary speech, we need consider only a few examples. The word "only" itself repays reflection on some of its uses. An announcement from an art museum might read in part:

> Only portraits of historical personages are included in the collection.

In this sentence, the word "only" functions as a variant quantifier but in a more complicated way than "any" and "every" and the like. We would be mistaken to suppose that its meaning could be reproduced in standard form by replacing "only" with the standard universal quantifier and completing the predicate term by adding reference to an appropriate universe of discourse. Another modification would also be required. We must reverse the order of the terms:

> All of the pictures included in the collection are portraits of historical personages.

Or we must replace the first term by its complement and change the quality:

> No pictures that are not portraits of historical personages are pictures included in the collection.

When abbreviations are put in the place of the terms, these two standard-form versions of the meaning of the original sentence would read *All C are P* and *No $\overline{P}$ are C* respectively. The two are equivalent, and either one could be derived from the other by one conversion and one obversion. Which is *the correct* translation is an arbitrary matter. The one replaces "only" with "all" and reverses the order of the terms; the other replaces "only" with "no" and replaces one of the terms, the first one, with its complement. Either correctly reproduces in standard form the significance of the original, and there is no significant basis on which to choose between them.

What we have just considered is a statement that fits the pattern *Only* ( ) *are* ( ). The addition of "the" to the beginning of this pattern might seem to be a slight difference, but it is a significant one. To express the meaning he intends, the writer of the museum's announcement would have had to formulate it this way:

> The only pictures included in the collection are portraits of histori-
> cal personages.

This is still another way of saying the same thing, and it can be translated into standard form by merely replacing "the only" with "all." The complications we encounter when translating sentences beginning with "only" do not arise with "the only."

It would appear that "the only" is just another substitute for "all," to be grouped with "any" and "every." This is true as long as we consider it solely as it functions at the beginning of a sentence. But, like "all" (and unlike "any" and "every"), it is subject to displacement into the middle of a statement. Then it no longer resembles "all" in its function, but it exhibits a parallel to "only" when it occurs at the beginning.

The statement

> Portraits of historical personages are the only pictures included in
> the collection.

could only be translated into standard form in logical English by reversing the order of terms as well as replacing "the only" with "all" and restoring it to the quantifier's usual place at the beginning of the sentence. We use "all" in the same way at the beginning and in the middle of a sentence; this is not true of our use of "the only." This is just a quirk of the language, the sort of thing that will always trip up the person who attempts to learn a language in terms of a limited number of simple rules. It is not that there are no rules at all, it is just that there are many of them. They cannot be expected to fall into any neat system but instead seem to present a welter of cross purposes and apparent inconsistencies.

One of the questions that frequently arises in connection with the interpretation of statements, such as those we have just now been considering, has to do with "convertibility." To say of a certain community, *only land-owners are eligible to vote,* must be taken to mean that *all those who are eligible to vote are landowners.* We might ask whether it does not also mean that *all landowners are eligible to vote.* If so, then neither of the standard-form statements by itself would represent an adequate reformulation of the original; the two of them together would. It would be as if the logical relationship signified when "only" is used as quantifier is convertible, which is not the case when the standard quantifier "all" is used.

In such cases, we may find it difficult to keep separate what we know or assume to be true from what is actually asserted by a sentence we are interpreting. If, for example, we believe that, in the community described, ownership of land is not only a necessary but also a sufficient condition of enfranchisement, we are very likely to assume that both of these facts (which are logically distinct) are included in the meaning of the statement. However, if someone were to say, *Only landowners are eligible to vote, and not even all of them are,* while he might be giving a false description of the actual conditions determining the right to vote, *he would not be contradicting himself.* If we wished to disagree, we would try to show, not that the statement is internally inconsistent, but that the facts are otherwise. We might, for example, challenge him to cite any other condition governing the right to vote besides ownership of land. If he could do so and also show that some landowners failed to fulfill it, we would be obliged to accept his statement and abandon our earlier opinion. We would not be obliged, however, to give up the view that *only landowners are eligible to vote;* we would merely correct our mistaken interpretation of it arising from factual assumptions that were not genuinely part of its meaning. This is not to deny that such statements do often suggest the additional meaning. As long as it remains possible to add *and not even all of them* or some similar qualifying clause, without inconsistency, they cannot strictly be said to mean anything beyond the minimum interpretation we initially attached to them.

6.5 SINGULAR TERMS

The discussion so far has concerned statements in which the terms have been general and of indefinite application. The use of terms of a definite, restricted application to one or more individuals requires some modification in the conclusions we have just reached. There are special difficulties arising in connection with distinguishing between general terms with an indefinite range of application (such as *landowners*) and terms that refer to a circumscribed group (such as *the owners of the land that borders on mine*). We shall avoid these obstacles by referring to singular terms—terms that are intended to refer to just one individual—either by a name or by a description that is meant to apply uniquely.[2]

Statements about specified individuals, statements with singular terms as their subjects, are called "singular statements." A particular species of such statements was among the first statements we considered, and they were translated into the +'s and 0's of the chart that served as our simple model of a logical system. For obvious reasons, they do not require a quantifier. We can treat the singular subject term as if it were distributed; although the statement concerns only one individual, it is the only individual referred to. We can say there are no individuals referred to by the subject term that are not asserted to be included in or excluded from the predicate term, whichever is indicated by the statement's quality. *Hubert Humphrey is a Democrat* and *Hubert Humphrey is not an old man* are both singular statements, one affirmative and the other negative. In neither case are we left in doubt concerning any individual referred to by the subject term; there is only one, and we need not even consider any others. In logical English, therefore, singular statements are in effect assimilated to universal statements because they are comparable statements with distributed subject terms. In the system to be taken up in Part Three, there will be a marked difference in the analysis of universal statements and singular statements, but the difference in the present system is minimal.

Interesting differences do arise when we consider singular terms in the context of the variants from standard form of the sort which were being examined previously. The statement

> Only Franklin D. Roosevelt has served three full terms as President of the United States

[2] *President of the United States during the Twentieth Century* is a general term applicable to Roosevelt, Harding, Eisenhower, Kennedy and others. *President of the United States for three full terms* is also a general term, which *happens* to apply to Franklin D. Roosevelt. We could use it without impropriety, even if there had been more than one such president. *The President of the United States who served three full terms* is not a general term but a singular term. It not only happens to refer to just one man but also is intended to do so. If the description did not apply uniquely to one individual, such a form of expression would be improper. Because it applies only to one person, we can use the description in this form, now called a "definite" description, as a way of singularly referring to him. There are complications in the analysis and interpretation of definite descriptions that have had important consequences for logical theory. We shall have to ignore them and simply take such expressions at face value to be the singular terms, akin to proper names, which they appear to be.

has as its terms the singular term, *Franklin D. Roosevelt,* and the general term, *persons who have served three full terms as President of the United States.* According to one of the patterns we have developed for translating statements beginning with "only" into standard form, the relationship between them might be expressed as *No $\overline{R}$ are T,* using $\overline{R}$ as an abbreviation for *persons other than Franklin D. Roosevelt* and *T* as an abbreviation for *persons who have served three full terms as President of the United States.* This form is somewhat more acceptable on interpretation than the alternative, *All T are R.* That is,

> No person other than Franklin D. Roosevelt is a person who has served three full terms as President of the United States

is idiomatically more acceptable than

> All persons who have served three full terms as President of the United States are Franklin D. Roosevelt.

The reformulation does not express all of what is meant by the original, however. Surely it is part of the meaning of the original statement that Franklin D. Roosevelt did serve three full terms, but this is not part of the meaning of *No $\overline{R}$ are T.* When a statement beginning with "only" has a singular term as subject, part of its meaning is expressed by the singular statement left when "only" is omitted. Unlike the former examples involving only general terms, it *is* self-contradictory to say *Only Franklin D. Roosevelt served three terms, and even he did not.* Of course, in the general case of the landowners, it would have been equally self-contradictory to say *Only landowners are eligible to vote, and even they are not.* However, there we could add, without self-contradiction, *even some of them are not.* With a singular term as subject, there is no such alternative. Consequently, we must interpret the statement about Roosevelt to include in its very meaning that he served three full terms *and* that no one else has done so. Both *R is T* and *No $\overline{R}$ are T* are essential to the expression in logical English of the original statement's entire significance. The two statements together constitute a complete and adequate expression in standard form of what is meant.

6.6 EXCEPTIVE STATEMENTS

Very closely related to "only" in function is the expression "no one but" or "no one except." *Only Franklin D. Roosevelt has served three full terms* could be changed to *No one except Franklin D. Roosevelt has served three full terms* without change of meaning. What this suggests is that we might well think of the function of "but" and "except" as that of forming complementary terms. The effect of such expressions is to divide a set into two complementary subsets. If applied to a singular term, the two "sets" are (1) the individual referred to by that term and (2) all the others in the universe of discourse. If applied to a general term, they are the class it refers to and its complement. It is typical of such exceptive statements that they require more than a single statement in logical English to capture their full meaning. In the example given, the universal negative would have to be accompanied by the affirmative singular statement:

> Franklin D. Roosevelt did serve three full terms as President.

The resemblance to the similar statement beginning with "only" is obvious. In the case of exceptive statements, however, the need to use two statements in logical English extends to cases in which there is no singular term.

> All of the animals in the zoo except the polar bears are taken inside for the winter

would not be adequately translated except by using both *All $\overline{P}$ are W* and *No P are W*. (The universe of discourse is *animals in the zoo*, P stands for "polar bears," and W stands for "those that are taken in for the winter.") Sometimes the exceptive clause does not specify what the distinction is.

> All but a few of the animals are taken in for the winter

indicates that there are exceptions, but what the distinguishing features of the exceptions are (that they are polar bears) is not indicated. The meaning in logical English would have to be formulated in terms of two statements in which the subject of each is what serves as the universe of discourse in the preceding example. The function of the statement is to indicate that some of the animals at the zoo are taken in for the winter, but not all of them. Its meaning in logical English would have to be rendered by combining *Some Z are W* and *Some Z are not W*.

A still more complex type of exceptive statement arises when the class excepted is itself subject to exceptions, that is, if the members of the class are not universally excepted. We interpreted *All but the polar bears are taken in for the winter* to include in its meaning a universal negative statement concerning the polar bears. This would not do for *All of the animals at the zoo except some of the polar bears are taken in for the winter*. Part of its translation must surely be *All $\overline{P}$ are W*, but along with that we must acknowledge both *Some P are W* and *Some P are not W*. This situation requires three statements in logical English to capture the meaning of the one exceptive statement with such a structure in ordinary English.

6.7   INADEQUACIES OF LOGICAL ENGLISH

We can see that there could be some objection to the treatment of *All but a few animals at the zoo are taken in for the winter*. In translating this into two particular statements in logical English, one affirmative and one negative, something seems to have been left out. What is missing is the proportional aspect suggested by the use of the exceptive form of statement together with the phrase "a few." "All but a few" indicates not only that there are exceptions, but also that the exceptions are in the minority. This proportional feature of the statement in ordinary English is not reproduced in the particular statements. When they are joined together, they remain compatible with every possibility that divides the subject class into two parts, whatever the proportional relation between them. What is more, this feature cannot be reproduced in logical English. The quantifiers of logical English are restricted to the universal and the particular. There is no provision for degrees of quantity between "at least one" and "all." Wherever a statement in ordinary English specifies more precisely the quantity of a statement, that aspect of its meaning must be sacrificed in translation. Whatever is not translatable as a universal statement must be translated as a particular statement or a pair of them. The entire range in English from "a very few" to "almost all" is indifferently to be translated as "some." The same holds true, of course, of the still more precise specifications of quantity involved in the use of numbers or percentages: two, three, twenty-five percent, fifty-one percent, and so on. But here, one might reply, we have moved from the realm of logic into that of mathematics.

There are other types of statement that seem to elude the grasp of logical English in a still more radical way. We have seen how the statements of logical English relate to affirmative and negative existential statements. Modeling our interpretation on the Venn diagrams and the algebraic versions of **A, E, I,** and **O** statements, we can interpret them as asserting or denying the existence of members in class products determined by combining one basic class with the other or with its complement. We should have no trouble, then, with existential statements in ordinary English as long as it is possible to interpret them in terms of two classes combined in a class product. But some such statements seem to involve only one term, representing a single class. *There are lions, there are no unicorns* seem to be respectively an affirmative and a negative existential statement in which only a single term appears. We must either find some implicit reference to a second class (*the class of existing things* has seemed a possibility to some logical theorists) or abandon the hope of reproducing the meaning of such statements, even partially, in logical English. The metaphysical convolutions that would have to go into settling this particular issue should rightly alarm us. Pleading the privilege of an elementary textbook, we pass them by.

6.7 EXERCISES (Adopted and adapted from Lewis Carroll's *Symbolic Logic*)

Apply the techniques and principles presented in the preceding chapters to the equivalents in logical English of the following arguments.

A. Examine these syllogisms according to the rules of quality and distribution.

1. Dictionaries are useful.
   Useful books are valuable.
   ___
   Dictionaries are valuable.

2. No misers are unselfish.
   No one but a miser serves egg-shells.
   ___
   No unselfish people serve egg-shells.

3. Some healthy people are fat.
   No unhealthy people are strong.
   ___
   Some fat people are not strong.

4. Everyone who is anxious to learn works hard.
   Some of the freshmen in your class work hard.
   ___
   Some of the freshmen in your class are anxious to learn.

5. No misers are generous.
   Some old men are ungenerous.
   ___
   Some old men are misers.

6. All uneducated people are shallow.
   The students in your class are all educated.
   ___
   None of the students in your class are shallow.

7. A badly managed business is unprofitable.
   Railways are never badly managed.
   ___
   All railways are profitable.

8. No Professors are ignorant.
   All ignorant people are vain.
   ___
   No Professors are vain.

9. Some unauthorized reports are false.
   All authorized reports are trustworthy.
   ___
   Some false reports are not trustworthy.

10. Improbable stories are not easily believed.
    None of his stories are probable.
    ___
    None of his stories are easily believed.

B. Complete these syllogisms with missing parts to satisfy the rules of quality and distribution.

1. No one who has not read the letter knows what it is about, but no one besides John has read it.

2. No one who exercises self-control fails to keep his temper, yet some professors do lose their tempers.

3. I never neglect important business. Your business is unimportant.

4. Some excise laws are unjust, and all the laws passed last week relate to excise.

5. Nothing intelligible ever puzzles me, so Logic must be unintelligible.

6. No children are patient and no impatient person can sit still.

7. None of my colleagues can lecture effectively today, since all of them have a cold.

8. Some obstinate people are not philosophers, for all philosophers are logical.

9. Prudent travelers carry plenty of small change; imprudent travelers lose their luggage.

10. Busy employees do not talk about their grievances all the time, but discontented ones do.

C. The following are arguments with more than two premises and with the conclusion to be drawn. Examine them according to the rules of quality and distribution and analyze them in terms of the basic principles of inference.

1. Disgruntled students are illogical. No one who can complete a formal proof is unrespected. Illogical persons are not respected.

2. None of the students in your class can do Logic. No lunatics are capable of following instructions. Everyone who is sane can do Logic.

3. No experienced person is incompetent. Some logicians are always blundering. No competent person is always blundering.

4. All of the old material in this file has been superseded. No book in this file which gives instructions for the use of magnetic tape is new. Nothing in this file which has been superseded can be of any use.

5. No goods in this store which have been bought and paid for are still on sale. None of the goods may be carried away unless they are labeled "sold." None of the goods are labeled "sold" unless they have been bought and paid for.

6. Showy talkers think too much of themselves. No really well-informed people are bad company. People who think too much of themselves are not good company.

7. No books sold here have gilt edges except the ones in the front of the shop. All of the authorized editions have red labels. All of the books with red labels are priced at $5 and up. Only authorized editions are ever placed in front of the shop.

8. All of the University of Minnesota men in this company play football. No one but the executives may use the executives' washroom. None of the foot-

ball players can play chess. My friends in this company all are from the University of Minnesota. All of the executives can play chess.

9. No husband who is always giving his wife new dresses can be an ill-tempered man. A methodical husband always has plenty of time for breakfast. No one who hangs his hat on the light fixture can be a man who is kept in proper order by his wife. A good husband is always giving his wife new dresses. No husband can fail to be ill-tempered if his wife does not keep him in proper order. An unmethodical husband always hangs his hat on the light fixture.

10. I never put a check I have received in that file unless I am anxious about it. All the checks I have received that are not marked with a cross are payable to bearer. None of them are ever brought back to me unless they have been dishonored at the bank. All of them that are marked with a cross are for amounts of more than $100. All of them that are not in that file are marked "not negotiable." No check of yours I have received has ever been dishonored. I am never anxious about a check I have received unless it happens to be brought back to me. None of the checks I have received that are marked "not negotiable" are for amounts of over $100.

PART TWO

Chapter 7

INFORMAL FALLACIES, I

Our discussions have, so far, concentrated on the presentation of the traditional formal logic. As a result, we have proceeded within a restricted and somewhat unrealistic framework. The reasons for this were explained as we began our study of logic: the formal structures of inference we have been considering are seen most clearly in isolation. These situations, however, rarely occur in isolation, and now is the time for us to enrich our discussion and bring it into a closer approximation to the actual course and context of human reasoning.

7.1 THE TRADITIONAL APPROACH TO FORMAL AND INFORMAL FALLACIES

In traditional presentations of logic, at this stage of development, there is usually a study of "informal fallacies." The traditional classification of all fallacies frequently divided the field into three general areas: "formal fallacies," "verbal fallacies," and "material fallacies." Formal fallacies were understood in relation to the formal rules violated, and we will not have occasion to touch on them in this discussion. Verbal fallacies, for which linguistic confusions are responsible, will be taken up in this chapter. The group of fallacies identified as material fallacies will be the subject of Chapter 8.

The significance of a study of informal fallacies and its place in practical logic have not always been made sufficiently clear. Often, these fallacies appear to be a collection of miscellany. The situation is even more confusing because different writers frequently offer different classifications of the generally recognized informal fallacies and even present different accounts of various types of fallacious reasoning. To some extent, as we shall see, these flaws are inherent in the very nature of the subject; it is, however, possible to keep them at a minimum. Our discussion of informal fallacies, while guided by the traditional presentation, will attempt to avoid some of the usual errors.

There are two general points common to the majority of discussions of informal logical fallacies. One concerns their definition, the other their classification. Although any argument that fails to fulfill the rules of validity is fallacious, logicians, in discussing fallacies, have been inclined to concentrate their attention on particularly interesting cases of fallacious reasoning. These are cases that are constantly recurring and that seem especially apt to be misleading; logic has attempted to identify and classify those logical mistakes that often present a delusive appearance of validity. Since the human capacity for making mistakes appears to be considerably greater than any logician's capacity for tabulating and organizing the various kinds of mistakes made, none of these classifications and descriptions ever seems to be entirely satisfactory.

Nevertheless, the very way in which the problem is posed makes it clear that the concept of a fallacy involves two distinct parts. One is logical: fallacies are *invalid* arguments. The other is psychological: fallacies very often *seem* to be valid, at least in the sense that they persuasively support their conclusions. The study of informal fallacies has generally been the study of *persuasive mistakes* in reasoning.

The traditional classification of formal fallacies under such titles as "fallacy of the undistributed middle term," "fallacy of illicit process," and so on, pays attention solely to the *logical* aspect of the fallacy. Such fallacies are defined by and are entirely subsidiary to the rules of the syllogism. They add nothing new to logical theory, and we were able to get along very well without special titles by defining errors in syllogistic reasoning directly by reference to the rule violated—Q1, D2, and so on. In traditional discussions of informal fallacies, the emphasis has always fallen on the other side, the psychological aspect. Many mistakes in reasoning are so obviously invalid as to be laughable, once they are recognized as such. The interesting questions that remain, however, are "Why should such a mistake ever have been made?" or "How could I have been such a fool?" The study of informal fallacies aims at some understanding of various causes that on occasion are responsible for our making fools of ourselves, logically speaking.[1]

7.2 THE CLASSIFICATION OF FALLACIES

Although classifications of fallacies vary, it is possible to recognize in all of them at least two principal classes that have been distinguished. A number of fallacies are traceable to mistakes that originate in language, while others have their roots elsewhere, usually in the emotions. In actual life, of course, the two types are frequently mingled, sometimes inseparably blended. In order to place our account of reasoning in the context of actual life and thought, then, we must take account of (1) certain features of the language in which arguments are expressed and (2) certain psychological features of human thought that tend to affect the accuracy of the reasoning process. We must be sure to understand that the introduction of such topics does not add anything new to the principles of logical criticism. The same rules continue to determine the validity of deductive reasoning. What we are concerned with are factors that tend to obscure the distinction between validity and invalidity and influence us to accept as valid arguments that are not.

We have already seen, in Chapter 1, that the ability to distinguish between good and bad arguments precedes the study of logic. This ability is a large part of what we call "common sense," but it has its flaws and limitations. The ordinary person, unaided by anything except his common sense, finds himself baffled and unable to reach a confident judgment when the line of argument becomes too complex. In the preceding chapters, our attention has been concentrated on the development of formal logic as an

---

[1] In the light of the remarks about the two aspects, logical and psychological, of an informal fallacy, it is now possible for us to see why this traditional expression is misleading and in what respect. The fallacy, considered in its purely logical aspect, may well be the violation of a formal rule. Consequently, formal fallacies and informal fallacies are not complementary classes within the universe of discourse, fallacies. Instead of speaking of the study of informal fallacies, it would be more accurate to speak of the study of the informal aspects of fallacies. This is not the only case in which an inaccurate but convenient expression takes the place of an accurate but cumbersome one.

instrument for extending the range of judgment indefinitely by substituting for the direct appeal to common sense the appeal to an organized system of principles. Now, in turning attention to informal fallacies, we are simply taking account of the fact that the direct judgment of an argument, unaided by such a system of principles, is not always accurate even when it is made confidently. Common sense is not just baffled, it is sometimes bamboozled. The study of informal fallacies is basically a study of various ways in which common-sense judgment, particularly when it is careless and offhand, can be victimized.

The obstacles that stand in the way of a clear understanding of informal fallacies are many and diverse. That discussion of this subject has often failed to bring out plainly the shift from a primarily logical orientation to a primarily psychological one has already been mentioned. Another source of confusion has been the failure to take account of the different kinds of reasoning and the different purposes that may be served by offering reasons. Because of this failure, examples of fallacious reasoning commonly appear to fall outside the scope of logical criticism entirely. They represent, in many cases, not so much attempts to support beliefs as attempts to influence action. Often, it is quite clear that the fallacious argument offered as an example could not reasonably be thought to lend deductive support to its conclusion. The most anyone would be led to believe is that it makes its conclusion more probable.

Other difficulties have arisen from the failure to maintain any clear basis of classification of fallacies. We shall attempt to identify both general classes and particular species of informal fallacies as clearly as possible, calling explicit attention to the distinguishing characteristics of each. Despite these criticisms, however, we shall still be guided by the list of informal fallacies that has been traditionally accepted, for many of these individual fallacies have become part of the store of knowledge of an educated man.

A basic and important distinction has already been drawn—the distinction between fallacies for which linguistic causes are responsible and those that arise from other causes, usually emotional ones. To err is human, but some errors are more human than others. The linguistic fallacies are errors that would be made by a machine if the language in which it "reasoned" contained some of the features that all human languages exhibit to some degree. The other fallacies are more directly determined by the conditions in which human reasoning occurs and by the peculiarities of the human mind. We shall call such fallacies "psychological" fallacies, so distinguishing them from the specifically linguistic ones. We shall consider the linguistic fallacies first.

7.3 LANGUAGE AND REASONING

For more than two thousand years, philosophers have acknowledged, more or less clearly, more or less radically, the pernicious effects produced by carelessness in the use of language. In modern times, attention to language has become one of the principal features of philosophical discussion. However, a glance at almost any modern textbook of logic will reveal that the treatment of *linguistic* fallacies ignores the implications of one important basic fact about the use of language: *language is used to communicate.* It is possible to talk to oneself, but that is nothing except a derivative function. The primary and indispensable function of language is interpersonal, public, and intentionally so.

There are numerous theories about the primitive origins of language, but it is clear that the effective functioning of a developed language is thoroughly dependent on social factors. The infant's use of language is only beginning to be the subject of careful, detailed scientific study. Without waiting for the results of any such studies, it is possible to say that no reasonable student of the subject would take seriously any attempt to deal with the problem without paying any attention to the baby's social contacts with parents, brothers and sisters, and other children. The theory that the development of speech is an innate result of maturation, independent of social factors, like the physiological (as against the psychological) manifestations of adolescence, is ludicrous. Language is not only used for communication; it is communicated, from one person, from one generation, to another. Furthermore, once its use is mastered, language is the medium of all but the most primitive interpersonal relations. It is, that is to say, not just one among many such media; it is the all-important one.

We are interested, not in a general theory of speech and language but in the relevance of the use of language to reasoning. At first glance, it would seem that there is a certain contrast between what has just been said about language and what might be said about thinking. Language may be indispensable to reasoning, but its public use does not seem to be. Using language privately is odd, but thinking private thoughts is not. It would be foolish to recommend that everyone talk to himself, but we believe everyone should think for himself. It is almost inconceivable that someone should spend a major part of his waking adult life in a soundproof room delivering a monologue, but if a man spends most of his time in his study thinking out the solution to a scientific or philosophical problem, he may be on his way to becoming a respected scholar.

But, one might object, the difference is not so great after all. The scholar in his study spends at least some of his time reading what others have written, and he publishes at least some of the thoughts he arrives at in his privacy. A scholar who literally spent all of his time thinking to himself would be as mad as the monologuist. The man who thinks for himself is bound to make use of information that, in large part, he has not gathered himself but learned from others. One is tempted to conclude from these observations that reasoning is as public as the use of language, as well as being dependent on it. The temptation rests on a confusion, however; a basic difference remains when the confusion is eliminated. The considerations advanced *do* show that reasoning is not detachable from interpersonal communication of some sort. The information on which our conclusions are based is ordinarily communicated to us by others; the conclusions we reach are ordinarily passed on to others, either as neutral reports or in attempts to persuade them to follow the same course of thought themselves. But the fact that the two ends of the process of reasoning extend into the public realm of our relations to others does not make the reasoning process itself something public and interpersonal. We depend on others for a significant part of our food and make use of a public system of waste-disposal, but that does not make the process of assimilation something interpersonal. It goes on in our own innards, and nobody else's.

In fact, the notion of an interpersonal inference is as absurd as a collective digestion. What is interpersonal is the *communication* of information and the attempts to persuade, and these are not to be identified with the process of reasoning itself. Communication by language involves two ends, what one says and what another understands; typically, these two ends have their loci in different persons. Inference involves two ends, premise(s) and conclusion; necessarily these must have their loci in the *same* person. James can say something, and John can understand it. It is impossible that James would conceive a premise with no conclusion and John a conclusion with no premise and together constitute two people drawing an inference. Two people may make the same inference in the sense of duplicating each other's processes of reasoning, not in the sense of dividing the effort. What may happen is that James may have some information from which he draws no conclusion and may communicate this information to John, who draws a conclusion from it and reports his result to James. This sort of thing goes on all the time. The *inference,* however, even in this case, is totally and privately John's. It became possible only when John took the information originally James's and made it his own, and its possibility then depended not at all on the intention to report back. The effect of language on reasoning can be felt directly *and* indirectly, then, in the light of this discussion. It is felt directly when it becomes significant that the premises and conclusions of the inferences we carry on "in our own heads" are formulated in a language. It is felt indirectly when the fact that we draw on information communicated to us by others takes on significance. It is one thing to make a mistake in inference because of some flaw in the language used in our reasoning. It is something quite different, not a mistake *in reasoning,* to misunderstand what someone else says and draw a conclusion accordingly, although it is still a mistake and one that affects our reasoning in the sense of affecting the conclusions at which we arrive.

There are a number of complications that emerge in connection with a serious treatment of language and reasoning, complications that are not adequately indicated in an account as brief as this has been. For example, a dialogue is not always a mutual exchange of information, as the preceding suggestion seems to assume. It can as easily be a dispute; when it is, we have a context in which special kinds of mistakes are likely to occur. Again, when conclusions are drawn from what someone else has said, they may be based not so much on the information he is understood to be communicating but on the way he chooses to communicate it, or the very fact that he has chosen to make such a communication at all. We cannot hope to give a complete and explicit exposition of all these complications; we shall therefore not go beyond the preceding remarks, which are essential to an adequate elementary understanding of the kinds of mistake traditionally treated under the heading of informal linguistic (or verbal) fallacies.

7.4 AMBIGUITY AND NONSENSE

In an earlier discussion, we were shown that the English language permits the same idea to be expressed in several different ways. At least it appeared to be the case; for our purpose, we can take it to be so. This fact can sometimes lead to errors in judgment about reasoning but not to errors in the actual process of reasoning itself. That is, it may make us think that some arguments are fallacious when they are really valid; it will not cause us to draw conclusions that are not logically derivable from their premises.

The language also permits different things to be expressed in the same way, and this does lead to errors in reasoning. When the same expression has two or more different meanings, it is said to be "ambiguous." In a sense, all linguistic fallacies can be regarded as fallacies of ambiguity. These fallacies arise because of the confusion occurring when a linguistic similarity has obscured a logical difference. Various species of linguistic fallacy can then be distinguished according to the particular origin of such a confusion.

A language is most suitable for purely logical purposes if, for every expression in it, there is one distinct meaning. Synonymy occurs when two expressions coincide in meaning, ambiguity when a single expression has at least two distinct interpretations. If we restrict attention to a single linguistic expression (thereby leaving synonymy out of account), we can say that the ideal, for logical purposes, of a single distinct meaning really represents a mean between the two extremes of *too little* and *too much*. Ambiguity is the extreme of too much, and the other extreme is "nonsense."

It is interesting and instructive to recognize that some of the same distinctions can be applied both to nonsense and to ambiguity. In fact, since it is easier to recognize a nonsense statement than an ambiguous one, these distinctions can be even more easily illustrated by examples of meaningless statements. *Double talk* is nonsense; Lewis Carroll's "The Jabberwocky" is a prototype in poetic form.

> 'Twas brillig and the slithy toves
> Did gyre and gimble in the wabe;
> All mimsy were the borogoves,
> And the mome raths outgrabe.

A statement is no more meaningful than its weakest link—if it contains just one meaningless constituent (leaving mere embellishments out of consideration) it makes no sense. Therefore, the simplest type of a nonsensical expression is one in which there is a nonsense word.

It is also possible to construct equally nonsensical expressions out of individually meaningful constituents by violating the rules governing their combination. Such rules, when they are explicitly formulated as part of a logical system, are called "formation rules." The rule requiring that statements in logical English be composed of quantifier, subject term, copula, and predicate term is such a rule. Unless there are rules governing the *formation* of statements, the mere existence of a vocabulary will not suffice for the creation of meaningful expressions. *All some are no* is nonsense, although each of its constituents can be part of a meaningful statement, either in logical English, where there is one straightforward formation rule, or in ordinary English, for which the formation rules, studied as grammar and syntax, are neither as explicit nor as rigid nor as thoroughly codified. It is possible, then, for a statement to lack sense either because it contains at least one constituent that has no meaning *anywhere* or because its constituents, each of which might contribute to a meaningful combination else-where, are arranged in a meaningless way.[2]

7.5 EQUIVOCATION AND AMPHIBOLY

An analogous distinction can be drawn within the domain of ambiguous statements. Some of them are ambiguous because they contain elements that are ambiguous. Others are ambiguous because their elements are put together in an ambiguous way. The two alternatives are not mutually exclusive and may even reinforce each other in particular cases. When an error in reasoning occurs because of ambiguous elements—two possible senses of a word or phrase being confused—it is called a "fallacy of equivocation." When the other type of ambiguity, arising from structure, is responsible, it is called a "fallacy of amphiboly."

An example of an argument committing the fallacy of equivocation follows:

> Since the laws of logic are *laws,* laws governing human reasoning, it is not really possible to violate them, not any more than an apple could violate the law of gravitation.

The ambiguous word here is "law," which does not have the same meaning in connection with logic that it has in connection with physics. We could make the distinction explicit using the phrases "normative law" and "scientific law." If this were done, the confusion between the two different meanings of "law" would cease, and the argument would lose its air of plausibility.

[2] The problem of discriminating between sense and nonsense can become a very subtle one, as various attempts at formulating a "meaning criterion" have revealed. Here is another Lewis Carroll poem:

> "'Tis the voice of the Lobster"; I heard him declare,
> "You have baked me too brown, I must sugar my hair."
> As a duck with its eyelids, so he with his nose
> Trims his belt and his buttons, and turns out his toes.

Unlike the "Jabberwocky," its constituents are meaningful English words, familiar to all of us. What is more, they are put together without violating any of the rules of grammar or syntax ordinarily recognized as governing the construction of meaningful sentences in English. Yet something is amiss. This is a trivial example, but the problem took an acutely serious turn for the philosopher earlier in this century when the allegation was made against metaphysical statements that they too were nonsense statements masquerading as meaningful expressions.

Now let us look at an example of an argument committing the fallacy of amphiboly:

"The author warns against a number of logical errors in his book."
"He must have written it very carelessly, then."

It will not be of any use for us to specify the meaning of any word or phrase taken by itself. What we must do is to make clear that what is in the book is the warning, not the logical errors. This can best be accomplished by arranging the amphibolous sentence to read:

"In his book, the author warns against a number of logical errors."

The perceptive reader may have noticed a difference between the fallacies of equivocation and amphiboly that have been offered as examples. The fallacy of equivocation can and does occur as a genuine error in reasoning. People have in their own thinking been led to draw conclusions about normative laws from premises appropriate only to descriptive scientific laws, just because the same word is used in both senses. The example of the fallacy of amphiboly is most *unlikely* to occur in the reasoning of a single person. There are clearly two people involved in the example, a speaker (or writer) and someone who misunderstands his statement because of its amphibolous structure. The error is more a mistake in interpretation than a mistake in reasoning. This is not an accidental feature of our examples but is typical of the two types of fallacy. Equivocation can lead to errors either in reasoning or in interpretation. Amphiboly is a source of the latter mistake only. In other words, the so-called fallacy of amphiboly is tied to the use of language as a means of interpersonal communication.

What this difference suggests is that the verbal link is not quite enough by itself to generate a fallacy of ambiguity in the strict sense. That a statement should have two distinct meanings will suffice to make it possible for a mistake in interpretation to occur. For it to be responsible for a genuine error in reasoning, it is also necessary for the distinct meanings to be related. The two senses of "law" are distinct, to be sure; it is important that they not be confused but they must also be related to each other. They share some features in common, in this case, generality. Both normative and scientific laws are, after all, laws in a more general sense. The distinction is between two species of a common genus. There is nothing comparable in the example given to illustrate amphiboly. There the only relation between the two meanings was the accidental fact that owing to the speaker's carelessness in the construction of his statement, either one could be attached to it. Examples of equivocation that are equally without any connection of meaning besides the purely verbal one would also be limited to the role of errors in interpretation. We can easily imagine someone hearing a statement about *catching flies* intended in the sense appropriate to baseball players but understanding it in the sense appropriate to field entomologists. It is impossible to conceive of any realistic case in which someone would reason from a premise appropriate to one context to a conclusion intended to apply to the other. Equivocation is much more likely to result in errors of reasoning, that is, fallacies proper, than amphiboly only because when an ambiguity is built into the vocabulary of a language it is much more likely to reflect some positive relationship of meaning than when it is merely the result of carelessness in sentence construction.

7.6 THE FALLACY OF ACCENT

Equivocation and amphiboly are the principal sources of ambiguity, but there are others that deserve attention. The general heading of fallacies of ambiguity usually also includes at least one other, the "fallacy of accent." Like amphiboly, it is more accurately described as a fallacy of interpersonal communication than a fallacy of reasoning proper. The meaning of a statement, even when the individual words and their relations are clear enough, may vary with the relative emphasis or accent placed on its constituents. Whether we count this as a true type of ambiguity depends partly on where we wish to draw the line between what is really meant by a statement and what is merely suggested. It is the *overtones* of meaning, the suggested implications, that are likely to vary as accent shifts, while the literal meaning, narrowly interpreted, remains the same.

A spoken statement is hardly as likely to provide any occasion for the fallacy of accent to occur as a written statement. With a written statement, unless an intended emphasis is indicated by setting the word or phrase apart from the rest of the sentence, there is considerably more freedom for variation of interpretation. With a spoken statement, the only serious possibility for such an error of interpretation arises from assuming an intended emphasis even when none is indicated by actual vocal inflection. Even that, we are inclined to suspect, would not occur except with the assistance of other influences. Consider the child who, having just been cautioned against using his color crayons on the kitchen wall, is then discovered busily decorating the dining room. If he protests his punishment on the grounds that he had been told not to color on the *kitchen* wall, he has passed the age of innocence. The fallacy of accent occurs when a conclusion is drawn on the basis of a pattern of accents other than the one intended, and the pattern of accents is much more clearly indicated in spoken than in written language.

Although the fallacy of accent may seem to turn on fairly subtle considerations, it can still be seriously misleading. In recording a preliminary interrogation in a murder case, a police stenographer might take down the statement, "My son could not have murdered the maid." Those present when the statement was uttered would have a clear understanding of it. But if the stenographer does not indicate in any way the speaker's emphasis, the statement written in the transcript might well lead further investigation in the wrong direction to pursue suggestions determined by different patterns of emphasis. No matter what the emphasis, there is a constant theme, perhaps best represented by speaking the sentence with no particular accent at all. But as one word or another is stressed, implications that go beyond this constant meaning are strongly suggested, even if they are not explicitly stated. If the word "son" is stressed, it is strongly suggested that *another* member of the family could have murdered the maid. Without such special emphasis, it would be erroneous to suppose that such an interpretation is intended. Notice that emphasis on other words would also be possible in this instance, and that each would have its distinctive implications for our interpretation of the statement.

7.7   AMBIGUOUS INDICATION

If mistakes that are really errors of interpretation rather than of reasoning are to be included in the consideration of informal fallacies, there is no reason why still another type of ambiguity should not be taken into account, although this is not often done. The resulting error might be called the "fallacy of ambiguous indication." There are some words that are *intended* to exhibit a kind of ambiguity (although it may be stretching a point to apply this concept to them, since each has a clear enough meaning when it is used). The meaning of each word varies with the circumstances of use: "now," "here," "there," "this," "that" are all used to indicate a time, a place, or an object that is determined not by a fixed definition but in relation to their use on a particular occasion. Use of the word is usually accompanied by a gesture of some sort.

It is necessary to distinguish the special sort of ambiguity that is part of the very function of words like "now"—let us call them indicator terms—

from the ordinary sort of ambiguity. We can distinguish different senses of "now" as well as note that its meaning, in any sense, depends on when it is used. "Now" can be used to mark a more or less indefinite present or a very precise one. (Spanish offers *ya, ahora,* and *ahorita,* which correspond roughly to "nowadays," "now," and "right now" respectively.) If an error occurs because of a confusion between two of these senses, there would be no reason not to class it as a fallacy of equivocation. The following exchange exemplifies such a confusion:

> "There are almost three million people in Paris now."
> "No, it's August and at least a million Parisians are out of town for the holidays."

The reply assumes a much more precise sense of "now" than was intended in the initial statement. Since both speakers are using the word at roughly the same time, the special ambiguity which the word exhibits as an indicator term plays no role. Another dialogue *does* seem to depend on ambiguous indication:

> (Mother, to child upstairs): "Are you in bed now, dear?"
> (A brief interval, during which the patter of feet is heard, then finally the child's answer floating down): "Yes, Mommie, I'm in bed now."

As in an earlier example, one is tempted to say that the child has passed the age of innocence. Nevertheless, the function of indicator terms makes them especially susceptible to mistaken interpretation; the resulting errors are very much akin to the other errors in reasoning or interpretation grouped under the heading "fallacies of ambiguity."

7.8 FALLACIES OF GRAMMATICAL ANALOGY

In the traditional lists and classifications of informal fallacies there is no group bearing the title that heads this section. The fallacies of composition and division, to which we turn next, have usually been regarded as special cases of fallacies of ambiguity. In a broad sense, they are; as we shall see, however, there are good reasons for considering them as members of a distinct category of linguistic fallacy. The expression chosen for this category, "fallacies of grammatical analogy," is one that has come into favor fairly recently because of the influence of the late Ludwig Wittgenstein and his followers. Many of Wittgenstein's admirers believe that most (and even all) of the traditional problems of philosophy have their origin in subtle mistakes for which that title is appropriate.

Like fallacies of ambiguity, fallacies of grammatical analogy occur because a linguistic (grammatical) similarity obscures a logical difference. Unlike fallacies of ambiguity, they do not depend for their specious plausibility on a confusion between two possible interpretations of an ambiguous statement and an unnoticed shift from one to the other. We must be able to recognize, in the case of a fallacy of ambiguity, two meaningful interpretations of the statement responsible. That there are two distinct interpretations may be discernible only on close examination, but they must be discernible as genuine alternative interpretations. This is not the case with a fallacy of grammatical analogy. Although some linguistic expression is involved, even on close examination, we discover no more than one meaningful interpretation. The persuasive force of the argument depends on an "interpretation" that really makes no sense at all. Its occurrence is possible not because the one statement possesses more than one meaning, but because *other* statements with the same kind of structure have an entirely different kind of logical significance. The same grammatical form need not always have the same logical function. Consequently, the function of one statement may mistakenly be confused with the function of another because of the analogy generated by their common form.

How grammatical analogy, rather than ambiguity proper, can be responsible for fallacious reasoning is best appreciated in terms of examples. Let us suppose that at the Mathematicians' Picnic a number of comely candidates are competing for the title of Miss Calculation. We are given the following information about them:

1. They range in age from 18 to 22 years.
2. They are 5 feet, 4 inches tall and measure 36–26–35 on the average.
3. The blondes outnumber the brunettes.
4. They are unmarried.

Let us now consider some conclusions that might be drawn about a subset of the contestants, the winners of various initial phases of the competition. Could we conclude that *their* ages range from 18 to 22, that *they* are 5 feet, 4 inches tall and measure 36-26-35 on the average, that there are more blondes than brunettes among them, and that they are unmarried? Only one of these conclusions can be drawn on the basis of the information given— the last one. The others are all examples, or would be if they were conclusions drawn from that information, of a fallacy called the "fallacy of division" in one of its more complex forms.

7.9 THE FALLACY OF DIVISION

The fallacy of division occurs when, from a fact about a group or a whole, we draw a conclusion that either explicitly asserts the same fact to be true of its members or parts or depends on the assumption that it is true of them. Its simplest and most explicit occurrence would be exemplified by concluding from the fact that the contestants are 5 feet, 4 inches tall on the average, that a particular contestant, say Angela Liebestod, is 5 feet, 4 inches tall on the average. Such a conclusion would really be nonsense, for we can speak of average height only with respect to a number of persons, never of a single person. (Perhaps we could make sense of it in special circumstances: We might say of Alice that her average height, during her adventures in Wonderland, was approximately the same as her height in the real world. But this still requires that she have had different heights at different times.) Averages, ranges, and number are properties of groups and not properties of their individual members; that is, they are "collective" properties. Being married or unmarried, on the other hand, is a property of the individual. When such a property is asserted of a group, it is said to be asserted "distributively," that is, of each of the individual members of the group.

The universal statements of traditional logic make their assertions concerning the members of the subject class distributively; they say nothing collectively of the subject class as a whole. The rules permitting valid syllogistic reasoning depend on this fact. Consequently, if these rules are applied (as in reasoning from an assertion about a group to a conclusion concerning a class included in it) to a case in which a property is asserted collectively and not distributively, the reasoning is fallacious. The grammatical analogy may be almost exact, but it supports no logical analogy.

It should be clear to us from this discussion that the sort of mistake exemplified by the fallacy of division in this instance is attributable to language. It occurs because we use the same grammatical form both collectively and distributively. *They are five feet four inches tall on the average* asserts a property collectively, that is, of the group as a whole. *They were unmarried on the day they entered the contest* asserts a property distributively, of each member of the group. The principle of the categorical syllogism can validly be applied in the latter case but not in the former. If it is mistakenly applied where it should not be, it is the misleading grammatical analogy that is responsible. We are obliged, then, to regard such mistakes as linguistic fallacies.

Whether they are fallacies of ambiguity is another question entirely. On reflection we will see that the answer must be in the negative. One opposing viewpoint contends that there *is* an ambiguity in the quantifier "all," which permits it sometimes to be used distributively and sometimes collectively. But in our example, there was no quantifier, only the plural form of the verb. Furthermore, none of the statements involved in our illustration are ambiguous. *They range in age from 18 to 22 years* is not open to two interpretations, of which one ascribes an age range collectively to the group while the other ascribes the same range distributively to each of its members. This latter is not one of the two possible senses, each capable of being confused with the other. It makes no sense at all. The most we can say is that the grammatical form of this sentence is capable of performing an entirely different sort of function. There is a similarity between saying that the same word or statement has more than one meaning and saying that the same statement form can be put to more than one use. There is also a difference, and it is in order to mark this difference that we choose to classify the fallacy of division and similar fallacies not with fallacies of ambiguity but as a distinct group of fallacies of grammatical analogy.

Examples of the fallacy of division involving such collective properties as averages, ranges, number, and other statistical measures offer particularly clear-cut cases of errors arising from grammatical analogy. Complications can, however, enter in with other examples. Some of these point in the direction of ambiguity, while others suggest an error that does not have its source in language at all. Here we will make no attempt either to pretend that these complications do not exist or to provide a finer, more highly resolved classificatory system that will do justice to them. The distinctive mark of the fallacies of composition and division is the confusion between collective and distributive properties; one of the chief sources of this confusion, even if it is not the only one, is grammatical analogy. That is the reason for advancing the present classification.

7.10 THE FALLACY OF COMPOSITION

The fallacy of composition is the opposite of the fallacy of division. In the fallacy of division, the error of reasoning occurs because a collective property is treated as if it were a distributive one. The fallacy of composition involves treating a distributive property as if it were collective. People who bet on all-star football teams are likely to be committing the fallacy of composition. The members of an all-star team are selected on the basis of their individual abilities. The superlative quality that goes into the definition of such a team is therefore a distributive property, belonging to the individual members of the team. To infer that the team has the same superlative quality collectively is fallacious. The team's effectiveness may be hampered by many factors that are irrelevant to the individual skills of its members—insufficient practice together or too much internal competition and rivalry, for example.

We have examined the most obvious difference between the fallacies of composition and division—the mistake of inferring from a distributive to a collective property as opposed to inferring from a collective property to a distributive one. There is another difference, which we ought not to ignore, that has to do with the relationship between the collective and distributive properties. Some collective properties are reducible to properties of individuals in a way in which others are not. A statistical average, such as an average height, is a function of the appropriate values for each individual. It is logically definable in terms of the heights of the individuals in the group. The group for which such a collective property is calculated may be an entirely arbitrary one, with no working relationships among its members; it need not be a functioning unit in its own right. The quality of an athletic team is a different matter. In speaking of it, we must treat the team as a unit with characteristics that depend not only on the quality of its individual members but also on the degree to which they can effectively integrate their activities. Teams seem to have properties in a way in which many groups still subject to statistical calculations cannot. Teams score points, have records of wins and losses, exhibit other features that are not *simply* reducible to corresponding features of their members. Whether they are reducible in a more complex fashion is another question that would lead us too far afield into metaphysical subtleties.

The same contrast can be seen perhaps even more clearly in terms of the legal difference between a partnership and a corporation. The debts of a partnership are debts of the partners, not in the sense that each partner owes what the partnership owes, but in the sense that the partners do have business debts in connection with the partnership; the debt of the business as a whole is equal to their individual debts as partners. The collective debt is reducible to individual debts. This is not true of the corporation and its shareholding members. The corporation owns its own assets and owes its own debts. The shareholder in a corporation that has borrowed money has not thereby acquired any personal business debt, whereas a partner in a partnership has acquired one (unless there are special provisions to the contrary in the terms establishing the partnership).

Despite this difference, it would be fallacious in either case to make inferences from the economic situation of the collective whole to the economic situation of the individual member. Even in a partnership, the collective bankruptcy of the business does not imply a distributive bankruptcy of the partners. One or more of the partners may have ample assets to cover his legal share of the debts (on the assumption that the partnership arrangement does not provide for unlimited responsibility of each partner). Of course, at least one partner must be bankrupt if the business is. In the case of the corporation, collective bankruptcy does not imply even that much. We are permitted, however, to say, "They are bankrupt," of a group of unrelated individuals distributively or of members of a partnership or corporation collectively. The grammatical analogy makes it that much easier to find mistakenly logical connections between the collective and the distributive functions of the plural grammatical form.[3]

To bring this discussion of the fallacies of composition and division to an end, we note again that these two fallacies are unjustified inferences involving groups to which properties can be ascribed either collectively or distributively. When a statement intended to describe the group collectively is made the basis of an inference to a statement asserting or presupposing the same distributive description of the individuals in the group, the fallacy is called the fallacy of division. When the inference runs in the opposite direction, from a statement properly understood to be distributive, describing the individual members of the group, to a conclusion asserting or presupposing that the same property applies to them collectively, the fallacy is called the fallacy of composition. The group may or may not be one that is treated as an entity in its own right (a team, a corporate person before the law); the properties ascribed to it collectively may or may not be simply reducible by definition in terms of properties that belong to the individuals composing it. Whichever may be the case, we have seen that a major factor contributing to the occurrence of these fallacies is the applicability of grammatically analogous linguistic structures for both the collective and the distributive ascription of properties to groups.

7.11 THE FALLACY OF REIFICATION

Any discussion of the fallacies of composition and division inevitably risks committing another fallacy that deserves to be called a fallacy of grammatical analogy also. This is the "fallacy of reification." It is a subtle

---

[3] These examples could be cited in favor of a closer tie with other fallacies of ambiguity. It makes sense to ascribe bankruptcy to individuals as well as to groups, whereas it made no sense to ascribe an average height to an individual.

and many-sided mistake that consists of conjuring substantial things out of the thin air of speech. Philosophers would be by no means in agreement on whether the preceding discussion has avoided the fallacy of reification. We have included remarks about classes and collective wholes and their properties. Are there really such things, or are they not merely ghosts or fictions called up by words that grammatically function as names function, but are not names? If there are no such things, for us to reason as if there were because there are linguistic expressions that misleadingly seem to be their names is for us to commit the fallacy of reification.

In discussing composition and division, our emphasis was on the way in which a property was ascribed to a group, distributively or collectively. Now our emphasis turns to the group, especially in those cases in which a property is ascribed to it collectively. Let us return to our football team:

1. They have a maroon and gold uniform.
2. They have an average weight of 204 pounds.
3. They have a powerful running attack.

The first of these three statements is a way of saying that each member of the team wears a maroon and gold uniform; it ascribes a property distributively to individuals. The second and third statements are of a kind that tempts us to talk of collective properties belonging to collective things, classes or composite wholes constituted by a number of individuals taken together. In statement 1, "they" refers to the members of the team. In the other two, "they" seems to be a way of referring to *the team itself*—if there is such a thing. We have agreed earlier that it makes no sense to speak of the average height of a single individual. We are now asking whether there is a collective entity, composed of individuals, that has as one of its properties an average height or weight. If not, to be misled by grammatical analogies into supposing that there is such an entity is to commit the fallacy of reification. The answer to this particular question has already been suggested in an earlier observation to the effect that statistical measures are reducible. Average weights are not measurable as such; there is no one object to be weighed. Averages are the result of a mathematical operation performed on figures obtained by measuring perfectly ordinary individuals. The grammatical analogy between *They have an average weight of 204 pounds* and *He has a weight of 204 pounds* conceals the complexity of what is really being asserted: *They have (as individuals) weights such that when all these figures are added together and then divided by the number of individuals, the resulting figure is 204 pounds.*

The question becomes more difficult, more important, and more controversial when the apparent subject of a collective property must constitute some functioning unit in order to have that property. Are there, that is to say, genuinely irreducible properties that can belong only to composite entities as such? Do "they" (the football team) have a powerful running attack in a sense that cannot logically be generated out of facts about the individual members of the team? Is a corporation a real social entity or only a legal fiction? Such questions arise again and again in philosophical contexts. They are especially central in metaphysics, in social and political philosophy, and in esthetics. All that can be asked of an introductory textbook in logic is that it illustrate the fallacy of reification where grammatical analogy does seem to generate beliefs in fictitious collective things. The discussion of more dubious cases should be left to more intensive philosophical analysis.

We should not assume that the fallacy of reification is responsible only for errors restricted to the region of alleged collective entities and their collective properties. The very fact that we speak of having properties and losing them is suspicious. Is a property something like a watch? The way we talk of thoughts and meanings has also proved to be full of pitfalls for the philosopher. To cite a glaring example, what does "nothing" mean? It must mean something, for it is not a nonsense word; but then "nothing" must be *something*. Let us break the argument off, but with eyebrows already raised. The fallacy of reification occurs whenever an entity is assumed to exist or have some property or other because there is a word that seems to name or describe it. The problems generated by so-called collective terms are just a special and especially important area. The grammatical analogy that holds among all nouns, indeed among all expressions that are permitted to serve as subjects of sentences, is the root of the fallacy of reification and hence of all sorts of disputes about what there is in reality.[4]

[4] A penetrating and provocative discussion of this general kind of problem is offered in a well-known article by Professor Gilbert Ryle, "Systematically Misleading Expressions." First published in the *Proceedings of the Aristotelian Society,* it has been reprinted in *Logic and Language, First Series,* edited by A. G. N. Flew.

Much less well known, but antedating Ryle's work by a quarter-century, Franz Brentano's "Supplementary Essays" to his *Classification of Mental Phenomena* (a new edition of relevant portions of *Psychology from an Empirical Standpoint*) are directed to the same problem. Portions of the essay, "Genuine and Fictitious Objects," are included in English translation in *Realism and the Background of Phenomenology,* edited by R. M. Chisholm.

7.12 CONCLUSION

The range of fallacies of grammatical analogy is by no means exhausted by the examples we have examined so far. There is a variety of miscellaneous cases of fallacious reasoning that seem to have their origins in misleading grammatical analogies. For example, it has been a favorite sport of the critics of John Stuart Mill (and even some of his sympathizers) to accuse him of having committed a fallacy of equivocation in the proof he offers in Chaper IV of his essay on utilitarianism. To prove that happiness is desirable, he points out that it is in fact desired. Mill's argument is brief enough to be reproduced without paraphrase.

> The only proof capable of being given that an object is visible is that people actually see it. The only proof that a sound is audible is that people hear it; and so of the other sources of our experience. In like manner, I apprehend, the sole evidence it is possible to produce that anything is desirable is that people do actually desire it.

Now there is nothing directly in Mill's words to support the charge that he has here confused two senses of the word "desirable," using one in his premise and the other in his conclusion. Neither is there anything in the dictionary to suggest that there are two such senses to be confused. If there is an equivocation, it is only because Mill has been led to introduce a new sense of the word. If so, what led him to it was the grammatical analogy between "desirable" and "visible," "audible," and so on. The most perceptive criticism to make is simply that Mill was misled by the grammatical analogy into supposing that the sort of evidence relevant to the one set of concepts was relevant to the other. The mistake, if it is one, lies in applying the standards of proof applicable to "visible" to the word "desirable," not in shifting from one sense of desirable to another. (This account is still an oversimplification of Mill's position, which has roots in the history of ethical theory as well as in the grammatical analogy singled out here.)

The fallacies of equivocation, amphiboly, accent, ambiguous indication, composition, division, and reification (and other miscellaneous fallacies of grammatical analogy) have been grouped together as linguistic fallacies because an error in the use or interpretation of language is the primary factor that makes for their occurrence. The error arises either from ambiguity or grammatical analogy. In view of the comments we made initially concerning the difficulties attending any attempt to classify fallacious reasoning, it should be unnecessary to remind ourselves that this grouping is not intended to be, and in the nature of the case could not be, an absolute and sharply defined one. It provides guidelines to an understanding of the way human reasoning can be led astray, no more. There are factors other than linguistic ones that undoubtedly contribute to the occurrence of any of these fallacies in particular circumstances. There may even be cases, especially in connection with the fallacies of composition and division, in which the linguistic factor is secondary. There are also other types of fallacious reasoning, which we will consider in subsequent sections, in which linguistic considerations play some role. If anything, as we turn to the fallacies considered in the next chapter, the prospect of achieving a neat scheme of classification, with no fuzzy edges, becomes still more remote. The kind of precision offered the student in other areas, even in other areas of logic, is simply not available here.

7.12   EXERCISES

Identify the informal fallacies of linguistic origin that occur in the following tale.

The Search for the Seal in the Bedroom

Mr. and Mrs. Earwicker thought they heard a seal barking in the bedroom. They told the servant, Kate, to go look for a seal in the master's bedroom. Kate returned with a seal she had found in the desk in the study.

"Kate, you idiot, not that sort of seal—the sort that barks. Now go look in the bedroom."(1)

"Yes, mum."

"Well, don't just stand there. Why don't you move along?"

"I can't, mum."

"Indeed! And why not, pray?"

"I've had a metaphysical insight, mum. Wherever I am, I'm here, ain't that right, mum? I can't be anywheres else but here, no matter what. Nor any nat'ral body can be somewheres else from where she is. Now that there master's bedroom is somewheres else. So if I was to have went there, I wouldn't be here—I'd be somewheres else and that's not the part of any nat'ral body."(2)

"Oh, you idiot! Wipe that silly grin off your face and get along with you!"

"Yes, mum, if I might have a bit of facial tissue, if you please, I'll try, mum."(3)

"Oh, stupid, don't bother! Now, about here and somewhere else. I'm going to show you you can move, despite your metaphysical insights. You like to dance, don't you, Kate?"

"Yes, mum."

"Then we'll pretend it's a little dance. Now suppose you take two steps forward, turn around, take two steps back and turn around again. Where will you be?"

"Right here, mum, where I am now. Two steps forward, you said, turn around, two steps back, turn around again, and here I am."(4)

"No, no, silly—the second two steps you take backwards, not back in this direction. You turn around after you take two steps forward and then take two steps backward and then turn around again."

"Yes, mum. Two steps forward, two steps backward, turn around and then turn around again. I'm right back where I am, see, mum?"(5)

"No! Do as I tell you. Two steps forward, then turn around, two steps backward, turn around again. Now keep on going and look for the seal in the bedroom."

Kate returned to her mistress reporting that there was no seal to be found in the master's bedroom. When this information was passed on, the master wanted to know how the silly girl expected it to be found there, since no one had ever suggested it had been lost there.(6) Shaun hoped it was not in *his* bedroom. Shem supposed it must be a walrus after all.(7)

The master insisted that he still heard a seal barking somewhere. "Find the bark," he proclaimed, "and you find the seal!"(8)

"But, begging your pardon, mum," protested Kate, "I've had me another metaphysical insight. That there seal's a right clever beastie, and when I'm looking for him in one room, he's off barking in another. I can't be looking for him in all the rooms at once. There's not one nat'ral person here, not even you nor the master, can be looking in all the rooms at once. That there beastie can't be found nohow."(9)

"Oh, Kate, don't be such a dolt. If we all looked together, we could surely find him. And if we could *all* find him, *you* could find him, so get on with it, girl!"(10)

Exit Kate, accompanied by hoots from the owl in the attic.

Chapter 8

INFORMAL FALLACIES, II

In this chapter, we will be dealing with the group of fallacies classified as material fallacies. We will make no attempt to treat these as though they shared a common, homogeneous nature. The most we can say along such lines has already been suggested in our introduction to the topic of fallacious reasoning in Chapter 7. The fallacies we will now consider seem to originate not in language but in human psychology; beyond that, there is little homogeneity to be found among them. We shall, however, consider four distinct main groups within which somewhat more positive and definite common features can be discerned.

8.1 FALLACIES OF RATIONALIZATION

Traditional lists of fallacies have always included several items that depend for their persuasive force on the arousal of feeling. Such fallacies have been gathered together as "fallacies of emotional appeal" in some classifications. The Latin names that have been attached to them do not always explicitly reflect their emotional character, and it is more important to bring this aspect to the fore in providing alternative English titles than to offer a literal translation of the Latin original. The "argumentum ad misericordiam" does translate literally into English: the *appeal to pity*.

The fallacy of appeal to pity occurs when an attempt is made to influence opinion by evoking the feeling of pity in those whose judgment is being manipulated. It is, for example, occasionally the practice of the lawyer for the defense in a criminal trial to play upon the jurors' sympathies in the hope that they will decide his client is innocent. It is apparently an ancient practice. Socrates felt the need to explain why he refrained from it during the course of his trial (which took place in 399 B.C.):

> . . . perhaps some one among you may be vexed when he remembers what he has done himself; he may have been in a case less important than this, and he may have entreated and prayed the jury with floods of tears, and paraded his children, to get all the pity he could, with many friends and relatives besides, but I, as it seems, will not do anything of the sort, and that too although I am probably at the last extremity of danger . . . thinking of reputation, as regards me and you and the whole state, it does not seem to me to be decent that I should do any such thing. (*Apology*, 34C)

The pity evoked must be directly involved in the formation of the opinion it is intended to influence. If a prosecuting attorney attempts to arouse the jurors' feelings of sympathy for the *victim* or his family, this should not be considered an example of the fallacy here being considered, the appeal to pity. It is not the jury's task to reach a conclusion about the victim, but to reach one about the defendant. Pity for the victim is not likely by itself to influence a judgment concerning the defendant. What influence it has will in all probability arise indirectly by virtue of intensifying retributive emotions. If these feelings are then fixed on the defendant, they may in a careless mind contribute to a judgment that he is guilty. For such a complicated process there is no neat pigeonhole in the traditional list of fallacies. When the fallacy of appeal to pity occurs, it is the feeling of pity itself that influences the judgment.

The "argumentum ad baculum" literally means the *appeal to the stick* and has usually been given a less metaphorical rendering in English as the "appeal to force." But the big stick is effective only insofar as it succeeds in arousing fear, and the most suitable title for the fallacy that has traditionally gone by this name would be simply the "appeal to fear" or the "fallacy of intimidation." The change in title would also have some merit in reducing the emphasis on physical force that is suggested by the traditional designation. The attempt to persuade by intimidating does not gain in logical acceptability merely because physical weapons are not involved. There may be moral advantages in one over the other; in terms of purely logical value, intimidation by threat of physical harm is on the same level with intimidation by threats of economic or social pressure. The essential characteristic of the argumentum ad baculum as a logical fallacy is the attempt to influence a person's opinion by threatening him with unpleasant consequences of some kind.

The "argumentum ad populum," literally *appeal to the people,* involves the arousal of feelings that individuals have as members of a group, that is, racial, religious, national, regional or local, or class feelings. It is really an "appeal to popular emotion." There is another sense that has sometimes been attached to the argumentum ad populum, and it involves an appeal to popular prejudices or "what everyone accepts." The two are not unrelated, for anyone who rejects what is taken to be true by everyone else is likely to be the object of strong and hostile group emotions. Still, the attempt to influence opinion by arousing patriotic or other similar feelings is clearly a different technique from the attempt to support a judgment by citing its general acceptance. The latter appeal belongs more to the sphere of the appeal to authority, which will be discussed in the next section, than to the fallacies that depend on emotional factors such as those we are presently discussing.

There is no clear limit to the variety of fallacies that might be distinguished in terms of the emotions they involve. They can be as diverse as the entire range of human feeling. We could take into account the fact that an effective and persuasive speaker may influence the opinions of his audience by playing upon the sense of pride and self-importance, and introduce the "argumentum ad vanitatem." The fact that love is blind, so that the lover can easily be induced to adopt the most extravagant opinions about the object of his affections, would also be relevant and would lead us to recognize the fallacy of "argumentum ad amorem." But the three that have been briefly discussed already, the appeal to pity, the appeal to fear, and the appeal to popular sentiment, will suffice to illustrate some of the general problems that arise in connection with all fallacies of this sort.

The incitement of fear or pity or patriotic sentiment is usually intended to achieve a practical result. Why, then, do these appeals have any place in a study of reasoning in the sense in which it is of interest to the logician? The logician's subject matter is inference, the sort of inference in which one belief is based on others. The problem of the relation of belief to feeling and action is not properly his concern. A political orator may attempt to generate in his audience an overwhelming surge of patriotic feeling in order to reinforce its dedication to a national cause or to sway its votes. A poster, by evoking pity, may be intended to increase contributions to a charitable organization. In such cases, there is nothing to be identified as logical argumentation, nothing to which logical criticism could be applied. The result aimed for is a practical one, not a belief that might be true or false. In order for a mistake in reasoning to occur, there must be reasoning in the first place or at least something closely enough resembling reasoning to warrant extending our concept of logic to include it. Certainly the minimal requirements is that there must be a belief based in some sense on other beliefs. What standards are to be applied to decide the reasonableness of "practical" conclusions, such as voting or making a contribution, is not a question of logic but of morals and ultimately of ethical theory.

Since appeals to emotion are not arguments in the logician's sense, we may well ask why a set of fallacious arguments should be defined in terms of them. Perhaps, historically, the correct answer is that little attention was paid to the distinction between supporting a practical decision or attitude and supporting a belief. All attempts to sway decisions, whether decisions about the truth or falsity of an opinion or decisions about the attitude to be adopted to a person or a proposal, were taken to be arguments and subject to the logician's criticism. The fact is, however, that we do not need to perpetuate this mistake in order to find a place for such fallacies as the appeal to pity or to fear or to popular feeling in our study. Insofar as they are capable of being considered within the scope of informal fallacies, they should be regarded not as fallacies of emotional appeal, but as "fallacies of rationalization."

Rationalization is sometimes used as if it were synonymous with *reasoning,* but we are using it here in a sense closely related to the meaning that has been attached to it in psychology. We mean it to be the human tendency to invent beliefs to justify our sentiments and behavior, whether or not these beliefs were the real basis of the feelings or actions they support. By virtue of this process, emotions can induce beliefs as well as practical attitudes and decisions. The beliefs are held because of the emotions and the need to justify them. The *because* here is not logical but purely psychological. No one would cite the emotion as the basis of the belief as one would cite a premise in support of its conclusion. No one would be likely to say that the *evidence* for his belief is his fear of what would happen to him if he did not accept it. Still, as a consequence of rationalization, emotional appeals can produce belief and at least mimic the psychological effect of logical reasoning. Despite the fact that on calm examination there is nothing even resembling logical validity about the emotional appeal, it can be persuasive in the sense of engendering a belief that might, in principle, have been the conclusion of a genuine and even valid inference.

In order for a fallacy to be involved, according to the analysis just offered, the outcome must be a belief, not a practical decision. But another distinction must also be made. The belief must be genuine and not a mere profession of one. This point is especially important in connection with the appeal to fear, although it is applicable elsewhere. The threat of force may succeed in causing someone to make statements contrary to his beliefs, but if that is all that is accomplished, we cannot properly speak of a fallacy. Galileo's fear of being tortured produced an official recantation and renunciation of his astronomical views. If the story is correct, and he walked away murmuring to himself, "eppur si muove" (but it *does* move), all that the threat had really brought about was a performance. We could speak of a change of belief involving fallacious inference only if he had gone off murmuring, "Well, maybe it doesn't move, after all." We must distinguish between one juror being moved by pity to vote "not guilty," although he is convinced to the contrary, and another being induced by the same emotion to believe the defendant is really innocent. The former has committed a legal or moral error, but only the latter offers a true case of fallacious "reasoning."

There are other ways in which emotions can influence opinions, as we shall see later in this discussion, where they will be regarded as factors secondary to other features of the fallacious argument. In the type of fallacy that we have considered here, it is the process of rationalization that is important; the emotion must serve as a psychological bridge between the beliefs that have aroused it and the beliefs that rationalize it. There is no *inference* at all; since the ultimate effect is to influence opinion, it is appropriate to consider such persuasive devices in the same context as those that are more properly described as mistakes in inference.

8.2 THE ARGUMENTUM AD HOMINEM

Two classical fallacies closely enough related to call for their being considered together are the "argumentum ad hominem" and the "argumentum ad verecundiam." The Latin name for the first of these is still in current use as its appropriate designation; literally, it means *argument to the man.* The second title is, in English, the *appeal to respect,* but this literal meaning is nowadays usually replaced by the expression "appeal to authority." A third fallacy, somewhat loosely connected with these two, will also be considered in this section, the "argumentum ad ignorantiam," *appeal to ignorance.*

What the argumentum ad hominem and the appeal to authority have in common is that they are both, in a sense, "arguments to the man," although this expression is applied only to the former. The working principle of both is the mention or description of a person who holds an opinion that is in dispute. The argumentum ad hominem represents an attempt to establish the falsity of an opinion by citing information about the person who holds it. The appeal to authority is an attempt to support the truth of an opinion by a similar procedure. This common pattern could be schematically represented as follows:

A says "S"

$\underline{A \text{ is} \dots}$ (If A is well known, this may be omitted.)

Therefore, S is $\begin{cases} \text{true (appeal to authority)} \\ \text{false (argumentum ad hominem)} \end{cases}$

S can be taken to represent any expression of opinion; the description of A will, of course, vary with the circumstances and the purpose of the argument.

There is no logical connection between facts about a person who happens to hold a given opinion and the truth or falsity of the opinion. (There is, of course, an exception; if a person holds an opinion about himself, the opinion is true or false by virtue of facts about the person who holds it. But even here, that he holds the opinion often does not provide any proper *evidence* of its truth or falsity.) Consequently, any argument of the form we have just indicated must be regarded as fallacious, with certain qualifications and clarifications that will emerge as we go on to consider the fallacies of argumentum ad hominem and appeal to authority in finer detail.

The persuasive force of the argumentum ad hominem can arise in at least three different ways, depending on the kind of information offered about the person whose opinion is being attacked. We can distinguish, therefore, three forms of this fallacy, which we will designate as the "emotive," the "circumstantial," and the "logical" forms. In the traditional treatment of fallacies, the argumentum ad hominem was most closely identified with the logical form, but more recently it has come to be associated with the emotive form. In this form, it depends for its persuasive force on an attempt to arouse a negative attitude or feeling toward the holder of an opinion. Its effectiveness is a consequence of our reluctance to identify ourselves with those we dislike or disapprove even to the extent of sharing any opinions with them. In that it involves arousing an emotion, in this form the argumentum ad hominem is similar to the fallacies we considered in Section 8.1; the role played by the emotion is entirely different here, however. The object of the emotion and the subject matter of the argument need not be related to each other at all for the argumentum ad hominem to occur. In the fallacies of rationalization, the subject matter of the disputed opinion *is* the object of the effective emotion.

When an opinion is attacked on the grounds that someone who holds it or advances it is prejudiced, it is easy to look on the mistake as just another example of the emotive form of the argumentum ad hominem. Such people are often, if not always, objects of disapproval. Furthermore, it is clear that such an argument is fallacious and has the ad hominem pattern. There is no logical connection between being prejudiced and being mistaken; it is perfectly possible for even a hopeless bigot to hold true opinions and even for his prejudices to be true themselves.

The emotive element, however, does not seem to be essential in such cases; it is possible to speak of biases that are, in a sense, "honest" and need not arouse any disapproval toward those who have them. The mere allegation of the bias as such, without any attempt to arouse an emotional reaction to it, may be independently the basis of another type of ad hominem fallacy, which we have designated as its circumstantial form. It can be appreciated in its purest form in such an example as this:

> The witness, who has just testified that he saw the defendant strike the first blow, was too far from the scene to have had a clear view of what was happening. Furthermore, from where he was standing, he could see nothing but the plaintiff's back. It is not true, then, that the defendant initiated the exchange of blows, as the witness alleged.

In this example we can find no reflection on the witness's character, no attempt to arouse a hostile attitude toward him, not even an imputation of prejudice or insincerity. It is purely and simply a matter of calling attention to the circumstances. It is said that the situation from which he observed a street brawl was such as to reflect on the reliability of his observation. There would have been nothing fallacious in going so far, but the conclusion actually stated in the example goes much further. It asserts that what the witness said had happened had not happened. The conclusion is not that the witness's testimony carries no weight, but that it is factually false. There is where the fallacy lies, and its effectiveness in this form is the result not so much of any emotions aroused but of a confusion between two quite different questions.

It is one thing to call into question a person's reliability or lack of it, another to consider the truth or falsity of his opinions. It is possible that a witness to a certain scene was incapable of having seen what he thought he saw (and duly reported); it is still possible that what he thought he saw was what had really happened. Once this is understood, it is easy enough to see that the testimony of the most unreliable witness may be true as to its content and that there is no logical bridge from his unreliability to the falsity of his opinions. The point of the example is not restricted to testimony in a court of law, and our witness has merely provided a particularly clear-cut example of the distinction that must be drawn. The point is not just restricted to physical circumstances, such as distance from the scene of a reported event. A bias, for example, could be regarded as a circumstance adversely affecting the ability to "see" certain facts and situations accurately or to have a vivid and full appreciation of them. A circumstance of this sort may well affect a man's reliability as a source of information, but again it would be a fallacy of the ad hominem type to suppose that we can draw from this any conclusions as to the truth or falsity of his opinions. To do that, we can only attempt to arrive at a more reliable account of the facts. These may or may not turn out to agree with the earlier report, however subject to possible distortion through bias it may have been.

The logical form of the fallacy of argumentum ad hominem occurs when an attempt is made to disprove an opinion by showing that someone who holds it also holds other views inconsistent with it. If correct, the charge of inconsistency places the person against whom it is lodged in an untenable position. He must give up one of the incompatible opinions, unless he is willing to abandon the principle of intellectual responsibility altogether and say, with Walt Whitman and other more poetic than logical minds, "I contradict myself? Well, then, I contradict myself." The fallacy does not lie in making the allegation of inconsistency. It lies in using the inconsistency to establish the falsity of a certain specified opinion, when all we know is that one of the set, but not which one, must be false.

The fallacy of argumentum ad hominem occurs most directly when an attempt is made to use something known about the person who holds a disputed opinion as evidence of its falsity. But when an opinion is being defended against attack, something may occur that is so similar in its logical purpose to the argumentum ad hominem that we would be quite

justified in assimilating it under this classification. If one's opinion has
been attacked, one way of meeting the criticism is to turn it back upon
the critic. This technique is known as "retortion." It is also known as the
"tu quoque" (*you, too*) argument. Like the argumentum ad hominem
proper, it can be a devastatingly effective rhetorical weapon, but it is not
genuinely a refutation of the criticism. To consider an example of a vulgar
kind, if one party to a dispute accuses his opponent of lying and the latter
replies with "You're another," each may well be correct in his assessment
of the other.

More sophisticated examples of this form of argument are usually directed at the correctness of more recognizably logical efforts at discrediting
an opinion. If, for example, we attempt to attack an opinion by showing
that it implies an absurdity, the reply may be that a similar line of argument would show our own opinions to imply a like absurdity. Here, again,
both opinions may be implicitly absurd, so that the attempted rebuttal of
the criticism is fallacious for very much the same reason that the argumentum ad hominem is fallacious. However, if the retortion successfully establishes the parallel, it will at least cause the critic to take thought and perhaps even to prefer abandoning that particular line of criticism over accepting its consequences for his own views.

8.3   THE APPEAL TO AUTHORITY

It would be tempting, for the sake of simplicity, to suppose that the
fallacy of appeal to authority is the exact opposite of the argumentum ad
hominem. The common pattern has already been mentioned; all that
would remain would be to fill in an appropriate description for the person
holding the opinion, *A,* and select *true* instead of *false* in the alternative
conclusion (see p. 175). But to do this would be to sacrifice accuracy for
the sake of the simplicity so attained. Not every argument of the form

> *A* says "*S*."
> *A* is. . . .
> _____
> Therefore, *S* is true.

is fallacious. It does not conform to the standards of deductive validity, as
it is quite impossible for the premises to be true and the conclusion false.
If we let the matter rest there, however, we would be making it seem
too trivial. More subtle discriminations are required if the fallacy is to
have any significance.

It is likely that most of our opinions are formed on the basis of reports
we have received from others, directly or indirectly, by word of mouth or

in print or from writings. To allege that whenever we arrive at an opinion in this way we are committing a fallacy would be absurd. The fallacy ordinarily called the fallacy of appeal to authority has a much narrower range of application, and we should carefully distinguish the examples of such a fallacy from all those cases in which we are legitimately influenced to accept an opinion as true on the basis of another's report.

We begin by observing that reports are normally taken to lend support to the opinions expressed in them. The connection is obviously not a deductive one, since no one would claim that false reports are logically impossible. It is furthermore a very special case of inductive support (see Section 1.4). One way of focusing attention on the distinctive character of the support offered by another person's report is by showing that the argument cannot be formulated without the use of quotation marks or indirect discourse:

> "*A* says '*S*'; therefore, the probability that *S* is true is greater than it would have been if he had expressed no such opinion."

Although the logical connection between the truth of an opinion and the report that it is true may be special, even peculiar in some respects, it is not logically erroneous to take serious reports seriously. This means that in the absence of considerations to the contrary, they must be taken as lending *some* support, *some* weight of the evidence in favor of the truth of the opinions they express, although it need by no means be regarded as decisive.

If a report is not to be taken as providing the normal degree of support for the opinion expressed in it, there must be positive reasons advanced to cause us to doubt the competence or reliability of the reporter. If the purpose of mentioning facts about the reporter that tend in this direction is to deprive the propositions he advances from enjoying the normal support his expression of them would involve, there is nothing improper in doing so. But that is quite a different matter from advancing evidence that tends to prove the proposition false. The argumentum ad hominem, especially in its circumstantial form, occurs when two distinct logical procedures are confused. One is an attempt to weaken the support that certain facts provide in favor of a disputed proposition. The other is to cite evidence tending to prove it false. Facts about the person who advances a certain opinion may serve the one purpose but not the other.

We can resume our consideration of the fallacy of appeal to authority by noting that the support a report lends to the proposition it advances may go considerably *beyond* the minimal support that comes of taking any serious report seriously. The reports of eye-witnesses, of experts, of intellectually sophisticated persons, and others specially qualified in some way count more heavily. We take such reports *more* seriously than we do those advanced by just anyone. That we do seems entirely proper. We seem to be faced with a suspicious paradox: nothing that can be said about the source of an opinion properly counts against it, but much that can be said about the source can strengthen the case for it. The seeming paradox arises only because of the ambiguity in "counts against" that has already been noted. One need only compare judgments about truth and falsity with judgments about the way a certain piece of information, such as a report, bears on the issue. True and false are exhaustive alternatives; there is no middle ground between them. When it comes to the assessment of evidence, however, there is a third possibility. A piece of information may be said to support the truth of an opinion or to support its falsity or to support neither. We can speak of degrees here, too, while we cannot speak of degrees of truth and falsity. An item of evidence may lend more or less support to the opinion. We may assign it more or less weight in making our considered judgment concerning truth or falsity.

When a statement is already supported by some evidence in its favor or appears to be, a new item of information may "count against it" in either of two ways. It may lend support to the contradictory opinion; it may deprive it of the support it seemed to have, at least to the extent of diminishing the degree of support the evidence in its favor seemed to provide. If a witness is demonstrated to be unreliable or incompetent, the support his testimony provided is weakened or lost altogether; the opposite opinion is not thereby positively strengthened.

> Decreasing the weight of supporting evidence is not the same thing as increasing the weight of opposing evidence.

The exposure of the error represented by the circumstantial form of the argumentum ad hominem is merely an application of this principle.

The preceding discussion has shown how it is possible to maintain, without inconsistency, that although reducing the weight of evidence in favor of a thesis does not directly strengthen the case against it, increasing the weight of evidence does strengthen the case for its truth. It is for this reason that it would be a mistake to regard every appeal to authority as fallacious. It is only when the appeal to authority is given greater weight than it deserves that a fallacy can be said to occur. The question to be considered is, therefore, what are the circumstances in which a report is likely to be given more weight than it deserves. The misleading title, "fallacy of appeal to authority," might well be replaced by the expression, "fallacy of exaggerated authority" or "fallacy of misplaced authority."

The authoritative character of an opinion tends to be overestimated as a result of two kinds of force. One is emotional: An expert is the object of some admiration and respect; all of his opinions, whether or not they have anything to do with the area of his special knowledge, are likely to benefit by reflected glory and therefore to be taken more seriously than they may deserve in some cases. The opinions of a physicist about physics are of incomparably greater weight than the layman's opinions. His political views may be of no more authority than the next man's. Nevertheless, they may well be given more serious attention, owing to the prestige arising from his scientific accomplishments and qualifications.

The other force that tends to exaggerate authority is the result of failure on our part accurately to distinguish and demarcate an expert's area of special competence. He may be an authority in one field where we are to take his pronouncements very seriously; he may not be an authority at all in fields that are perhaps very closely related to his field. The layman is likely to regard the opinions of a recognized medical specialist as equally authoritative throughout the medical sciences. He is ordinarily unable to appreciate the precise limits of an area of specialization or the extent to which specialized knowledge in one narrow field may be independent of other areas. What "an outstanding psychologist" has to say about success and happiness in marriage attracts attention and takes on an appearance of authority. The outstanding psychologist may be a confirmed bachelor whose eminence and reputation have been justly earned during many years devoted to experimental investigations concerning the visual acuity of a variety of lower mammals. Picture, if you will, the eager writer of Timely Tips for Teens and 'Tothers interrupting a fond and mutually myopic tête-à-tête between the distinguished Professor Augenforscher and a marmot, to ask him his opinion of the double bed! If, despite our protests, the columnist insists, and puts the rhetorical question: "What mere layman would have the audacity to challenge Professor Augenforscher's opinion on a matter of psychology?," there is an answer: "No one," if the matter concerns the visual acuity of rodents; "Anyone," if it concerns anything else. The failure to make necessary distinctions of this sort is one source of the fallacy of exaggerated authority.

8.4 THE ARGUMENTUM AD IGNORANTIAM

In the preceding discussions of the argumentum ad hominem and the appeal to authority, we have placed much emphasis on the distinction between reducing the weight of evidence for an opinion and introducing evidence that counts against it. By not confusing the two, we can avoid the ad hominem fallacy completely and avoid some of the confusions that arise in connection with the use of authority. What is traditionally titled the "argumentum ad ignorantiam" (in English, usually the *appeal to ig-norance*) represents the confusion in its extreme form. The absence of evidence for an opinion is taken to show that it is false. Or, conversely, the absence of evidence against it is taken to be evidence for it. Once again, we must note that although what is not true is false, it is not the case that what has not been proved true has been proved false. The fact that we have no reason to accept an opinion is not a reason for denying it.

It is sometimes suggested that there are certain contexts in which the argumentum ad ignorantiam is correct, just as, within proper limits, the appeal to authority is correct and in fact unavoidable. The outstanding example of such a context is the court of law operating under the tradi-tional procedures of Anglo-Saxon justice. If the prosecution fails to prove the defendant's guilt "beyond a reasonable doubt," the jury is obliged to find him innocent. Here appears to be a case, then, in which the absence of sufficient evidence for one conclusion is taken as sufficient grounds for asserting the contradictory conclusion. A juryman would seem to be obliged by our legal system (assuming that the defense counsel has not positively proved his client's innocence) to abandon one of the principles of intellectual responsibility.

There is another way of regarding the trial situation. On this alternative view of it, we can avoid being forced to say that in some contexts, reasoning is correct that would be fallacious elsewhere, even though there is no significant difference in the nature of the conclusion to be established. The traditional Anglo-Saxon principle is stated in these terms: the defendant is to be presumed innocent until he has been proved guilty. The presump-tion of innocence exists at the trial's outset. The prosecution is obliged to overcome it; if the prosecution fails to do so, it prevails. The prosecution's failure to prove guilt is not to be regarded as a *new* reason for concluding that the defendant is innocent. It simply leaves whatever reasons there were for the initial presumption of innocence in force. There is, therefore, no occurrence of the fallacy of argumentum ad ignorantiam. The verdict of innocence is not independently supported by the prosecution's failure. In fact, the reasons supporting it are entirely independent of the particular circumstances of a given trial and the particular evidence offered by one side or another. They lie not so much in logical considerations pertaining to the relation of evidence and conclusions as in considerations of morality and justice. The initial presumption of the defendant's innocence is an expression of a moral opinion that has nothing to do with the facts of a particular case. It is based on the belief that it is better for a guilty party to go unpunished than for an innocent party to be punished unjustly. The case for the presumption of innocence is basically an ethical one. Perhaps the introduction of extralogical reasons for adopting an opinion itself represents a lapse from perfect intellectual responsibility. The third choice available to the juryman serving in the criminal courts of Scotland (who may bring back a verdict of "not proven") represents, from a purely logical point of view, a sounder position. Even so, if the Anglo-Saxon tradition, with its initial presumption of innocence, contains a logical flaw, it is not the error of letting an opinion be supported by the absence of evidence to the contrary. It is the error, if it is an error, of letting an opinion be supported by ethical considerations that are logically irrelevant to the question to be determined and the concrete evidence on one side or the other.

8.5 FALLACIES CONCERNING ESSENCE, ACCIDENT, AND CAUSE

Of any object (or person) many true statements can be asserted. Some of these are "essential" with respect to our understanding of what the object is. Without them, the object would not be what it is understood to be. Other statements depend on "accidental" conditions and circumstances. When such factors are altered, we may say the object has changed, but we are not obliged to say that it has been transformed into an entirely different thing. When a bachelor marries, he ceases to be a bachelor; if he becomes bald, that makes no difference to his bachelorhood [1]—he remains a bachelor. Having or not having a wife is an *essential* characteristic as far as bachelorhood is concerned. Having or not having hair is an *accidental* one. A precise account of this distinction, including its historical roots and all of its philosophical ramifications, would take us deep into the innermost reaches of logical theory and metaphysics. We must be satisfied with the rough account just presented, for here our concern is with the extent to which such a distinction is relevant to our study of fallacious reasoning.

In view of the abstract and elusive character of the distinction between essential and accidental truths about an object or person, it is hardly surprising that the traditional lists of fallacies should have included some that

---

[1] It makes no logical difference. Whether it makes any practical difference in his prospects of remaining single is a matter of speculation that will not be entered into.

are born of confusions between the two. Like the fallacies of composition and division, which arise out of a common confusion generated by grammatical analogy, such an error can occur in either direction. Taken in one direction, the fallacy is traditionally called the "fallacy of accident" and in the opposite direction, the "converse fallacy of accident." The same errors[2] bear resounding Latin titles: *argumentum a dicto simpliciter ad dictum secundum quid*[3] and *argumentum a dicto secundum quid ad dictum simpliciter.*[4] The Latin titles, or rough translations of them, bring out the nature of the errors involved more explicitly than do the customary English designations.

The fallacy of accident occurs in arguing from a statement asserted of an object simply, that is without reference to accidental circumstances, to a conclusion that presupposes that the assertion had included the accidental circumstances. In other words, it consists in treating an accidental feature as if it were essential. The classic example, without which no discussion of fallacies could be complete any more than the discussion of syllogism could be complete without reference to human mortality, concerns a piece of meat that is purchased one day and eaten the next.

> The meat you bought yesterday was raw. You say you ate it today; therefore you must have eaten some raw meat today.

When someone says of a piece of meat that he bought it yesterday, he is speaking of it simply as that certain piece of meat. It remains the same piece of meat when it is cooked, for there was no intention of making the state of the meat when purchased an essential feature of the reference to it. The conclusion of the fallacious argument depends on the contrary assumption, that the condition of the meat is one of its identifying or essential characteristics and must therefore be included implicitly in any simple reference to it.

The converse fallacy of accident occurs when a circumstance that is essential to the truth of the premise is ignored in the conclusion, as if the premise had been asserted simply, without reference to any such circumstance, instead of requiring it. It is therefore an argument from a statement asserted under a given condition (a dicto secundum quid) to a statement

---

[2] Some writers have objected to the identification, insisting that the fallacy of accident is to be distinguished from the fallacy named by the Latin designation given here.

[3] Arguing from a statement made simply to a statement made under some (special) condition.

[4] Arguing from a statement made under some (special) condition to a statement made simply.

asserted simply and unconditionally (ad dictum simpliciter). Different forms of the common error might be distinguished according to whether the qualifying circumstance is stated or left implicit, known or unknown. The student of logic who argues that a given syllogism violates one of the rules of quality or distribution and is therefore invalid, without first having determined whether the syllogism is in standard form, commits an error of this sort. It is explicitly stated that the rules determine validity or invalidity only for syllogisms in standard form. To ignore this qualification and apply the rules indiscriminately to any syllogism whatsoever, in standard form or not, we would be arguing from a principle true under the condition of standard form to a conclusion that depends on that same principle being true in the simple sense.

The qualifying condition need not be explicitly stated. If that is the case, the possibility of our reasoning fallaciously is increased, of course. If a child is told that when beans are planted in the ground, they will produce bean-stalks, he may plant the left-over baked beans from supper, hoping they will grow and that he can then do battle with giants. No one told him that the beans should not have been cooked, so there is some excuse for his mistake, more excuse than there is for the logic student of our previous example. But certainly that was an implicit condition of the assertion that beans will grow into beanstalks. It was taken for granted, so that the *dictum* was as genuinely *secundum quid* as if a condition had been explicitly stated. (In this case, that the beans have not been cooked is not an essential feature of the beans themselves. Being cooked or raw is no more essential to beans than it is to beef. The condition is essential, however, to the truth of the general principle about growing beanstalks from beans. That principle is intended to concern uncooked beans only.)

We can speak of still another occasion for the occurrence of this fallacy if there are in fact qualifying conditions under which certain statements are true, but which are not only unstated but unknown. An argument based on a biased sample is the most common representative of the fallacy in this particular form. The facts about the elements of the sample may hold only under special conditions that are accidental features of those particular items and not true of the general class from which the elements of the sample are drawn. The generalization based on them, however, is expressed as a dictum simpliciter, without reference to any such special conditions. In this form, the fallacy is sometimes called the "fallacy of hasty generalization." Randomness is important in a sampling procedure because, in a random sample, the possibility of special conditions, unknown to the investigator, having any importance is minimal.

The examples considered first are sufficient to indicate that it is misleading to identify the converse fallacy of accident with hasty generalization.
The examples of fallacious reasoning provided by the careless logic
student and the would-be giant-killer both involved the very reverse of
generalization. In each case, we applied a general rule (with either a
stated or an implicit restriction) to a specific case but without taking the
restrictive condition into account. When we generalize, we take facts about
specific cases and make them the basis of a general conclusion. What is
common to all three is the failure to take into account in the conclusion,
whether it is specific or general, the special conditions required by the
premises.

A discerning reader may have noticed that there is another difference
between the first two examples and the third. What is logically essential
to a statement is not entirely unknown, for it depends on the information
that the premise tended to convey. Someone who says that the rules of
quality and distribution determine the validity of arguments in standard
form knows that the restriction to standard form is essential to the truth
of his statement. Someone who says that beans will produce beanstalks
knows that he does not intend this principle to apply to baked beans, although he may think it unnecessary to make the qualification explicit. A
hasty generalization, or a conclusion derived from a biased sample, can
occur without anyone's being aware of it. The reason is that instead of
logically essential features, which are determined by meaning, being left
out of account, causally essential features may be ignored.

This distinction requires some expansion of the initial discussion of
essential and accidental characteristics. Being unmarried is logically essential to bachelorhood, for it is involved in the very concept itself. Other
factors, in the case of a given bachelor, may be essential in another, somewhat weaker sense. If they were not true, he would not be a bachelor.
When put that way, the resemblance to logically essential features is apparent. Of any bachelor, we can say that as a matter of logical necessity, if he
were not single, he would not be a bachelor. Let us suppose, however, that
of some bachelors, it is true that if they had not been disappointed in love,
they would not be bachelors. Even if we could say this of all bachelors, it
would still be incorrect to say that it is a matter of logical necessity. Having been disappointed in love is no more logically essential to bachelorhood
than is being bald. But of a given man, it may be causally so important that
without the disappointment in love, he would not be a bachelor. Of conditions that play such a role in relation to some truth or other, we can say
that they are causally, although not logically, essential conditions. This does

not offer a more satisfactory account of causally essential conditions than did our opening discussion of the logically essential conditions, but it will have to suffice for our present purposes.

The confusions between essential and accidental features or circumstances we discussed previously in terms of what is logically essential could be expected to have some counterparts in the context of the causally essential. We have concentrated our attention in this area on the "fallacy of false cause." The conclusion, when the fallacy of false cause occurs, is the assertion of a causal relationship. In other words, it is the claim that something or other is causally essential to a given fact. The premises on which the claim is based involve only an accidental association, insufficient to establish a genuine causal dependence. Among the most common associations are those that depend on a temporal relationship. If one thing frequently follows another, it is often assumed that it must be caused by the other. When this is the root of the fallacy, it is called the fallacy of "post hoc, ergo propter hoc"—*afterwards, therefore because of,* to offer a somewhat loosened translation. That one event precedes another may be an entirely accidental circumstance; therefore, it is not sufficient by itself to establish a causal relationship. The temporal relationship is only one basis of the fallacy of false cause, however. Mere accompaniment may also lead to the assumption of causal relation. Cicero advised his fellow Romans to buy no British slaves, "for Britons are too stupid to serve satisfactorily as slaves." Even assuming that his assessment of the mental attainments of the Britons of his day was correct, the assumption suggested by his advice, that their being British was the cause of their stupidity, can be rejected. Other factors, such as lack of the educational and cultural opportunities enjoyed by the citizens of Rome, were more likely to have been responsible. If so, it would be correct to say that "if he had the educational and cultural opportunities available in Rome, he would not be so stupid"; it would not be correct to say that "if he were not British, he would not be so stupid." The latter relationship would be relegated to the status of an accidental one, not one of the causally essential conditions of the phenomenon of stupidity in Britons.

The fallacy of false cause is the analogue of the "fallacy of accident." That is, it depends upon treating an accidental circumstance as if it were essential, with the difference between what is essential and what is accidental now turning on causal relationships rather than logical intentions. However, as far as causal relations are concerned, our attention having been concentrated on this form of fallacy, there is no reason why we should not identify a causal fallacy analogous to the converse fallacy of accident.

Such a fallacy would occur if a (causally) essential condition of a phenomenon were to be treated as if it were a merely accidental circumstance. Philosophers have often propounded the doctrine of the subjectivity of "sense qualities": many, if not all, of the qualities we perceive are alleged to exist only when they are being perceived. The presence of an observer is a causally essential condition of the existence of the quality. Locke, for example, held this view of what he called secondary qualities—color, taste, smell, sound, and others—although he did not think it true of primary qualities—size, shape, motion, solidity. Bishop Berkeley thought it true of all qualities. If these philosophical views are correct, then the assumption of the ordinary man, uncorrupted by philosophy, to the effect that colors, tastes, and sounds exist even when there is no one perceiving them at all represents a fallacy. The error could be described as drawing a conclusion concerning a phenomenon that leaves out of account one of its essential causal conditions. An expression such as "converse fallacy of false cause" would have little to recommend it. A more appropriate title for this sort of error might be "the fallacy of neglected cause."

It would be convenient for us to summarize briefly the fallacies that we have been considering in this section. A statement may be made or a term used with such an intended meaning that, unless certain conditions are fulfilled, it could not be true. Such conditions are then logically essential to the intended meaning. Other conditions, the presence or absence of which does not affect the truth of the intended meaning, are called accidental. A confusion about what is meant to be essential and what is meant to be accidental is the source of the fallacy of accident and the converse fallacy of accident. When an argument depends on counting an accidental feature or circumstance among those which are essential, it bears the former title. When an essential feature is neglected, and the argument proceeds as if it were not intended to be essential but figured as a mere accident, the converse fallacy of accident is the correct designation.

We can make similar observations in connection with causal explanations. Certain conditions that accompany an event are essential to it; if they did not hold, the event would not occur. Other conditions are accidental circumstances; the event might or might not occur whether they are present or absent. When an argument proceeds as if the accidental circumstance were among the essential conditions, it commits the fallacy of false cause. When, among a set of essential conditions, one or more of them is unnoticed or left out of account and so treated as if it were not among the causal factors responsible for the phenomenon, we have proposed that the mistake be called the fallacy of neglected causes. What are the correct procedures for distinguishing between essential and accidental conditions, either logical or causal, remains an open question here, of course. Part of the answer lies in either a theory of meaning or a metaphysical analysis of the nature of being; part of it lies in a correct theory of scientific method and the nature of scientific explanation.

8.6 FALLACIES IN PROOF

A fallacy, as it was originally defined in Section 7.1, is an argument that appears to be correct but is not. The last three fallacies we will examine require the definition to be stretched somewhat. They represent arguments that appear to be proofs but are not, although they may be valid so far as the reasoning itself is concerned. Of course, an argument that includes at least one false premise cannot be a proof. But the arguments we are to consider in this section can be seen to be faulty even without showing that one of the premises is definitely false.

If we could use any premise we pleased, we could prove anything we please. With an unlimited choice of premises, the distinction between valid reasoning from an arbitrarily selected set of premises and proof would collapse. As we have defined proof, the choice of premises in a true proof is restricted to statements that are true. We cannot select such premises as will support a desired conclusion, without regard to their truth or falsity. Therefore, while a premise remains in doubt, we rightly regard an argument as falling short of a strict proof.

To the requirement that in a proof the premises of the argument must be true, we must add a further qualification. The premises must be available or capable of being known independently of the conclusion itself. If the conclusion is appealed to in establishing the truth of one of its own premises, the argument is flawed. The premise may be true, and the reasoning may be valid. However, under these circumstances, we could not say that the argument establishes the conclusion, for in truth it depends upon it.

A valid argument serves a useful purpose in a rational dispute if it establishes a point to the satisfaction of both parties, because they both accept its premises. If it does not settle the matter, it may still serve a useful purpose by bringing out into the open one of the roots of the dispute. It may, that is, pinpoint a certain premise or premises on which there is no agreement as yet and to which further controversy may turn with a hope of ultimately reaching agreement as one party or the other becomes persuaded that he was mistaken. Neither of these useful purposes is served if the disputed conclusion is itself included among the premises, although the argument is valid. When this occurs, we speak of a fallacy, although in an extended sense. The fallacy is called "begging the question" or "arguing in a circle." Its Latin title is *petitio principii,* which originally had a somewhat narrower significance but is now generally taken to refer to any argument that presupposes its own conclusion among its premises. An argument that begs the question neither settles the issue nor throws any new light on its foundations. The original question is merely placed in a more complicated context. To the unwary, the brave show of argumentation may be much more persuasive than a straightforward declaration, unsupported by argument, would be. However, the circular argument represents no advance over the simple assertion whatsoever.

One way we can describe the fallacy of petitio principii would be to say that it is the unwarranted assumption of the conclusion itself among the premises of an argument that is supposed to prove it. There are still other ways of smuggling in the conclusion, besides making it a premise of its own proof. Instead of baldly asserting an opinion that is likely to be challenged, another statement may be made; one which would be inappropriate unless the disputable opinion were true. John Stuart Mill speaks of "question-begging epithets," counting their occurrence as a separate form of fallacy. To say of a theological opinion, "That heresy must be banned," is to take for granted that it is heresy. This may be a disputable point and even the heart of the matter being debated. The application of the epithet "heresy" to an opinion before its heretical nature has been demonstrated is a way of "begging the question," although it does not take precisely the form of arguing in a circle.

One technique of obliquely introducing a controversial opinion without arguing for it, even without directly asserting it, has traditionally gone by the name of the "fallacy of complex question." When the fallacy of complex question occurs, instead of making a statement that would be inappropriate unless the controversial opinion were true, we raise a question that depends on the same presupposition. To ask, "Should the heresy of Sabellianism be extirpated by violent means or should it be tolerated, in the hope that it will wither away of itself?" is to presuppose that Sabellianism is really a heresy. A simpler, and painfully familiar example, as familiar in logical treatises as human mortality and immutably raw meat, is the question: "Has he stopped beating his wife?" To be drawn into answering such a question is to accept as fact, perhaps without even clearly realizing that one has done so, an opinion that would have been challenged if it had been directly asserted.

It should be obvious that there is a common technique underlying both the use of the question-begging epithet and the use of the complex question. In either case, an opinion that ought to have been supported is simply presupposed, introduced without argument and even without explicit statement. When someone argues in a circle, we can at least recognize the occurrence of an elementary form of argument. With these other devices, there is no argument but merely the attempt to smuggle an opinion into the controversy while attention is being distracted elsewhere. There is no adequate reason for singling out the fallacy of complex question for special attention, as has usually been the case. It would be preferable to give a common designation to every attempt to gain acceptance for a questionable thesis by introducing it under cover of another statement that presupposes it. The "fallacy of illicit presupposition" would seem to be an appropriate general designation, whether the fallacy takes the form of making an assertion that contains a question-begging epithet or by raising a question that could not properly arise unless some opinion, not yet established, were so.

The fallacy of "ignoratio elenchi" (*ignorance of the refutation*) or *irrelevant conclusion,* like petitio principii, involves reasoning. The reasoning may be valid, as it may also be in petitio principii. In fact, going beyond petitio principii, it may even prove its conclusion. The argument may be, as reasoning and as proof, impeccable. Where, then, lies the mistake? It is to be found in the fact that the conclusion proved is the wrong conclusion. It does not bear upon the issue that was supposed to be in dispute. If someone is called upon to prove one thing and instead proves something else, no matter how sound his argument may be, a mistake has been made. Such a device may have great persuasive force, but its force is derived not from the correctness of the argument but from the confusion between what was supposed to have been proved and what has been proved. An argument aimed to demonstrate that a certain opinion ought to be abandoned, because it is false, may be countered by a defense of freedom of speech. Freedom of speech calls for the elimination of restrictions on the *expression* of opinions, although they may in fact be false. The arguments advanced in favor of freedom of speech are therefore irrelevant to the question of whether a given opinion should be *accepted* as true. To advance them in favor of the latter contention is to commit the fallacy of irrelevant conclusion. It is important to know not only just how much an argument really proves but also whether what it proves has anything to do with the question at issue.

8.6 EXERCISES

A. Following the disturbances at the county seat, some serious accusations were leveled at the Police Department of Caligula County. Analyze the following fragments from private conversations, public speeches, letters to the editor, and so on, in the light of the preceding discussion of material fallacies.

1. Our Chief of Police has devoted his entire career to the development of an able and dedicated police force. If it were true that his officers have behaved as they were accused of behaving, it would be a bitter disappointment to him, on the very eve of his retirement. That would be too bad.

2. I have looked up the court records. It turns out that at least some of the individuals who are supposed to have been beaten up so badly were not innocent at all but were tried and found guilty.

3. The police of Caligula County are by nature gentle and even kindly men. To the many citizens who have observed them helping old ladies across the street, playing games with underprivileged children, and otherwise engaged in beneficent community activities, these charges are incredible.

4. Who is behind these accusations? A seedy bunch of trouble makers, who want only to do damage to the good people of Caligula County, and a disgruntled newspaper editor trying to revenge himself for the many traffic fines he has paid and to distract attention from the much more serious misconduct of which he has long been suspected.

5. No one who appreciates the way the members of the police force feel about these charges—they're really all broken up by them—would have any inclination to believe them.

6. If you will check the police records, you will find that every one of these alleged incidents has been thoroughly investigated. No evidence of misbehavior on the part of a policeman has yet turned up. The falsity of the charges can be considered as demonstrated.

7. Of course, if there were really anything wrong in the Police Department, the investigations may not have been entirely reliable. But in fact they have shown that there is nothing wrong, and so their reliability must be granted.

8. That the principal of the high school supported some of the allegations is, all things considered, just further evidence against their truth. He is a fine man, to be sure; but as the uncle of one of the alleged victims, he is inevitably inclined to be sympathetic with their point of view.

9. Modern police work calls for extensive training and firm discipline. Police officers generally are highly trained and qualified professionals, hardly the sort of people who would be guilty of conduct like that which has been

charged against the police of Caligula County. We must therefore reject those charges.

10. You have often denounced such allegations against public officials in the past, on the grounds that even if they were true, their tendency would be to endanger law and order. Consistency requires that you repudiate the criticisms of the Caligula County Police Department.

11. Sir Asphodel Cannabis, the internationally renowned British expert on forensic procedure, has expressed his confidence that the police officers of Caligula County are guiltless.

12. Support your local police! Without a police force, a civilized community would be an impossibility, order would collapse, our great and prosperous Caligula County, built out of the wilderness by our pioneer forefathers, would sink back into barbarity.

13. If our cops thought for a moment that you believed any of those stories about them, they'd beat you to a pulp.

14. On many an occasion, you have made your opinions known when unfair attacks have been circulated concerning our public officials. Why do you not denounce with equal vigor the unfair charges that have been leveled at the police of Caligula County?

15. The case that has been made against the Caligula Police is based on exactly the same sort of evidence that the police cited in claiming that the alleged victims of brutality had really attacked *them*. But the critics' own friends and supporters have objected to the Police Department's arguments, and so they must repudiate the accusations made against the police.

16. Effluvia DeBayou, last year's Caligula County Consolidated High School's Homecoming Queen, declared that she didn't believe any of the stories are true. In fact, her very words were: "I declare, honey, I don't believe any of those stories are true." Her opinion should carry some weight, at least among the younger set.

17. Everything happened so fast; there was so much confusion that it was impossible for anyone to observe accurately what was going on. It is plain, then, that any person who flatly asserts that he was struck by a policeman is going beyond the evidence available.

18. The day after the trouble that generated all these wild accusations, Police Sergeant Bloodwort reported for duty with a black eye. It is not the police, but their critics, who were guilty of brutality.

19. The alleged victims were dangerous, violent persons, attacking the most fundamental principles of our way of life. I don't for a minute allow that they were mishandled by the police; if they had been, they would have had it coming. They're the sort of scum no decent patriotic citizen wants to have anything to do with.

20. There have been no good arguments advanced in defense of the Caligula

County police. Every one of them has turned out to be fallacious. The truth of the allegations has become clear for all to recognize.

B. Analyze any fallacious or misleading aspects of the following story.

1. Angela Liebestod, a beautiful girl from Meridian, Mississippi, won the local beauty contest and went up north for the national contest. Her mother accompanied her as chaperone. Arrangements had been made for some of the contestants to be escorted to a dance by members of the Guard of Honor at a nearby military academy. The somewhat anxious Mrs. Liebestod was much relieved, for she was confident that her daughter's honor would be well protected.

2. Her confidence was shaken, however, on learning that a lecture had recently been given on the social effects of loose morals among young people at the military academy. It was shattered entirely when she discovered that her daughter's escort was also a member of the academy's football team, which had been described in print as "lean and hungry with a smooth, well-oiled attack relying on a mixture of bone-crushing power and the finest passes you've ever seen." In fact, on reading this she swooned, and when she revived she firmly forbade Angela to have anything to do with "that awful boy."

3. Angela countered not with a criticism of her mother's faulty logic but by citing their next door neighbor in Meridian, a Mr. Tillicum who had once lived in Wisconsin, who had told her before she left that those Yankee boys were really very nice. Mrs. Liebestod replied that she had heard quite another story from Betsy Tillicum, and Angela became quite angry and said Betsy Tillicum was jealous and spiteful and anything *she* said about boys was bound to be a lie. She then burst into tears and wailed, "They are, too, nice boys. Just think how miserable I'll be if I have to stay here with you while all the other girls go to the dance! And besides, you don't know anything about my date, so you can't say he's not a perfect gentleman, so he *is!*"

4. There was no further discussion and Angela went to the dance. She reported on her return that she had had a wonderful time and had made a simply glorious impression on everybody—when she entered the ballroom with her date, there had been a burst of applause. But her mother wasn't interested; all she wanted to know was whether Angela had rejected in a ladylike manner the improper advances that had been made to her.

PART THREE

Chapter 9

ELEMENTS OF SYMBOLIC LOGIC

9.1 COMPOUND STATEMENTS

The system we turn to in Part Three is sometimes referred to as "modern," sometimes as "symbolic" logic. Neither expression goes to the heart of the matter. The logical system studied in Part One is by no means antiquated; it can be given, as we have seen, a thoroughly symbolic presentation. The significant distinguishing feature of the new system, the one that does go to the heart of the matter (at least provisionally), is that its symbols relate statements to each other. Previously, we worked with a system that related class terms. The elementary constituents of the first system were class terms, those of the new one are to be statements. The one is a logic of simple or categorical statements, the other is a logic of compound statements. The distinction has some far-reaching consequences, to which we shall turn attention shortly. We must, however, first come to understand some elementary facts about compound statements. Let us consider the following story.

The Tragical History of Michael Ogee

Michael Ogee had lived all of his life in a small town in the Midwest. Although it was a college town, with some pretensions to culture, they did not turn in the direction of *haute cuisine*. In fact, Mr. Ogee had never tasted a broiled mushroom. Presently, the eager recipient of a travel grant for architectural research, he was in France—not Paris—and a trip to the capital was planned. Mr. Ogee and his wife happened on a small bistro that offered among its appetizers broiled mushrooms; in a spirit of adventure, he ordered them. He found them delicious. "These mushrooms," he said to his wife, "are quite good." In his halting French, he expressed his enjoyment to the waiter, who replied, *"Oui, monsieur, tous les champignons sont bons."* That "all mushrooms are good" seemed rather a sweeping generalization, possibly rooted more in Latin enthusiasm than in sober fact; Mr. Ogee resolved to look into the matter.

The trip to Paris was made as planned. In the first restaurant they visited, broiled mushrooms were on the menu, and Mr. Ogee's first pleasant experience was repeated. His wife commented that they did not appear to be exactly the same kind as he had eaten before. "The waiter may have been right, my dear," he replied. "It is possible that all mushrooms are good to eat." He fell into the habit of ordering broiled mushrooms at every opportunity; after enjoying them on several more occasions, he reported, "I believe that all mushrooms *are* good to eat."

When Mr. and Mrs. Ogee returned to their home in the country, the weather was fine; they found an early opportunity to take a hike in the nearby woods. In a shady spot, Mr. Ogee discovered a large number of what appeared to be mushrooms. He picked them and took them home, where his wife broiled them for supper. It was a sad mistake, for they were of the poisonous variety. Mr. Ogee was fatally stricken. "Alas," he whispered as he breathed his last, "it is false that all mushrooms are good to eat."

As logicians, we must steel ourselves to the tragic fate of Mr. Ogee and direct our attention solely to what is logically interesting about his story: the waiter's assertion and Mr. Ogee's three comments.

1. All mushrooms are good.
2. It is possible that all mushrooms are good.
3. I believe that all mushrooms are good.
4. It is false that all mushrooms are good.

Of these four statements, the first is simple and the other three are compound. By a simple statement, we mean one that does not contain any complete statement as a part of the whole sentence. The waiter's assertion is not absolutely simple, of course; it does contain several words. If we view the statement in terms of logical analysis, we can consider it as a universal affirmative statement containing the usual parts—quantifier, subject term, copula, and predicate term. We can, therefore, say that it has constituents.

The significant feature differentiating it from the other three is that none of its constituents is, in itself, a complete statement. Each of the other assertions contains an expression that is, by itself, a complete statement (in this case the same statement—*all mushrooms are good*). We can now say that the defining characteristic of a "compound statement" is that it contains at least one part that is also a complete statement capable of being true or false.

We can draw an important distinction among our three compound statements: the statement within each of them is capable of being true or false, but whether it is true or false makes no difference to the validity of the entire statement in the first two cases. It might be *possible* that all mushrooms are good, whether or not it is in fact true. Someone might *believe* that all mushrooms are good, whether it is in fact true or false. We cannot say this of the last statement. If *all mushrooms are good* is a false statement, then the opinion expressed with Mr. Ogee's dying breath is a true one. If, to the contrary, it is true that *all mushrooms are good* (perhaps he picked some toadstools), then his opinion must be false. In brief, the truth of Mr. Ogee's last opinion depends entirely upon the truth or falsity of the statement it contains. A compound statement that has this property is called a "truth-functional compound"; the truth or falsity of the compound is determined by the truth or falsity of the statement or statements contained in it.

It is obvious that it is possible to form compound statements, and truth-functional ones, that contain more than one constituent that is a statement. Every time we use the word "and," for example, we are forming a truth-functional compound statement. It has two constituents that are statements, and it will be true only if both of its constituents are true. The logic of compound statements we are about to investigate will deal with truth-functional compound statements only. We can construct logical systems to deal with compounds that are not truth-functional, such as "modal compounds" formed with "possible," "impossible," "necessary." We shall not, however, attempt to do so in this book.

9.2 SYMBOLISM AND ITS ADVANTAGES

We have seen that there are different ways in which what is essentially the same logical system can be formulated. The system we discussed in Part One was expressed in terms of three different languages: logical English, Venn diagrams, and algebraic notation. All three of them were in a sense artificial languages, but only the last two were artificial in the sense of being constructed of made-up symbols. Logical English was artificial only because of the restrictions imposed upon it as to vocabulary and structure. The statements included in it could be understood, although not always with as much precision as necessary, by anyone familiar with ordinary English language; they were merely a selection from statements available within the limits of the vocabulary and grammatical and syntactical rules of English.

This was not true of the languages of Venn diagrams and algebraic notation. The latter, although apparently borrowed from the language of algebra, would not be understood in its distinctively logical function by the mathematician who is familiar with the algebraic use of its forms only. The letters functioned as abbreviations for class terms instead of numbers. Consequently, the expressions "equal to 0" and "unequal to 0" could not be understood in the sense given to them in mathematics. When they are used in connection with class terms, as in algebraic notation, it is better to think of them merely as abbreviations for "There are . . ." and "There are no. . . ." Their use in connection with class terms at all is the result of the combined forces of a historical confusion[1] and convenience. Their function in the logical context is as artificial as the Venn diagram system or the + and 0 of the chart that served as our original model.

The system with which we shall be occupied in this part makes use of an artificial language consisting of symbols some of which have been borrowed from the stock of mathematics, like those of algebraic notation. It is all the more important, since it will not be presented alongside another formulation of the same system in English, to recognize that the symbols here have a distinctively logical function, not a mathematical one. It is not

---

[1] The idea of a "mathematical logic" was once taken much more literally than contemporary logicians would think appropriate. It was once thought that logic could be turned into algebra, that the rules of logic were really mathematical rules in disguise. Nowadays, what is emphasized is the usefulness for logical purposes of the basic technical instruments of mathematics—a clear system of abbreviations and symbols and a clear set of primitive rules and axioms. Logic does not borrow the concepts of mathematics but its way of handling them. One of the reasons for supposing that logic could be turned into mathematics was the existence of certain formal analogies between some of the basic rules of mathematics and some of the basic principles of logic. The use of the expression "logical product" for a class identified as including everything (and only such things) belonging to both of two classes (see p. 98), is a case in point. It is a mistake, an exaggeration, to say that this is *really* a kind of multiplication. It is legitimate to say that there are certain analogies between numerical and logical products, between multiplying two numbers and grouping together the common elements of two classes. The analogies have to do with the formal rules governing both operations.

the concepts of number, equality, multiplication, addition, and so on that are being borrowed from mathematics but the technical advantages inherent in using symbols clearly and unambiguously defined, rather than the expressions of a natural language with their shifting and imprecise meanings.

The advantages to be gained by the use of artificial symbols should be plain. The advantage of using abbreviations is most obvious, although not necessarily most important. It permits not only a saving in printer's ink but also clearer insight into the logical structure of a statement and increased guarantees against error in the application of logical rules. Anyone who recalls some of the difficulties encountered in connection with the initial presentation of logical English will realize that a system using artificial symbols enjoys other advantages over systems formulated in the expressions of familiar discourse, even if they are restricted to a few chosen basic words. We recollect the unsystematic failure of the combination of the universal quantifier "all" with the negative copula "are not," to produce reliably what would ordinarily be interpreted as a universal negative statement. We recollect the need to restrict the particular quantifier "some" to only one of its meanings, the weaker one that does not include an implicit "but not all." Similar difficulties are likely to arise for any system that attempts to derive its basic logical expressions from the same source, hence the almost universal emphasis among modern systematic logicians on "symbolic logic," that is, a logic that makes use of a set of artificial symbols rather than the words and forms of ordinary language. This is not to say that the result is apt to be in any way superior to a language that has grown up gradually and unsystematically during the history of some human group. There is still much that can be said in English, for example, that cannot be said in any system of symbolic logic yet invented. Possibly some of it ought not to be said. Some of it may accomplish ends that are totally irrelevant to the ends aimed at by a logical system. Still, there are some things we can say in English that we ought to be able to express within the framework of a comprehensive systematic logic and yet cannot be expressed in any existing framework utilizing only the commonly accepted symbolic devices. Certain nontruth-functional compounds, for example, have no adequate counterpart in most versions of symbolic logic, although there have been attempts to incorporate them into more comprehensive systems.

None of these considerations, however, detract from the advantages of an artificial symbolism that we have cited. And the interplay between a systematic logical framework using such symbols and the unsystematic structure of our ordinary language may well help to illuminate the latter, even if it cannot entirely be replaced.

The advantages of artificial symbols lie in their very artificiality. The vague, ambiguous, occasionally unsystematic features of ordinary speech are given to us; we cannot shake them off. In extreme cases, we have seen that it is better to sacrifice some of the systematic neatness of our logical language than to attempt to eliminate these flaws by fiat. (An example was the introduction of "no" as an extra quantifier in logical English.) Because the symbols are artificial, we start fresh; we are in control of them as we cannot be in control of expressions borrowed from any preexisting language. If the symbols are ambiguous, it is because we made them so. The results of combining them in a certain way cannot be other than we expect. At worst, we may not know what to expect because we have specified no rule to cover the case. However, that is much more easily remedied than coming upon something that runs counter to our systematic expectations because of some quirk in the language for which we are totally unresponsible. It is time, then, to consider more carefully than we have before how one might go about introducing artificial symbols for logical functions, specifically for the logical functions important to a system involving truth-functional compound statements.

9.3   INTRODUCTION OF SYMBOLS

There are three ways in which we can introduce an artificial symbol. The first, and most obvious, is by direct translation from ordinary language. The advantages to be gained by this method are solely those that arise from abbreviation. We can introduce a single artificial symbol to take the place of the cumbersome English expression "It is false that. . . ." At somewhat less gain, we can introduce a single symbol to replace the three letters joined in the English word "and." Obviously, this method cannot bring the other advantages belonging to a system of artificial symbols; whatever flaws exist in the expressions of a nonlogical language chosen for translation will attach themselves to their artificial substitutes, unless special instructions are given. No such difficulties arise in connection with the functions we have just mentioned, but they do arise with others. One important type of truth-functional compound, for example, is expressed in English by "either . . . or. . . ." The trouble is that this expression, like "some," has two different functions in English, one weaker and one stronger. The stronger use includes an implicit "but not both," analogous to the "but not all" implicit in the stronger sense of "some." Consequently, any symbol introduced as a translation of "either . . . or . . ." will be ambiguous in the same way, if its introduction is not accompanied by a special provision to the effect that it is to serve just *this* function or *that* one of the functions served by the English expression.

In order to avoid the reference back to some counterpart in English, we can introduce logical symbols with which to construct truth-functional compound statements in a more systematic manner by using a truth table. This will be the second of our three ways of introducing them. A truth table presents all of the possible combinations of truth or falsity for a set of elementary statements. For the present, we need consider truth tables for only one or two statements. A single statement is either true or false, and these are the only two possibilities.[2] Using T as an abbreviation for "true" and F as an abbreviation for "false," we can represent the two possibilities for some proposition or other, represented by $p,$ on a simple table:

$$\begin{array}{c} p \\ \hline T \\ F \end{array}$$

The first example of a compound truth-functional statement we encountered was one that involved only a single statement as a constituent. The statement was combined with "It is false that" to form a compound that had the property, as we saw, of being truth functional. When the statement that occurred within it was true, the entire compound was false, and when the constituent statement was false, the entire compound was true. The result of putting "It is false that" in front of a statement is, in English, to produce a statement that has an opposite truth value to the statement it is applied to. The function of the expression is to contradict or negate. This function can be exhibited on a truth table by showing both the truth values for the elementary statement p and the truth values for the compound formed by putting an artificial symbol for the negation ($\sim$) in front of it:

$$\begin{array}{cc} p & \sim p \\ \hline T & F \\ F & T \end{array}$$

This table of truth values, or truth table, is a compact way of expressing two items of information:

[2] At least they are the only two we will consider. There have been attempts to devise three-valued and even multivalued logical systems, but they are beyond the scope of an introductory treatment.

Line 1: When p is true, $\sim p$ is false.
Line 2: When p is false, $\sim p$ is true.

The first column includes the possible truth values for the elementary statements involved; in this case only one, p. The other column indicates the corresponding truth value of the compound formed by combining p with the logical sign $\sim$. Notice that although the English expression for negation—one of them at least—has been mentioned, the symbol $\sim$ has not been introduced as merely a translation of it. We have not been saying that $\sim$ means "It is false that" but rather that $\sim$ and "It is false that" have the same function, which is exhibited in the truth table. The same method could be used to explain the function of "It is false that," and we could use it to exhibit the intended function of $\sim$ quite independently of any side remarks about its English counterpart.

In order to introduce, by the same technique, symbols for forming truth-functional compounds with two constituents (like "and" in English), the truth table must be more complex. There are four possible combinations of truth values for any two distinct statements, represented by p and q on the left-hand side of the table following:

p	q	$p \cdot q$
T	T	T
F	T	F
T	F	F
F	F	F

In the third column we write the corresponding truth values for each of the four cases when p and q are joined by the symbol $\cdot$ in a compound. This truth table is therefore a compact way of representing four items of information, which together define the function of the logical symbol:

Line 1: When p is true and q is true, $p \cdot q$ is true.
Line 2: When p is false and q is true, $p \cdot q$ is false.
Line 3: When p is true and q is false, $p \cdot q$ is false.
Line 4: When p is false and q is false, $p \cdot q$ is false.

Notice that the compound is true only when *both* of the constituents are true. It serves the same function as "and" does in English. It is important, however, for us to see that its function was sufficiently defined by the truth table, not by any reference to a corresponding word in English. In fact, we knew that it had the same function as "and" only *after* its function had been exhibited on the truth table. The correct name for the function is "conjunction."

The function called "disjunction" (or inclusive alternation) is the weaker sense in which "either . . . or . . ." is used, without the implicit "but not both." The symbol that expresses it is exhibited on the following truth table:

p	q	$p \vee q$
T	T	T
F	T	T
T	F	T
F	F	F

There is no ambiguity about the use of v, as there is about "either . . . or. . . ." By definition on the truth table, the compound formed by v *is* true when both of the constituents are true. A symbol intended to have the other function of "either . . . or . . ." must be introduced separately, by an appropriate array of truth values.

The symbol for a function called "material implication" is introduced as follows:

p	q	$p \supset q$
T	T	T
F	T	T
T	F	F
F	F	T

All sorts of difficulties arise if we attempt to introduce $\supset$ as a translation of some specific counterpart in English. We shall use it, however, as an abbreviation for "If . . . then . . ." and other expressions in English of *implication*. The difficulty is, first of all, that "If . . . then . . ." does not express just one type of relationship in English, but a family of them. We cannot identify the "If . . . then" of *If that is a circle, then its area is equal to* pi *times the square of its radius* with the "If . . . then" of *If that is a glass of water, then it will quench your thirst,* nor either of these with *If the French Revolution had not occurred, then the map of Europe would be different today.* Secondly, it is impossible for us even to pick out *one* of the several uses of "If . . . then" and say of it that its function is material implication as defined on the truth table. What all of the functions of "If . . . then" have in common with the function assigned to $\supset$, that is, material implication, is that the compound cannot be true when the first part, called the "antecedent," is true, and the second part, called the "consequent," is false. Material implication, one might say, is a minimal sort of implication. All of the senses of implication we ordinarily find it useful to express may go somewhat beyond it, but all share with it this one basic feature. For this reason, we use $\supset$ as an abbreviation for "If . . . then" in the same spirit as we used "some" as a translation for "most" and other quasi-numerical quantifiers. It is the closest approximation possible within the limits of our artificially constructed language.[3] Statements of material implication, because of the relationship they have to "If . . . then" statements, are also called "hypothetical" statements.

There is one more symbol in common use for elementary work in symbolic logic: $\equiv$. It represents the relation of "material equivalence." Two statements are said to be materially equivalent when both have the same truth value. The function of this symbol, which forms a compound asserting such a relation to hold between its constituents, is exhibited by a truth table with the following pattern:

p	q	$p \equiv q$
T	T	T
F	T	F
T	F	F
F	F	T

Instead of presenting a separate truth table for each symbol, we can exhibit them all on a composite truth table, each with its own column. In Table 9.1 the names of the symbols commonly used and the names of the functions or relationships they represent are given as well as the symbols themselves. This table presents the essential vocabulary of the system of compound statements, sometimes called the "sentential" or "propositional" calculus.

It has already been mentioned that there is still a third method, besides the translation of familiar words in abbreviations and the construction of truth tables, by which we can introduce artificial symbols. Certain symbols that have already been introduced by one of those methods can then be used to define other symbols. The key to this process is a characteristic of the logic of compound statements that has no counterpart in the traditional

---

[3] There is nothing paradoxical, then, about what have been called paradoxes of material implication—any material implication is true if its consequent is true or its antecedent is false, whatever the other constituents may be. That is how the function is defined on the truth table; that is the end of the matter. The peculiar air of paradox arises only when we think it correct to say that $\supset$ *means* "If . . . then." Of course we will, if that is how $\supset$ has been introduced as a symbol. All the more reason, then, for introducing it independently by the truth-table method. When we regard $\supset$ as an independent symbol, defined by a truth table, it is easy to understand its status. To insist on identifying it with "If . . . then" is somewhat like thinking that "some" *means* "most," because we are forced to use "some" as a substitute for "most" in translating from ordinary English into logical English.

TABLE 9.1

Elementary constituents		Negation	Conjunction	Disjunction	Material implication	Material equivalence
		Curl	Dot	Wedge	Horseshoe	Triple bar
p	q	$\sim p$	$p \cdot q$	$p \vee q$	$p \supset q$	$p \equiv q$
T	T	F	T	T	T	T
F	T	T	F	T	T	F
T	F	F	F	T	F	F
F	F	T	F	F	T	T

system. Since a compound statement is still a statement, it can be made a constituent of a compound itself. Of this procedure we shall have more to say later. For the present we need consider only some very simple cases. The truth value of a statement with the form $\sim p \vee q$ would be arrived at by determining the truth value of its constituents. It makes no difference if one of the constituents is a compound statement, as its truth value is determined by the function assigned to $\sim$. If we make up a truth table for the compound exhibiting all the possible circumstances, the result would look like this (a reference column for the negation of p has been provided):

p	q	$\sim p$	$\sim p \vee q$
T	T	F	T
F	T	T	T
T	F	F	F
F	F	T	T

A comparison of the resulting pattern of truth values in the final column with the composite truth table shows that it is the same as the pattern of truth values used in defining the function of $\supset$. We could, if we wished, introduce $\supset$ by saying that $p \supset q$ means $\sim p \vee q$. We have found that the truth-functional effect of combining p and q with $\supset$, as in the former compound, is exactly the same as that of combining them with $\sim$ and $\vee$, as in the latter. Material equivalence is also usually introduced by definition in this way, as meaning the conjunction of two material implications that have the same constituents but in the reverse order:

$$p \equiv q \quad \text{means} \quad (p \supset q) \cdot (q \supset p)$$

Obviously, for us to apply this method, some symbols must be taken as basic. Which ones we select will depend on various considerations and will vary according to the purpose for which the system is intended.

The functions that we have been considering are the ones commonly in use in elementary modern logic. One of the reasons for this is that they all have counterparts, within the limitations described, in English. Of course, there are other ways, besides those mentioned in the preceding discussion, to express the same functions in English. The expressions that we have mentioned so far are by no means the only resources we have for constructing compound statements in ordinary discourse. Not only "and" but also other grammatical conjunctions such as "but," "yet," "although," "nevertheless," are available to form logical conjunctions. This is not to say that all of these words have exactly the same function in English. So far as we attend only to their use as forming truth-functional compounds, they do. They do have other functions, however; in these respects they are differentiated.

The task of interpreting the truth-functional compounds of ordinary language becomes still more complicated when we turn our attention to the many ways in which implication and equivalence can be expressed. If we neglect the aspects in which the material implication of our system falls short of a complete rendering even of "If . . . then," there are still problems. The same expression may function somewhat differently in different contexts, even in its truth-functional aspect. We encountered much the same situation in connection with the various ways of expressing categorical statements in English, and "either . . . or" has already provided an example in the present context. (Interestingly enough, "neither . . . nor," so obviously related to "either . . . or," does not share its ambiguity. It asserts that both components are false. *Neither the butler nor the maid witnessed the crime* would be symbolized as $\sim B \cdot \sim M$.)

The word "only" was used with class terms to form categorical statements equivalent to universal statements in logical English. Combined with "if," it forms an important truth-functional logical expression. "If and only if" is one way of expressing material equivalence (plus whatever nontruth-functional significance may be intended), as in *The defendant will be convicted if and only if the jury believes the butler's testimony*. The truth-functional aspect of the meaning of this statement asserts that the component elementary statements are either both true or both false, that the implication holds both ways.

Standing by itself, "only if" is open to a stronger or a weaker interpretation, very much like "only" as a categorical quantifier. *Only grandmasters are capable of playing every variation of the Blackmar-Diemer gambit without making any mistakes* certainly means to assert that all persons capable of playing every variation of the Blackmar-Diemer gambit without making a mistake are grandmasters. It might be understood also to mean that all grandmasters are capable of the performance. Similarly, *We will go tobogganing only if the temperature rises above 0°,* certainly means to assert that if the temperature does not rise above 0°, we will not go tobogganing. But whether it also means to assert that if the temperature does rise, we will go, is not so clear. The safest course to follow is to interpret statements of the form *p only if q* to mean nothing but *if not q, then not p,* unless the context makes it quite clear that *if q, then p* is also intended.

"Unless" is another word that is used to express an implicative type of relationship, possibly an equivalence in some contexts. *We will not go tobogganing unless the temperature rises above 0°* certainly means that if the temperature stays below 0°, we will not go tobogganing $(\sim R \supset \sim T)$. Whether the speaker also intended to say that we will go tobogganing if the temperature rises above 0° is not quite so clear. If he did, his statement could be truth-functionally interpreted as $R \equiv T$. The more positively framed statement, *We will go tobogganing, unless the temperature stays below 0°* does seem to intend the implication to hold in both directions, that is, to be truth-functionally equivalent to $T \equiv \sim S$. However, if there is any unresolved doubt as to the intended meaning of a statement, the weaker interpretation should be preferred in translating it into symbolic language.

As we have seen, the truth-functional connectives of the symbolic system all have counterparts with the same function in the English language. There is no reason why the vocabulary of a symbolic system should be restricted in this way. A truth-table definition can be used to introduce any symbol, whether or not the function assigned to it is performed by any simple expression in English. For theoretical purposes, one of the most useful logical signs has a function that lacks any simple expression in English. It is the "stroke function" (or the Sheffer stroke function, after its inventor, the late Henry Sheffer of Harvard University), represented by the symbol /. Once it has been defined by the truth-table method, it is possible to use it to define all of the other symbols introduced so far. The truth table that defines it has the following form:

p	q	p/q
T	T	F
F	T	T
T	F	T
F	F	T

Of course there are complex expressions in English that have the same truth-functional effect, but they are all built up out of other expressions. Examples are:

It is false that *p* and *q* are both true.

(The stroke function is contradictory to conjunction, as can be seen by comparing the truth tables for each.)

Either *p* or *q* is false.

For ordinary purposes, however, the stroke function is not used. If any of the symbols are to be defined instead of being introduced by truth tables, either ∼ and v or ∼ and · are taken as basic.

9.3 EXERCISES

A. Reconstruct from memory the truth-table definitions of negation, conjunction, disjunction, material implication, and material equivalence. Check against the table on p. 207 and correct any mistakes.

B. Invent compounds to fulfill the following conditions.

1. A compound having the same truth-value pattern on a truth table as the pattern that is used to define conjunction but including the signs for negation and disjunction only.

2. A compound with the same truth-value pattern as the one in problem 1, but including the signs for negation and implication only.

3. A compound having the same truth-value pattern on a truth table as the pattern used in defining material implication but including the signs for negation and conjunction only.

4. A compound with the same truth-value pattern on a truth table as the pattern used in defining material equivalence but including the signs for conjunction and implication only.

5. A compound with the same truth-value pattern as the one in problem 4 but including the signs for conjunction, disjunction, and negation only.

6. A compound having the same truth-value pattern on a truth table as the pattern used in defining disjunction but including the signs for negation and implication only.

7. A compound with the same truth-value pattern as the one in problem 6 but including the signs for negation and conjunction only.

8. A compound defining negation in terms of the stroke function.

9.4 LEVELS OF COMPLEXITY

There are two basic points on which our understanding of how the new system works must depend. We have already noted these points in Section 9.3, but it would be well to recall them before going on. First of all, the result of combining a statement or a pair of statements with one of the logical signs is a new statement, a compound statement. As a statement, it can be a constituent of a new compound formed by using one of the logical signs. Consequently, there is no theoretical limit to the complexity of statements that can be formed. No matter how complex a statement may be already, since it is a statement, it is always permissible for us to place ~, the negation sign, in front of it or to connect it with some other statement by the sign for conjunction, disjunction, or any of the other signs available.

The second point is that all such compounds are truth functional. The logical tasks performed by the different signs that enter into them were exhibited and distinguished by different patterns on the truth table. When we know the truth values of any two statements, the truth value of any compound made up by combining one or both of them with one of the logical signs can be determined directly by reference to the truth table that defines the logical symbol's function. We need only refer to the line corresponding to the known truth values of the constituent statement.

When we are confronted by a compound statement in which there are already compound constituents—the possibility stressed in the first point—its truth value will still be a function of its constituents. At least one of them, we are supposing, is compound. If we are given the truth values of the constituents, simple or compound, we can still determine the truth value of the whole directly by referring to the defined function of the logical sign. It makes no difference that the constituents are compound. If we are not given the truth value of a compound constituent, it must first be determined by referring to the truth values of *its* constituents. In general, what we need is a procedure for determining the truth value of a statement, no matter how complex it may be, if we know only the truth values of its most elementary constituents. (This has already been simply illustrated in connection with the definition of material implication.)

No matter how complicated its structure may be, a compound statement can always be seen as a construction built up step by step from elementary statements by using truth-functional signs. We can illustrate the construction of a complex truth-functional compound by showing how the following statement is built up:

$$[A \text{ v } (B \cdot \sim C)] \supset (Q \text{ v } R)$$

We begin with its elementary constituents:

$$A \quad B \quad C \quad Q \quad R$$

By attaching $\sim$ to C and connecting Q and R by v, these compounds are initially formed:

$\sim C \qquad Q \vee R$

Then we form the following compound, which combines one of the elementary constituents with a compound already formed:

$B \cdot \sim C$

Now this compound becomes a constituent of a disjunction; on the other side of the disjunction is the elementary statement A:

$A \vee (B \cdot \sim C)$

Finally, this compound is connected by $\supset$ to the disjunction of Q and R that we formed previously, and we have the entire statement:

$[A \vee (B \cdot \sim C)] \supset (Q \vee R)$

Our example also illustrates how the structure of a compound statement is indicated by the use of parentheses and brackets of various kinds. For very complicated cases, a system of dots is used. Such signs provide a kind of punctuation. They are not essential to the logical significance of the system; in the so-called Polish notation, their function is performed by the order in which the components of the compound statement are written. In our notation, they are necessary to avoid ambiguities that would otherwise occur. Suppose, for example, that we wished to form a disjunctive statement with A as one of its constituents and $B \supset C$ as the other. Writing $A \vee B \supset C$ would not suffice to express clearly what was intended. It does not permit a distinction between a disjunctive statement with A and $B \supset C$ as its constituents and a hypothetical statement with $A \vee B$ as its antecedent and C as its consequent. In order to indicate that it is the former compound that is intended and not the latter, we enclose $B \supset C$ in parentheses: $A \vee (B \supset C)$. This shows that as far as the symbol $\supset$ is concerned, $B \supset C$ functions as a unit, as one of the alternatives. If we intended to make the hypothetical statement, we would have to enclose $A \vee B$ in parentheses, showing that as far as $\supset$ was concerned, that compound functioned as a unit, the antecedent: $(A \vee B) \supset C$. If either one of these two possible compounds is to be incorporated into a statement of still greater complexity, we must enclose it within parentheses again. It is convenient to utilize different kinds of parentheses where some compound units are included in others. A compound that includes internal parentheses will be enclosed in square brackets when it becomes a constituent of some still more complex statement. One that already includes a unit enclosed in square brackets will be enclosed within { }, and so on. With one exception, a compound statement functioning as a constituent of a more complex statement must be enclosed in brackets of some kind or other. The exception occurs when we form a compound by negating a statement: $\sim p$ is always taken to be a unit without having to be enclosed in parentheses. Actually, the function performed by parentheses and brackets could also be performed by the numerical indices we are about to introduce, but parentheses and brackets do serve to bring out the grouping of constituents in a compound statement very graphically. This advantage justifies their continued use despite the difficulties that can arise with statements of particularly high levels of complexity.

It will be useful for us to keep track of the various intermediate levels of complexity between the entire compound and its most elementary constituents. We shall indicate such levels or degrees of complexity by numerical indices attached to the letters and logical signs making up the compound. We begin by defining a 0-level statement as one containing no logical signs whatsoever. A first-level statement is one that contains only one logical sign. The level of complexity of statements containing more than one logical sign is determined according to the level of the most complex constituent within it. A statement that contains at least one first-level constituent, but none of any greater complexity, is assigned to the second level and given the index 2. A statement that contains at least one constituent of the second level, but none higher, is at the third level, and so on. The level of complexity for an entire compound is one higher than the level of its most complex constituent. The level of complexity belongs to the entire compound, but it is convenient to identify it by attaching a numerical index to the logical sign that goes into making up the compound.

9.4 EXERCISES

Distinguish the various levels of complexity in each of the following compounds by writing the appropriate numerical index above each elementary constituent and logical sign. Example:

$$\overset{0\ 1\ 0\ \ 3\ 2\ \ 0\ 1\ 0}{(p \vee q) \cdot \sim(p \supset r)}$$

A. $\sim(\sim p \vee \sim q)$

B. $\sim(p \cdot \sim q)$

C. $\sim(\sim p \cdot \sim q)$

D. $(\sim p \vee \sim q) \cdot (p \vee q)$

E. $p \supset (q \cdot \sim q)$

F. $(p \cdot q) \vee (\sim p \cdot \sim q)$

G. $(p \supset q) \cdot (q \supset p)$

H. $\sim p \supset q$

I. $\sim(p \supset \sim q)$

J. $\sim \sim(p \vee q) \supset [(q \supset r) \cdot \sim p]$

9.5 EVALUATION CHARTS

We are now in a position to set up a method for determining the truth
value of a compound with more than the first level of complexity, given
only the truth values of its elementary or 0-level constituents. It is, first of
all, necessary for us to determine the levels of complexity of its compound
constituents. As we explained in Section 9.4, a compound including nothing
but elementary statements with an associated logical sign would be at the
first level of complexity; a compound containing a first-level compound
would be at the second level; and so on. As we noted before, every compound is at a level one degree higher than that of its most complex component. We will indicate levels of complexity by the use of numerical
indices.

We can represent distinctions in levels of logical complexity as differences
in spatial level on an "evaluation chart." We prepare such a chart by drawing horizontal lines to divide the space beneath the statement to be evaluated
into rows or levels. All the logical signs with the index 1 are then written
in the first row below the position in which they occur in the statement.
Signs with the index 2 are written on the second level below a line drawn
across the first row, those with the index 3 are written on the third level
beneath a line drawn across the first two, and so on. The result for the
statement that has been serving as our example will look like this:

$$0\ 3\ \ 0\ 2\ 1\ 0\ \ \ 4\ \ \ 0\ 1\ 0$$
$$[A \lor (B \cdot \sim C)] \supset (Q \lor R)$$

0			$\sim$		$\lor$
1		$\cdot$			
2	$\lor$				
3			$\supset$		
4					

The rows are labeled according to the truth values that will appear in
them. In the first row, labeled 0, the truth values of the elementary 0-level
constituents of the statement are written. Each of them will be either in a
box all by itself or in one that contains just one logical sign. The truth
values for the first-level constituents, which will appear in the row
labeled 1, are determined by the 0-level truth values and the definitions of
the logical signs. If there is no logical sign, the same truth value is carried
unchanged into the next row. If a truth value occurs after the $\sim$ sign, the

opposite value is written in the next row, below the sign. If there are two truth values and a logical sign, the truth value of the compound, given those truth values for its constituents, is written in the next row. The result will be a set of truth values for all the first-level constituents of the statement. They, too, will occur either alone or together with only one logical sign. The process can be repeated for the next row, in which the values of the second-level constituents are determined, and so on, until the truth value for the entire statement has been reached. If we were to assume that A is true, B false, C true, and Q and R false, the evaluation chart for the various intermediate levels and the entire statement would take this form:

	0	3	02	1	0		4	0 1 0
		$[A$ v	$(B \cdot$	$\sim$	$C)]$	$\supset$	Q v	R
0	T		F	$\sim T$				F v F
1	T		$F \cdot$		F			F
2	T v		F					F
3		T				$\supset$		F
4						F		

9.5 EXERCISE

Construct evaluation charts for the ten statements in Exercise 9.4. Determine the truth value of each when p is occupied by a true statement, q by a false one, and r by a false one.

9.6 TRUTH TABLES

We can construct for compounds with higher levels of complexity the same sort of truth tables that we used to exhibit the logical function of the basic signs. Each line of truth values on a truth table corresponds to a distinct pattern of truth values on an evaluation chart. We can construct the truth table systematically by referring to the index number indicating levels of complexity. We place in the column on the extreme left the 0-level constituents. Next we provide a set of columns for the first-level constituents, then a set of columns for the second-level ones, and so on. Finally, we provide a column at the extreme right for the truth values the entire statement takes under each of the possible circumstances represented by a distinct combination of truth values for its elementary constituents.

This is how the columns would be headed on a truth table for the example in Section 9.5:

$$
\begin{array}{cccccccc}
1\;0 & 0\,1\,0 & 0\,2\,1\,0 & 0\,3 & 0\,2\,1\,0 & 0\,3 & 0\,2\,1\,0 & 4 & 0\,1\,0 \\
ABCQR & \sim C & Q \text{ v } R & B \cdot \sim C & A \text{ v } (B \cdot \sim C) & [A \text{ v } (B \cdot \sim C)] \supset (Q \text{ v } R)
\end{array}
$$

The two columns immediately to the right of the five for the elementary constituents are for the first-level statements, $\sim C$ and $Q \text{ v } R$. The logical signs in these two statements occur in the first row of the evaluation chart. The next column is for $B \cdot \sim C$, a second-level compound represented in the second row of the evaluation chart; the next column is for the third-level constituent, since there is no other second-level constituent; and the last column is for the entire statement. In more complex statements, there might be several columns for each of the intermediate levels.

The number of rows required for a full truth table will depend on the number of distinct combinations of truth values for the 0-level statements that are possible. This depends on the number of 0-level statements. If there is only one, there are just two possible truth values, as we have seen. That is why the truth table in which the function of $\sim$ was exhibited needed only two lines. If there are two constituents, there must be four rows, since each of the two possible values for the one can be combined with true or false for the other. When there is a third statement, each of the possible combinations for two can be combined with its truth and each can be combined with its falsity, giving a total of eight possibilities. It is clear that the number of possible distinct combinations is doubled every time another statement is added at the 0-level, for each of the already existing possibilities can be combined with *true* for the new statement and each with *false*. The number of lines needed on the complete truth table will be a power of 2, the power being the number of distinct 0-level statements involved. A truth table for the example we have been using would require 32 lines, because it contains five distinct 0-levels constituents; 2 to the fifth power is 32. Table 9.2 shows the eight lines of a complete truth table for another example, with only three distinct 0-level constituents.

A theoretical understanding of how a truth table is constructed for a compound proposition is important, but we can do as well in the principal purpose of constructing such a truth table by using an evaluation chart. In practice, therefore, we will not need to prepare huge and complicated tables with many rows of distinct combinations of truth values for the elementary constituents and many columns of components of various levels of complexity.

TABLE 9.2

P	Q	R	~P	~R	~P v ~R	Q v ~R	(~P v ~R) ⊃ (Q v ~R)
T	T	T	F	F	F	T	T
F	T	T	T	F	T	T	T
T	F	T	F	F	F	F	T
F	F	T	T	F	T	F	F
T	T	F	F	T	T	T	T
F	T	F	T	T	T	T	T
T	F	F	F	T	T	T	T
F	F	F	T	T	T	T	T

We have now developed the elementary features of a language. The idea that inspires this language, the idea with which modern logic begins, is that of a truth-functional compound statement. It is as fundamental here as was the idea of classes and their relationships for the system studied in Part One. In the succeeding chapters, we shall develop, as we did in Part One, a set of principles and tests of valid inference for arguments including compound statements of this type.

9.6 EXERCISE

Construct full truth tables for each of the compounds in Exercise 9.4.

Chapter 10

ARGUMENTS AND VALIDITY

The basic logical concepts of premise, conclusion, validity, and the related concepts will retain the meanings they have had this far, as we continue our discussion of symbolic logic. An argument, as before, consists of at least two statements, one of which is the conclusion. The same general types of argument considered in the system in Part One recur in the new system. Some arguments are such that the conclusion is derived from just a single premise—these are the immediate inferences. Others, to be valid, require more than one premise in support of the conclusion. The distinction between direct and indirect inference also arises in symbolic logic, but how it applies depends upon the principles of inference that are taken to be basic. (Because of the greater complexity and scope of the new system, it will be convenient to have the number of principles of inference greater than the five principles governing arguments in the system of logical English and its companion languages.) Of course, the distinction that is fundamental to all systems of logic—the distinction between valid and invalid arguments—applies in symbolic logic too.

218

10.1 TESTS OF VALIDITY

It will be useful for us to distinguish among three ways of determining the validity of arguments involving compound statements. These three methods of testing validity correspond fairly closely to the methods of introducing symbols discussed in Section 9.3. Symbols could be introduced, we pointed out then, by relating them to familiar expressions in the language we ordinarily speak, treating them as abbreviations. Secondly, we could introduce them by the use of truth tables, in which the function each symbol was intended to perform was exhibited systematically on the table. Thirdly, once we had introduced certain symbols to be taken as basic or primitive, others could be introduced in terms of them by definition. We could cite the following examples as illustrating the three procedures:

1. $\sim$ = *It is false that*   (Definition in terms of familiar expressions)
2.

p	q	$p \vee q$
T	T	T
F	T	T
T	F	T
F	F	F

(Definition by a truth table)

3. $p \supset q$ means $\sim p \vee q$ (Definition in terms of basic symbols in the system)

In testing the validity of an argument we can, first of all, interpret the various symbols occurring in it in terms of their counterparts in English and then "apply common sense." This can be done whether or not the symbols were introduced by a comparable procedure. All it means is that we are relying on our presystematic capacity for telling a valid argument from an invalid one, at least in simple cases, as we used the unsystematic expressions of ordinary language as a basis of definition in the first method of introducing symbols. The second procedure for determining validity makes use of a truth table. In the third, the validity of certain argument forms having been previously established, the validity of others is demonstrated by indirect inference.

In the traditional system, at least as far as logical English is concerned, only the first and the third methods were used. The principles of immediate inference and the syllogism were established as basic principles of inference by appeal to their obvious validity in the light of common sense. All other valid arguments were shown to be so by the method of indirect inference: each direct step in the demonstration was justified by appeal to one of these basic principles. This was not quite true of the traditional system as it was set forth in the language of Venn diagrams, for there we had a more mechanical way of establishing the validity of a syllogism. Once the premises were set down on the pattern, the conclusion appeared automatically. It was not necessary to reflect on the relationship between premises and conclusion or to appeal to common sense—either the conclusion was already there when the premises were written down or it was not. Such a test depends on the nature of the systematic device being used rather than on our presystematic capacities for logical criticism.

10.2 THE TRUTH TABLE
AS A TEST OF VALIDITY

There are obvious advantages to having a perfectly clear-cut systematic procedure for establishing the validity of all argument forms, even those that function as basic rules of inference. In the system now being developed, unlike the system built up in terms of logical English, we are in a position to enjoy those advantages. The truth table can be used to determine the validity or invalidity of any argument capable of being formulated in the language of truth-functional compounds. For this reason, truth tables, rather than any appeal to extrasystematic judgment, give us the theoretical basis for all tests of validity applicable to arguments involving compound statements.

The point of using a truth table is this: A complete truth table includes *all the possibilities,* that is, all the possible combinations of truth values for the elementary statements that enter into the compounds. Since the compound statements are truth-functional compounds, the table can include a truth value for the entire compound in each of the possible sets of circumstances defined by various combinations of truth values for its constituents. On a truth table, we can determine the truth values taken by each of a set of compound statements under each of the possible sets of circumstances. If one of the statements is the conclusion of an argument and the others the premises, all that remains to be seen is whether there is any possibility of the premises being true and the conclusion false. We can ascertain this by scanning the various sets of truth values. If no such combination occurs, we can say none is possible; the truth table exhausts all the possibilities. *An argument is valid if there is no possibility of the premises being true and the conclusion false.*

We can illustrate the procedure by a simple example. Here is one of the principles we will take to be basic when we turn attention to indirect inference:

$$p \supset q$$
$$\underline{q \supset r}$$
$$p \supset r$$

This is the principle of "hypothetical syllogism" (HS). Its resemblance to the categorical syllogism studied in Part One is plain. It includes three basic constituents (statements rather than terms, now); two occur once in the premises and once in the conclusion, while the third occurs twice in the premises.

Actually, there is a slight inaccuracy of expression here. The pattern of marks given does not really constitute a fully specified argument; it is a pattern of argument or an "argument form." Unless the letters S, M, and P are being used as abbreviations with meanings specified for them, the same is true of the patterns we considered in our earlier discussion of the categorical syllogism. In the case of the syllogism, if the constituents were to be specified, as they are not in the abstract argument form, they would be class terms. Here, if the constituents to occupy the places indicated by p, q, and r were to be specified, they would be statements. They could even be compound statements; if so, they would still be functioning as elementary constituents as far as the argument form is concerned.

On the same strict usage, it would be incorrect to refer to a compound formed of p, q, r, and so on together with logical signs as a compound statement. It is really a "compound statement form," which would be a statement if its elementary constituents were specified. Therefore, we will follow the convention that the use of the lower case for the p, q, r series will be for the purpose of indicating places for statements to go. Capital letters, appropriately assigned, will be used as abbreviations for specific statements.

We can now return to our example of the truth table as a test of validity. If one thinks of the statements in the example as the counterparts of "if . . . then" statements, the validity of the principle can readily be established by the first method, appeal to common sense. We are now interested in how it can be established by reference to a truth table. The truth table must include columns for each of the constituents of the argument. Because there are three distinct 0-level statements involved, it must include eight lines (see Table 10.1).

Scanning the table shows that there are only two possible sets of circum-

TABLE 10.1

p	q	r	$p \supset q$	$q \supset r$	$p \supset r$
T	T	T	T	T	T
F	T	T	T	T	T
T	F	T	F	T	T
F	F	T	T	T	T
T	T	F	T	F	F
F	T	F	T	F	T
T	F	F	F	T	F
F	F	F	T	T	T

stances in which the conclusion is false and that in both of them one of the premises is also false. There is, then, no line and no possibility in which the premises are true and the conclusion false. The argument is, as we have consistently defined validity all along, valid.

10.3 THE EVALUATION CHART AS A TEST OF VALIDITY

The limitations of the truth table for determining validity should be obvious. It requires the construction of a complete truth table with columns for every statement that appears as premise or conclusion in the argument. It is not at all unlikely or unheard of for an argument to involve many more than three 0-level statements as constituents of the various compound statements that make it up. In the absence of a machine to perform the task for us, the complete truth table procedure becomes hopelessly unwieldy in such cases. Fortunately, the principle involved can be applied without need for constructing a complete truth table: we can use an evaluation chart.

The crucial question on which validity turns is this: Is there a possibility, that is, is there at least one line on a truth table in which the premises are true and the conclusion is false? Let us pause for a moment and ask what it is that determines the combinations of truth values that are possible as rows on a truth table. In order for a set of truth values for the various elementary statements and compounds formed from them to be one of the possibilities in a complete truth table, it must be consistent. This means that each elementary statement must preserve the same truth value in every occurrence and that the truth value of every compound must be as required by the truth values of its components and the truth-table definition of the symbol relating them. A set of truth values that does not meet this criterion cannot occur as one of the possible sets on a complete truth table. In determining validity by the truth-table method, we are not concerned with all of the possible rows for their own sakes; we are interested only in knowing if one certain kind of combination is possible, that is, consistent.

It has already been noted that a given pattern of truth values on an evaluation chart corresponds to a row of truth values on a complete truth table. This fact makes it possible to reformulate our question in terms of evaluation charts: Is it possible to construct a consistent pattern of truth values on the evaluation chart in which each of the premises of the argument being tested is assigned the value "true" and the conclusion assigned the value "false"? If it is, there will be such a row on the complete truth table. If not, there will be none; the argument must be valid. The only change in our method of constructing an evaluation chart, a very slight one, is that it will include several compound statements instead of just one. The premises can be partitioned off from the conclusion by a double vertical line and the premises partitioned off from each other by single lines. We can study an example in the following chart, prepared for the principle of hypothetical syllogism:

	$p \supset q$	$q \supset r$	$p \supset r$
0	$\supset$	$\supset$	$\supset$
1			

If we assign F to the conclusion and T to each of the premises (all first-level compounds), it turns out that we must either assign inconsistent values to one of the elementary constituents or assign a truth value to a compound that is contrary to the requirements set by the symbol's truth-table definition. An F under the symbol in the conclusion column requires that it have a T to its left and an F to its right. These same values must then be assigned to the same elementary statements where they occur elsewhere. In order for the premises each to have T beneath them, we must avoid having a T to the left and an F to the right of *their* symbols. But with the values for p and r that have already been fixed, the only way to avoid such a combination is by placing a T under the first occurrence of q and an F under its second occurrence. The original pattern is therefore impossible.

We are now ready to illustrate the same procedure by a more complicated example in which its superiority to the method of constructing a complete truth table is obvious.

$$p \supset (q \text{ v } r)$$
$$s \supset (t \text{ v } u)$$
$$\sim(\sim q \supset t)$$
$$\sim(r \text{ v } u)$$
$$\overline{\sim p \cdot \sim s}$$

The evaluation chart for this argument will look like the following chart.

	Premise 1	*Premise 2*	*Premise 3*	*Premise 4*	*Conclusion*
	0 2 0 1 0 $p \supset (q \text{ v } r)$	0 2 0 1 0 $s \supset (t \text{ v } u)$	3 1 0 2 0 $\sim (\sim q \supset t)$	2 0 1 0 $\sim (r \text{ v } u)$	1 0 2 1 0 $\sim p \cdot \sim s$
0	| v	| v	| $\sim$ |	| v	$\sim$ | $\sim$
1	$\supset$	$\supset$	| $\supset$	$\sim$	·
2			$\sim$		
3					

When *T*'s are placed below the lowest signs in the premise columns and *F* below the last sign in the conclusion column, we are immediately forced to place *F*'s in the spaces that have the $\sim$ over a space with *T* (that is, in the row for truth values of second-level compounds under the third premise and in the row for truth values of first-level compounds under the fourth premise).

In the chart that follows, the assumed values for premises and conclusion on which the test of validity depends are in italics. The values immediately determined by them are in boldface.

	Premise 1	*Premise 2*	*Premise 3*	*Premise 4*	*Conclusion*
	0 2 0 1 0 $p \supset (q \text{ v } r)$	0 2 0 1 0 $s \supset (t \text{ v } u)$	3 1 0 2 0 $\sim (\sim q \supset t)$	2 0 1 0 $\sim (r \text{ v } u)$	1 0 2 1 0 $\sim p \cdot \sim s$
0	| v	| v	| $\sim$ |	| v	$\sim$ | $\sim$
1	$\supset$	$\supset$	| $\supset$	$\sim$ **F**	·
2	*T*	*T*	$\sim$ **F**	*T*	*F*
3			*T*		

For the third premise, we must place a *T* to the left and an *F* to the right of the $\supset$ immediately above. For the fourth premise, we must place an F on each side of the v immediately above. Once the marks just noted have been determined, there are still others that are fixed. Again, on the next chart, marks already determined are in italics and those determined by them in boldface.

Premise 1	Premise 2	Premise 3	Premise 4	Conclusion
0 2 0 1 0 $p \supset (q \lor r)$	0 2 0 1 0 $s \supset (t \lor u)$	3 1 0 2 0 $\sim (\sim q \supset t)$	2 0 1 0 $\sim (r \lor u)$	1 0 2 1 0 $\sim p \cdot \sim s$
0	| v	| v	| ~ |	**F v F**	~ | ~
1	⊃	⊃	| **T ⊃ F**	~ *F*	·
2	*T*	*T*	~ *F*	*T*	*F*
3			*T*		

Now we have reached the row labeled "0"; the values for the elementary constituents r and u, have been fixed; we must assign them consistently wherever else they occur as well.

Premise 1	Premise 2	Premise 3	Premise 4	Conclusion
0 2 0 1 0 $p \supset (q \lor r)$	0 2 0 1 0 $s \supset (t \lor u)$	3 1 0 2 0 $\sim (\sim q \supset t)$	2 0 1 0 $\sim (r \lor u)$	1 0 2 1 0 $\sim p \cdot \sim s$
0	| **v F**	| **v F**	| ~ |	| *F* v *F*	~ | ~
1	⊃	⊃	| *T* ⊃ *F*	~ *F*	·
2	*T*	*T*	~ *F*	*T*	*F*
3			*T*		

One more step (taking into account the values in level one for the third premise) and we fix the values for q and t.

Premise 1	Premise 2	Premise 3	Premise 4	Conclusion
0 2 0 1 0 $p \supset (q \lor r)$	0 2 0 1 0 $s \supset (t \lor u)$	3 1 0 2 0 $\sim (\sim q \supset t)$	2 0 1 0 $\sim (r \lor u)$	1 0 2 1 0 $\sim p \cdot \sim s$
0	| v	| v	| **~F** | **F**	| v	~ | ~
1	⊃	⊃	| *T* ⊃ *F*	~	·
2	*T*	*T*	~ *F*	*T*	*F*
3			*T*		

This has repercussions in the partitions for the first and second premises and ultimately for the conclusion. It can be left to the reader to pursue them until he discovers that the F beneath the conclusion represents a value contrary to what is required by the definition of · and the values assigned to its constituents.

Where the assignment of T to the premises and F to the conclusion does not force an inconsistent assignment of truth values to the elementary constituents or the assignment of a truth value to a compound that is inconsistent with the values that appear for its components, we must conclude that such a pattern of truth values is possible. It therefore will occur on a complete truth table, proving the argument to be invalid. Sometimes there is only one such row, possibly more, perhaps many more. It is a sufficient demonstration of invalidity to have shown that at least one exists. We can do this by showing a pattern on an evaluation chart in which all the requirements of consistency in assigning truth values to 0-level statements and correctness in determining the truth values of compounds have been fulfilled with the premises all assigned T and the conclusion F. The two following examples illustrate invalid arguments. In the first one, there is only one such pattern. As long as the T's beneath the premises and the F beneath the conclusion are all preserved, any other change in the pattern of truth values will result in an inconsistency. As it stands, the pattern is consistent and corresponds to one row of the complete truth table. The argument is consequently invalid.

	Premise 1	*Premise 2*	*Premise 3*	*Conclusion*
	0 3 1 0 2 0 $A \lor (\sim B \cdot C)$	0 3 0 2 1 0 $D \supset (A \cdot \sim C)$	1 0 2 0 $\sim A \lor D$	1 0 $\sim B$
0	$T \mid \sim T \mid F$	$T \mid T \mid \sim F$	$\sim T \mid T$	$\sim T$
1	$T \mid F \cdot F$	$T \mid T \cdot T$	$F \mid T$	F
2	$T \lor F$	$T \supset T$	T	
3	T	T		

In the second example, there are still open possibilities. The truth values written down are all required by the conditions imposed by writing T below the premises and F below the conclusion. The truth value of E is not fixed by those assumptions. They are compatible with either truth value for E, and there will be two rows on the complete truth table in which the premises are true and the conclusion is false:

	Premise 1	Premise 2	Conclusion
	0 1 0 2 0 1 0 $(E \lor F) \supset (G \lor H)$	1 0 3 1 0 2 0 $\sim G \supset (\sim E \cdot F)$	0 1 0 $F \lor H$
0	v F | T v F	~T | | F	F v F
1	⊃ T	F | | · F	F
2	T	F ⊃ F	
3		T	

As the foregoing examples illustrate, in a simple way, the use of the evaluation chart for the purpose of testing the validity of an argument requires some new ways of determining[1] truth values on the chart. Although they are merely derivatives of the basic truth-table definitions, they represent a much more significant addition to the logical repertoire than the relatively minor adjustment in the construction of the chart itself. So far, we have considered how the truth value of a truth-functional compound is determined by the truth values of its constituents. In testing validity, we begin by asking whether it is possible for the compounds that constitute the premises and the conclusion of the argument to have a certain combination of values—*true* for the premises, *false* for the conclusion. We say nothing at the outset concerning the values for the elementary constituents. The problem is not what their assigned values determine about the values of the compounds. We must know whether it is possible to assign a consistent set of values to them that will result in that combination of truth values for premises and conclusion that is crucial to the question of validity.

The basic working pattern on the evaluation chart consists of a single logical sign and the spaces for truth values that are directly related to it. Except in the case of the negation sign, these are the spaces on either side of a sign and directly below it. For the negation sign, they are the spaces directly to its right and directly below it. Under certain circumstances (including that of the negation pattern), a single truth value will determine the other truth values in the pattern. In some circumstances, a single value will determine one of the others by itself, so that the third space in the pattern is open to either truth value, which one being a matter of indifference to the rest of the pattern. To indicate such a situation, we introduce

[1] In what follows, we shall speak of the "determination" of truth values on the chart. It should be understood that this so-called determination is not on the basis of information given initially but only in terms of conditions that are arbitrarily specified for the purpose of deciding whether they are possible.

a special sign *I*. When it appears, the space it occupies can be filled in with either *T* or *F* without affecting the other marks. *I* does not stand for a third truth value but for indifference to whether one truth value or the other is written, the conditions imposed by the logical sign having been already fulfilled. Once we have introduced *I* for this purpose, whenever a single truth value in a pattern does not suffice to determine the other marks, we can use two truth values to determine the third.

The list on page 229 contains the full set of rules governing the determination of marks on the chart. The table below shows the various patterns in which such determinations can be made. (In the table, determinations that represent only the direct application of the truth-table definition of the compound are omitted.)

DETERMINATION OF MARKS ON AN EVALUATION CHART [a]

When the logical sign is:				
~	·	v	⊃	≡
~**F** *T*	**T · T** *T*	**F v F** *F*	**T ⊃ F** *F*	**T ≡ T** *T*
~**T** *F*	*T ·* **F** *F*	*F v* **T** *T*	**F ⊃ F** *T*	**T ≡ T** *T*
~**I** *I*	**F** *· T* *F*	**T** *v F* *T*	*T ⊃* **T** *T*	**F ≡ F** *T*
	F · **I** **F**	*T v* **I** **T**	*F ⊃* **I** **T**	**F** *≡ F* *T*
	I *· F* **F**	**I** *v T* **T**	**I** *⊃ T* **T**	*T ≡* **F** *F*
	I · I *I*	**I v I** *I*	**I ⊃ I** *I*	**F ≡ T** *F*
				F ≡ **T** *F*
				T *≡ F* *F*
				I ≡ I *I*

[a] The marks in boldface are required by the other marks in the pattern.

1. Truth values must be consistent.
2. Any sign with truth values on each side must have below it the truth value required by its definition.
3. Any sign with *I* below it takes *I* on each side.
4. A box with no logical sign must have the same mark as the space below it.
5. A space directly to the right of a negation sign must have the opposite truth value from the space below it.
6. A v with *F* or a · with *T* below it must have that value on each side.
7. A v with *T* or a · with *F* on either side must have the same value below it and takes *I* on the other side.
8. A v with *T* or a · with *F* below it and the opposite value on one side must have the same value (as the one below it) on the other.
9. A ⊃ with *F* below it must have *T* on the left and *F* on the right.
10. A ⊃ with *T* on the right or *F* on the left must have *T* below it and takes *I* on the other side.
11. A ⊃ with *T* below it and *T* on the left or *F* on the right must have the same value on the other side.
12. A ≡ with *T* below it must (or with *F* below it must not) have the same value on each side.

10.4 CONDENSATION OF THE EVALUATION CHART

The concluding example in Section 10.3 is a special and an especially simple case of a more general problem. We can no more expect that the assignment of truth values to the premises and conclusion of an argument will automatically determine every mark on the chart than that it will determine every truth value. Even if the argument is valid, it will not necessarily do so. All that the validity test requires is that it be impossible to fill them all without creating an inconsistency somewhere. In some cases, such an inconsistency can be established *without* determining every value on the chart. In general, the presence of undefined values is an indication of neither validity nor of invalidity. Validity is established only by showing that, on the assumption that the premises are true and the conclusion is false, an inconsistency is forced. Invalidity is established only by showing that, having assigned these values for premises and conclusion, it is still possible to specify every other value on the chart without generating any inconsistency. Even after the initial assumption has resulted in the fixation of some values, as long as some are left undetermined, it is pertinent to ask whether there is a possibility of completing the chart by filling in the undetermined values.

After those values that are determined by assuming the premises true and the conclusion false have been entered in the chart, not all of the blanks will have the same status. Some of them may have been filled in not with a truth value but with the mark *I*. As far as the question on which the validity test turns is concerned, the *I* represents as affirmative an answer as does a definite truth value. In a sense, it is even more affirmative. The presence of a definite truth value in a space is an indication that the chart, as far as this position is concerned, can be filled in consistently if and only if it is filled in with the specified truth value. The presence of an *I* indicates that as far as that position is concerned, it has been established that it is possible to fill it in without creating an inconsistency *no matter which* truth value is specified.

For all spaces occupied by either a definite truth value or an *I*, the question we are interested in has been answered in the affirmative. It *is* possible to fill those spaces without generating an inconsistency. The question that has not yet been settled is whether it is possible to fill all of the remaining spaces without generating an inconsistency somewhere. To answer it, we need consider only the remaining blank spaces and the truth values that are logically tied to them. We can answer the question by assigning first one truth value and then the other to each of the elementary constituents. If it is impossible, on either value assigned, for the evaluation chart to be filled in consistently, the argument will then have been proved valid. If one of the assignments results in a finished and consistent chart, the argument will have been proved invalid. We shall now develop an efficient procedure for determining which of these alternatives is correct in a given case.

At the outset, the blocks on an evaluation chart are all completely open. None of the spaces in which truth values are to be assigned are occupied. Some of the blocks are empty, containing no marks at all; the others contain a single logical sign. We begin the validity test by assigning truth values to the empty blocks at the bottom of each column. To premises, we assign *T* and to the conclusion, *F*. This assignment of values may then determine other marks, *T, F,* or *I,* according to the rules presented in Section 10.3. When those values are filled in, the chart may contain open and closed blocks and some that are half closed. (The expression describes a block with two spaces for truth values, of which only one is occupied.)

All of the blocks on a finished evaluation chart are closed and the question of validity or invalidity is settled. An unfinished chart, which leaves the question still unanswered, contains at least one block that is open or only half closed.

The first step in continuing the validity test when the initial assignment of values to premises and conclusion has not resulted either in an inconsistency or in a finished and consistent chart is to purify the chart of all irrelevant marks. The result will be like the chart in its initial stage. The only closed blocks will be completely closed and will have open blocks above them but none below. First of all, we cross out all portions of closed blocks that do not have an open block above them. The following chart has been so modified:

	Premise 1		Premise 2			Conclusion		
	$A \cdot (B \supset C)$		$[(A \vee C) \supset D] \equiv (\sim B \vee D)$			$\sim C \supset (D \equiv B)$		
0	T	$\supset$	$T \vee I$		$\sim$	$\sim F$		$\equiv$
1	T	T	T	$\supset$	$\vee$	T	$\supset$	F
2	T						F	
3	T			$\equiv$				
4			T					

Now there remains to be eliminated only the half closed block in level 1 of the second column.

Any half closed block can be replaced by an empty block or an open block with a $\sim$ as its logical sign. Consider first of all the half closed blocks that can arise when the value T is filled into one side of an open block. The following possibilities will be represented. (In all other cases, a T on one side of a sign will determine both related marks.)

$$T \cdot \quad \cdot T \quad T \supset \quad T \equiv \quad \equiv T$$

In all of these configurations, the truth value that appears below them will be identical with the truth value that is filled into the single blank space remaining in the half closed block. For example, if we close $T \cdot$ by filling in the blank space with T, a T must appear below. If the same blank space should be filled in by an F, the same value would then appear below the block. So it is with the other four combinations. What this means is that a block containing a T, a logical sign, and a blank space behaves on the chart exactly as if it were an empty space. Whatever value is filled into the blank portion of the compound will appear at the next level below it. Consequently, we can eliminate any such combinations from an evaluation chart without affecting the results. The $T \supset$ in the second column in our example can be crossed out.

We next consider the half closed blocks that can contain an *F*. There are these possibilities:

$$F \text{ v} \qquad \text{v } F \qquad \supset F \qquad F \equiv \qquad \equiv F$$

Whichever value is filled into the first two, those with a v on either side of the truth value, the same value will appear below. An *F* with a v on either side behaves like an empty block. Such a combination can be crossed out and the blank space remaining will provide for results identical with those that would have been produced by the half closed block. The other three possibilities, in which *F* appears in combination with ⊃ or ≡, cannot be treated as equivalent to empty blocks. In each of these cases, the truth value of the entire compound will be the *opposite* of the truth value filled into the blank space. For example, if the blank space at the left of ⊃ *F* is filled in with a *T*, the opposite truth value, *F*, will appear in the level below. If it is filled in by an *F*, a *T* will appear below. These half closed blocks are consequently equivalent to open blocks in which ∼ is the logical sign. Any such combination of F with ⊃ or ≡ can be crossed out and replaced by a ∼ written at the left of the remaining blank space.

The purification of an unfinished evaluation chart by eliminating irrelevant closed and half closed blocks involves, as we have seen, the three steps listed below:

1. Crossing out all closed blocks and portions of closed blocks that do not have an open block above them.
2. Crossing out the marks in half closed blocks containing *T* or v.
3. Crossing out the marks in half closed blocks containing *F* combined with ⊃ or ≡ and writing a ∼ at the left of the remaining blank space.

The following chart illustrates all the procedures used in purifying the unfinished evaluation chart resulting from the initial assignment of values to the premises and conclusion:

	Premise 1	*Premise 2*	*Conclusion*
	$(A \supset B) \text{ v } (C \supset \sim A)$	$(A \text{ v } B) \supset (C \text{ v } D)$	$A \supset [B \cdot (C \text{ v } \sim D)]$
0	T ⊃ | ∼T	T v I | v	T | | | ∼
1	| ⊃ F	T ⊃ T	T | | | v
2	v	T	T | ·
3	T		T ⊃ F
4			F

The values indicated are those that result from assigning *T* to both premises (P1 and P2) and *F* to the conclusion (C). The truth value of *A* is thereby determined, since it is the antecedent of the conclusion, a hypothetical statement. The same value is assigned to *A* wherever it calls for a value at the 0 level, and other values are then determined accordingly.

The 0 level now includes three closed blocks: $\sim T$ in P1, $T \vee I$ in P2, and *T* in the conclusion. Since none of them stand underneath an open block, they are all to be crossed out. They have no further relevance in the determination of truth values. The 0 level also contains a half closed block, $T \supset$, in P1. It is still relevant to the determination of values, but it functions as a blank space does. It too can be crossed out; the empty portion of the block will suffice. When the procedures just described have been carried out, the 0 level on the evaluation chart will look like the following example.

	Premise 1			Premise 2				Conclusion	
0	$T \supset$		$\sim T$	$T \vee I$	v	T			$\sim$

In level 1, in the column for the first premise, we again encounter a half closed block: $\supset F$. Such a pattern performs the same function as an open block with $\sim$ on its left. We can replace it by that arrangement. Level 1 in column P2 is a closed block. It cannot be entirely eliminated, since the truth value on the right stands beneath an open block. The portion $T \supset$, which does not have an open block above it, has no further relevance and can be crossed out. We can also cross out the truth value under *A* in the conclusion. Level 1 should then look like the figure below.

	Premise 1			Premise 2				Conclusion	
1		$\sim$	$\supset F$	T	$\supset$	T	T		v

The result of purifying the entire evaluation chart of irrelevancies is depicted in Section 10.5. There we shall consider how to proceed with the validity test with the chart still incomplete but reduced to those marks and spaces that are significant to the purpose.

10.5 COMPLETION OF THE VALIDITY TEST

We now have to consider an evaluation chart that resembles the original chart in the following respect: it consists of columns of open blocks above single truth values. The truth values at the bottom of the columns determine no values in the blocks above them, however. We can continue the validity test only by trying first one value and then the other for each elementary constituent in turn, until a decision is settled.

If we assign a truth value to one of the elementary statements and determine the other marks fixed by that assignment, we can obtain three possible results. They are the same three that had to be considered when we made the initial assignment of truth values to premises and conclusion:

1. An inconsistency will be generated.
2. The values for all the remaining blanks will be filled in without inconsistency.
3. Some of the blanks will remain either open or only half closed.

If the initial assignment of truth values generates an inconsistency, this is sufficient by itself to prove validity. If the choice of one value for an elementary statement generates an inconsistency, validity has not yet been established. It is still possible, perhaps, for the other truth value for the same elementary statement to permit a consistent chart to be completed. If an inconsistency is generated when both values are assigned, it constitutes a demonstration of validity.

The other two possibilities have the same significance as when they result from the assignment of truth values to premises and conclusion. A chart that is completely filled in without any inconsistency proves the argument to be invalid. (We are always presupposing, of course, the initial assignment of T to all premises and F to the conclusion.) A chart that is incompletely filled in calls for further investigation.

We can use the example from Section 10.4 to illustrate each of the possible outcomes that we have just identified. The elementary statements for which truth values are as yet undetermined on the chart that results from the initial assignment of values are B, C, and D. If we take B to be true, the result will be a completed and consistent chart. If we take C to be true, an inconsistency is generated. If we assume D to be true, the chart will remain incomplete. Ultimately, of course, a complete and consistent chart will emerge no matter which of these choices is adopted. It is just that that result comes about directly if we assign T to statement B, not upon assigning T to either of the other elementary statements. The full application of the procedures introduced in Section 10.4 would produce the following chart:

	Premise 1				Premise 2			Conclusion			
	$(A \supset B)$ v	$(C \supset \sim A)$			$(A$ v $B)$ $\supset$ $(C$ v $D)$			$A \supset [B$ · $(C$ v $\sim D)]$			
0	$T \supset$		$\sim T$		T v I		v	T			$\sim$
1		$\sim$	$\supset \acute{F}$		T	$\supset$	T	T		v	
2	v				T			T			
3	T							$T \supset$	F		
4								F			

Were we to assign to statement *B*, the value "true" and then determine values accordingly, the chart would be completed as is the following one.

	Premise 1			Premise 2		Conclusion			
	(A ⊃ B) v (C ⊃ ~ A)			(A v B) ⊃ (C v D)		A ⊃ [B · (C v ~ D)]			
0	*T* ⊃ *T*	*F*	~ *T*	*T* v *I*	*F* v *T*	*T*	*T*	*F*	~ *T*
1	*T*	~*F* ⊃ *F*		*T* ⊃ *T*		*T*	*T*	*F* v *F*	
2	*T* v *T*			*T*		*T*	*T* ·	*F*	
3	*T*					*T* ⊃	*F*		
4						*F*			

The result we have obtained by assigning to *B* the value "true" is sufficient for a validity test. The argument has been shown to be invalid and there is no need for any further investigation. We proceed to the other elementary statements solely for purposes of illustration. The assignment of "true" to statement *C* permits no consistent completion of the chart. Somewhere an inconsistency will be generated; if it is repaired, another inconsistency will be forced somewhere else. The pattern of truth values that emerges most directly upon assigning *T* to statement *C* is illustrated in the following chart:

	Premise 1			Premise 2		Conclusion			
	(A ⊃ B) v (C ⊃ ~ A)			(A v B) ⊃ (C v D)		A ⊃ [B · (C v ~ D)]			
0	*T* ⊃ *T*	*T*	~ *T*	*T* v *I*	*T* v *T*	*T*	*F*	*T*	~ *I*
1	*T*	~*T* ⊃ *F*		*T* ⊃ *T*		*T*	*F*	*T* v *I*	
2	*T* v *F*			*T*		*T*	*F*	*T*	
3	*T*					*T* ⊃	*F*		
4						*F*			

B has been assigned inconsistent truth values (*T* in the column for the first premise and *F* in the conclusion). It is necessary to continue the validity test by trying the assignment of *F* to statement *C*. The result would be a complete and consistent chart in this case.

The need for trying the assignment of *F* to statement *C* presents a difficulty. The original chart has already been filled in with values determined by the assignment of *T* to *C*. We must either identify or erase those marks, or we must construct a new chart. Either alternative represents an inefficient method we would do well to avoid. Fortunately, a more efficient approach is available. When truth values are assigned on a chart and other values determined by them written in also, the resulting chart can be purified by the procedures introduced in the preceding section. We can therefore represent the result of assigning a truth value to an elementary constituent by the condensed chart produced by determining values accordingly and thereupon eliminating any irrelevant marks.

A subsidiary condensed chart representing the outcome of assigning the value T to a given elementary statement can be constructed by identifying all of the areas on the chart that would be eliminated as irrelevant when the chart is purified. The condensed chart would include only those portions of the original not so identified. These areas can be distinguished if we apply the following set of instructions.

We begin by approaching a space in the 0 level directly below an occurrence of the elementary statement we have chosen to work with and move to the area directly below it. Having done this, we must next carry out the following instructions, as they become applicable:

1. If the box of which the area is a part is blank, or contains a v on either side or contains a $\supset$ to the left, we continue to the area immediately below the box and continue to follow these instructions (1–4).

2. If the box contains a · or a $\equiv$ on either side or a $\supset$ on the right, we draw a line under the box as far as the logical sign, including it but not the area on the other side of it.

3. If the box contains a T, we draw a line under the entire box. If it contains an F, an inconsistency has been generated; we try to assign F to the selected elementary constituent on the original chart.

4. If the box contains a $\sim$, we continue to the area immediately below the box, and apply the following instructions:

    A. If the box contains no logical sign, or a · on either side or a $\supset$ on the right, we continue to the area immediately below and continue to follow these instructions (A–D).

    B. If the box contains a v we draw a line under the box as far as the logical sign, including it but not the area on the other side. If it contains a $\equiv$ on either side or a $\supset$ on the left, we draw such a line *and* place a $\sim$ in the area on the subsidiary chart that corresponds to the area not underlined.

    C. If it contains an F, we draw a line under the entire box. If it contains a T, an inconsistency has been generated; we try to assign F to the selected elementary constituent on the original chart.

> D. If it contains a ∼, we continue to the area immediately below the box and apply the original set of instructions (those numbered 1–4).

We are to apply these rules until all occurrences of the selected elementary constituent have been dealt with. All those portions of the original chart that do not stand above one of the lines we have drawn are to be reproduced as a subsidiary chart. Values can then be determined as called for on the subsidiary chart, which abstractly offers the same possibilities as the original: a completed and consistent chart, an inconsistency, or a chart in which some spaces have not yet been filled in. These possibilities have the same significance we have attached to them already.

The subsidiary chart that we would produce upon assigning *T* to statement *C* would be quite simple. Illustrated first is the result of having drawn lines under portions of the chart according to the instructions we have just presented.

	Premise 1			*Premise 2*			*Conclusion*			
	$(A \supset B)$ v $(C \supset \sim A)$			$(A \lor B) \supset (C \lor D)$			$A \supset [B \cdot (C \lor \sim D)]$			
0	*T* ⊃		∼ *T*	*T* v *I*		v	*T*			∼
1		∼	⊃ *F*	*T*	⊃	*T*	*T*			v
2		v			*T*		*T*		·	
3		*T*					*T* ⊃		*F*	
4							*F*			

When only those portions of the chart that have not had lines drawn beneath them are reproduced, very little of the original chart remains:

	Premise 1	*Premise 2*	*Conclusion*
	B		B
0			
1			
2			
3	T		F

The inconsistency is obvious, and we would proceed immediately to try the assignment of *F* to the same statement on the original chart.

We have now considered the results of selecting first *B* and then *C* as the elementary constituent to be provisionally assumed true. There remains

D. The selection of *D* produces a different result from either of the preceding illustrations. The outcome is neither a complete and consistent assignment of marks nor an inconsistency but a subsidiary chart in which some spaces remain empty. Again, we show first the full chart with the underlining called for by selecting *D* to be assumed true. The second is the subsidiary chart that is created by reproducing only those portions of the full chart that do not stand above one of those lines:

	Premise 1				*Premise 2*			*Conclusion*		
	$(A \supset B)$ v $(C \supset \sim A)$				$(A$ v $B) \supset (C$ v $D)$			$A \supset [B \cdot (C$ v $\sim D)]$		
0	*T* ⊃			~ *T*	*T* v *l*		v	*T*		~
1		~ ⊃ *F*			*T*	⊃	*T*	*T*		v
2		v				*T*			*T*		·
3		*T*							*T* ⊃	*F*	
4									*F*		

	Premise 1		*Premise 2*	*Conclusion*	
	B v	*C*		*B* ·	*C*
0					·
1		~			
2	v			·	
3	*T*			*F*	

To sum up this discussion, we note that subsidiary charts are dealt with by the same procedures as the original charts: we determine all marks that can be determined. From here on, if we find it is necessary to go on, we apply the usual principles. If the blanks are filled in consistently, invalidity is shown. If an inconsistency arises in a subsidiary chart, we must assign the value *F* to the selected elementary constituent of the chart from which it was derived, determine truth values, and begin the process again. If blanks remain, we create a new subsidiary chart, and so on. Again, it is to be emphasized that only a highly artificial or complicated argument would require the procedure to be continued at length. It is in fact a particularly powerful procedure providing a rapid determination of validity or invalidity for even very complex arguments.

10.5 EXERCISES

Using evaluation charts, determine the validity or invalidity of the following arguments.

A. $O \supset (P \cdot M)$
$M \supset \sim P$
——————
$\sim O$

B. $A \supset (B \vee C)$
$B \supset (A \vee C)$
$\sim C$
——————
A

C. $A \vee B$
$C \cdot \sim A$
——————
$B \vee D$

D. $I \supset (J \vee K)$
$J \supset (K \supset L)$
$\sim L$
——————
$\sim K$

E. $A \supset \sim(B \vee C)$
$B \supset (C \supset D)$
$\sim D \supset \sim C$
——————
$A \cdot C$

F. $\sim(C \vee B)$
$D \vee B$
$\sim(D \supset A)$
——————
$A \vee C$

G. $(A \vee B) \supset C$
$\sim(C \cdot A)$
$A \equiv \sim D$
$D \supset (B \vee C)$
$(E \vee D) \supset B$
$B \supset [F \cdot (A \vee E)]$
——————
$C \supset A$

H. If March comes in like a lion, it goes out like a lamb; and if March comes in like a lion and goes out like a lamb, there are floods in April. There were no floods in April, therefore it is false that March came in like a lion.

Chapter 11

PRINCIPLES OF
INFERENCE AND PROOFS

In Chapter 10, we have seen how the validity or invalidity of an argument can be determined on a truth table or, more economically, on an evaluation chart. These methods both fall within the second of the three general methods we distinguished at the beginning of our discussion of validity. They are both truth-value tests. The first method we distinguished was the appeal to common-sense judgment. The third involved the use of indirect inference, so far illustrated in derivations of conclusions from premises using the language and basic rules of inference from traditional logic. In this chapter, we will both present a set of basic principles of inference for compound statement and consider their application in the construction of proofs.

We will recall that in order to apply the technique of indirect inference in demonstrating the validity of an argument, we must have at our disposal a set of basic principles that have already been established by some other method (or that we may have laid down arbitrarily). These principles provide the justification for each of the successive steps in a proof by indirect inference. The system we studied in Part One presented five such principles, the four principles of immediate inference (CONTRAD, LIM, CONV, and OBV) and the principle of the syllogism (SYL). Because of the greater complexity of the system of truth-functional compounds, we will need more basic principles to appeal to. In fact, we shall introduce more such principles than we actually need, since some of them could be established by indirect inferences justified by the others. Since our aim is not so much ultimate theoretical simplicity as it is usefulness in analyzing common types of argument, there need be no objection to the procedure.

11.1 THE PRINCIPLE OF REPLACEMENT

The first principle we will consider is the "principle of replacement."

> If two statements are equivalent, either one may be put in place of the other.

We have already made use of the same principle in extending the scope of the rules of the syllogism so as to determine the validity of arguments not in standard form (see Section 5.3). There will be no harm in recalling the considerations that we cited then in justifying it. We have defined validity in terms of possible combinations of truth values. Any change in an argument that leaves unchanged the possible combinations of truth values for its constituent premises and conclusion will not affect the argument's validity. But in saying that two statements are logically equivalent, what we mean is they must have the same truth value. Replacing the one with the other will have no effect on the validity of any argument, therefore. We should note that a statement can be replaced by one of its equivalents whether it stands alone or as a constituent of a statement with a higher level of complexity. Since all compounds in the system are truth functional, the truth value of the compound will not be affected by a change that does not affect the truth values of its constituents.

Because there are various useful cases of equivalence between compound statements, we do not cite the "principle of replacement" when we apply it to justify one of the steps in an indirect inference. Instead, we identify the particular pattern of equivalence making the principle applicable. The types of equivalence patterns we are to use for truth-functional compounds are discussed in the following pages.

Association (ASSOC)

All compound statements in which the same constituents are related by
a v only or by a · only are equivalent no matter what way the constituents
are associated in groups by parentheses.

$(p \cdot q) \cdot r$ and $p \cdot (q \cdot r)$ and $p \cdot q \cdot r$ are all equivalent. So are: $(p \vee q) \vee r$
and $p \vee (q \vee r)$ and $p \vee q \vee r$.

There are three points that we should note before going on to the other
equivalences, although they will apply there also. First, it is not quite
accurate to say that the expressions exhibited are equivalent. The constituents of the expressions, p, q, and r, are not statements but statement-
variables, as previously noted in Chapter 10. They are places in which
statements (of any kind) may be inserted. Consequently, it is more exact
to say that any statements formed by consistently replacing the statement-
variables in those expressions by statements will be equivalent. Thus, if
A, B, and C represent statements, we could justify the replacement of
$(A \vee B) \vee C$ by $A \vee (B \vee C)$ by citing the principle of association.

The second point to note is that in the third line of each example,
$(p \cdot q \cdot r \cdot$ and $p \vee q \vee r)$, there is a pattern that we could describe as multiple conjunction or disjunction. Our truth-table definitions of conjunction
and disjunction introduced these relations for pairs of constituents. A
pattern in which the conjunction sign appears more than once, linking a
set of constituents without any internal grouping by parentheses at all,
can be understood as an extension of simple conjunction. Like simple
conjunction, the multiple conjunction is false if any one of its constituents
is false; otherwise it is true. In similar fashion, a multiple disjunction is
true if any one of its constituents is true; otherwise it is false.

The third point is that in a specific application of this principle, the constituents of the conjunction or disjunction may be compound statements
themselves. Thus, we can replace $(A \cdot X) \vee (B \vee C)$ by $[(A \cdot X) \vee B] \vee C$,
citing the principle of association. As far as the application of that principle
is concerned, $(A \cdot X)$ merely functions as one of the disjuncts. Its own
internal complexity is ignored. We may now turn to the rest of the equivalences to be used in connection with the principle of replacement:

Commutation (COMM)

All compound statements in which the same constituents are related by
a v only or by a · only are equivalent, no matter in what order the constituents appear.

To take the simplest examples, $(p \cdot q)$ and $(q \cdot p)$ are equivalent; $(p \vee q)$ and $(q \vee p)$ are equivalent.

Tautology (TAUT)

Any conjunction or disjunction in which the constituents are the same statement is equivalent to that statement.

$p \vee p$ is equivalent to p

$p \cdot p$ is equivalent to p

Double Negation (DN)

Any compound formed by attaching an even number of $\sim$'s to a statement is equivalent to that statement.

$\sim \sim p$ is equivalent to p

DeMorgan's Theorems (DeM)

The negation of a disjunction is equivalent to the conjunction of its negated constituents. Similarly, the negation of a conjunction is equivalent to the disjunction of its negated constituents.

$\sim(p \cdot q)$ is equivalent to $\sim p \vee \sim q$

$\sim(p \vee q)$ is equivalent to $\sim p \cdot \sim q$

Definition of Material Implication (MI)

A material implication is equivalent to the disjunction of its negated antecedent with its consequent.

$p \supset q$ is equivalent to $\sim p \vee q$

Definition of Material Equivalence (ME)

A material equivalence is equivalent to the conjunction of two implications in which the constituents of the material equivalence are respectively antecedent and consequent in one and consequent and antecedent in the other.

$(p \equiv q)$ is equivalent to $(p \supset q) \cdot (q \supset p)$

An alternative, which practical considerations make it useful to include, is provided by first conjoining the two constituents of the material equivalence, then conjoining their negations, and then making a disjunction with these two compounds as its constituents.

$(p \equiv q)$ is equivalent to $(p \cdot q) \vee (\sim p \cdot \sim q)$

Distribution (DIST)

The conjunction of two disjunctions is equivalent to the disjunction of all the conjunctions formed by pairing each constituent of the one with each constituent of the other. Similarly, the disjunction of two conjunctions is equivalent to the conjunction of all the disjunctions formed by pairing each constituent of the one with each constituent of the other.

a. $(p \cdot q) \vee (r \cdot s)$ is equivalent to
$$(p \vee r) \cdot (p \vee s) \cdot (q \vee r) \cdot (q \vee s)$$

b. $(p \vee q) \cdot (r \vee s)$ is equivalent to
$$(p \cdot r) \vee (p \cdot s) \vee (q \cdot r) \vee (q \cdot s)$$

SPECIAL CASES

c. $p \vee (q \cdot r)$ is equivalent to $(p \vee q) \cdot (p \vee r)$

d. $p \cdot (q \vee r)$ is equivalent to $(p \cdot q) \vee (p \cdot r)$

These latter two special cases can easily be derived from the general cases listed as *a* and *b,* under distribution, by applying the principle of tautology. In fact, *a* and *b* are themselves special cases of a still more general form in which the principle of distribution could be exhibited. We have already accepted the possibility of writing statements in the form of multiple conjunctions or multiple disjunctions. (See the discussion in connection with the principle of association.) Cases *a* and *b* represent the form taken by DIST when the conjunctions and disjunctions are simple, having only two constituents. The rule as stated could apply just as well to multiple conjunctions and disjunctions. We could then represent the most general form for one kind of case as follows:

$$(p_1 \vee p_2 \vee \ldots p_m) \cdot (q_1 \vee q_2 \vee \ldots q_n)$$

is equivalent to

$$(p_1 \cdot q_1) \vee (p_1 \cdot q_2) \vee \ldots (p_1 \cdot q_n) \vee (p_2 \cdot q_1)$$
$$\vee (p_2 \cdot q_2) \vee \ldots \vee (p_2 \cdot q_n) \vee \ldots$$
$$\vee (p_m \cdot q_1) \vee (p_m \cdot q_2) \vee \ldots \vee (p_m \cdot q_n)$$

Students of mathematics will recognize the procedure followed in multiplying sums. Unlike mathematics, where the sum of two products is not subject to the same rule, in applying the principle of distribution, we can construct an equivalent for the disjunction of two conjunctions by the same method, merely reversing the roles played by the $\cdot$ and the $\vee$.

Exportation (EXP)

A hypothetical statement with a conjunction as its antecedent is equivalent to a statement in which the conjunction sign has been replaced by an implication sign (the $\cdot$ by the $\supset$) and the original indices of complexity have been reversed.

$$\overset{1}{}\overset{2}{}\qquad\qquad\overset{2}{}\overset{1}{}$$
$$(p \cdot q) \supset r \text{ is equivalent to } p \supset (q \supset r)$$

Transposition (TRANS)

A hypothetical statement is equivalent to another hypothetical statement with the same constituents negated and in the opposite order.

$$p \supset q \text{ is equivalent to } \sim q \supset \sim p$$

SPECIAL CASE: *Partial Transposition*

By combining the principles of exportation and transposition, we can arrive at a special principle, which might be identified as partial transposition but which will be justified in particular occurrences in indirect inference merely by reference to the principle of transposition (TRANS) itself. Partial transposition represents the equivalence of a hypothetical statement that has a conjunction as its antecedent with another hypothetical statement in which the consequent and one of the conjuncts have both been negated and have exchanged places. For example,

$$(p \cdot q) \supset r \quad \text{and} \quad (p \cdot \sim r) \supset \sim q$$

constitute an equivalent pair.

11.2 BASIC ARGUMENT FORMS

The principles of equivalence or various equivalence patterns that we have just introduced are all intended to provide occasions for the application of a single "rule of replacement," which permits the substitution of any statement or constituent of a statement with another expression that is equivalent to it. We proceed now to a presentation of what are more properly the "principles of inference" or "basic argument forms" of the system.

1. *Simplification* (SIMP)

Any constituent or group of constituents of a set of conjoined statements may be inferred from that set given as a premise.

$$\frac{p_1 \cdot p_2 \cdot p_3 \cdot \ldots \cdot p_n}{p_1}$$

or p_2

or $p_1 \cdot p_2$

and so on

2. *Conjunction* (CONJ)

From any set of statements asserted separately, the conjunction of the same set of statements may be inferred.

$$\frac{p_1, \; p_2, \; p_3, \; \ldots, \; p_n}{p_1 \cdot p_2 \cdot p_3 \cdot \ldots \cdot p_n}$$

3. *Addition* (ADD)

From any statement, a disjunction including that statement as one of its disjuncts may be inferred.

$$\frac{p}{p \vee q}$$

4. *Absorption* (ABS)

Any statement may be conjoined to both sides of an implication.

$$\frac{p \supset q}{(p \cdot r) \supset (q \cdot r)}$$

SPECIAL CASE (derivable by conjoining the antecedent to both sides and applying tautology and commutation respectively to the two sides of the result):

$$\frac{p \supset q}{p \supset (p \cdot q)}$$

5. *Hypothetical Syllogism* (HS)

From any two hypothetical statements such that the consequent of the first is the antecedent of the second, a hypothetical conclusion that has the antecedent of the first as antecedent and the consequent of the second as consequent may be inferred.

$$\frac{\begin{array}{c} p \supset q \\ q \supset r \end{array}}{p \supset r}$$

The general principle to be stated here is not given a separate name of its own. Instead, names are given to two special cases, as indicated below. From two premises, the constituents of which are respectively a set of one or more hypothetical statements, and the set composed of their antecedents, a conclusion can be inferred having as its constituents all of their consequents, subject to the following conditions:

6. The conclusion will be a conjunction if both premises are conjunctions:

$$\frac{\begin{array}{c} (p_1 \supset q_1) \cdot (p_2 \supset q_2) \cdot \ldots \cdot (p_n \supset q_n) \\ p_1 \cdot p_2 \cdot \ldots \cdot p_n \end{array}}{q_1 \cdot q_2 \cdot \ldots \cdot q_n}$$

SPECIAL CASE: *Modus Ponens* (MP)

$$p \supset q$$
$$\underline{p}$$
$$q$$

That is, this is the special case when there is only one hypothetical statement. The general pattern could be derived from it by using the principles of simplification and conjunction.

7. The conclusion will be a disjunction if either premise is a disjunction and the other premise a conjunction.

a. $(p_1 \supset q_1) \vee (p_2 \supset q_2) \vee \ldots \vee (p_n \supset q_n)$
$$\underline{p_1 \cdot p_2 \cdot \ldots \cdot p_n}$$
$$q_1 \vee q_2 \vee \ldots \vee q_n$$

b. $(p_1 \supset q_1) \cdot (p_2 \supset q_2) \cdot \ldots \cdot (p_n \supset q_n)$
$$\underline{p_1 \vee p_2 \vee \ldots \vee p_n}$$
$$q_1 \vee q_2 \vee \ldots \vee q_n$$

SPECIAL CASE: *Constructive Dilemma* (CD)

$$(p_1 \supset q_1) \cdot (p_2 \supset q_2)$$
$$\underline{p_1 \vee p_2}$$
$$q_1 \vee q_2$$

The principles still to be separately identified could all be thought of as being derived according to a formula reminiscent of the principle of partial transposition—they can be constructed by negating the conclusion and one of the premises of an argument form already given and exchanging their places.

8. *Modus Tollens* (MT)

From a hypothetical statement together with the negation of its consequent, the negation of its antecedent may be inferred.

$$p \supset q$$
$$\underline{\sim q}$$
$$\sim p$$

Modus tollens has the relation described to modus ponens. The second (nonhypothetical) premise and the conclusion have been negated and exchanged.

9. *Destructive Dilemma* (DD)

From a premise that conjoins two hypotheticals and another premise

that disjoins the negations of their consequents, a conclusion can be derived
disjoining the negations of their antecedents.

$$(p_1 \supset q_1) \cdot (p_2 \supset q_2)$$
$$\underline{\sim q_1 \lor \sim q_2}$$
$$\sim p_1 \lor \sim p_2$$

Destructive dilemma, we might note, is *not* a derivative from constructive
dilemma by the formula now being applied. Its original would be the
anonymous argument form in which both premises are conjunctions.

$$(p_1 \supset q_1) \cdot (p_2 \supset q_2)$$
$$\underline{p_1 \cdot p_2}$$
$$q_1 \cdot q_2$$

If the second premise and the conclusion are negated and exchanged (and
replaced with equivalents according to DeMorgan's theorems) the result
will be the form identified as destructive dilemma.

10. *Disjunctive Syllogism* (DS)

From a disjunction and the negation of all but one of its constituents, the
remaining constituent may be inferred. In the simplest case:

$$p \lor q$$
$$\underline{\sim p}$$
$$q$$

This principle is derived by the formula from the principle of conjunction, together with some equivalences. We can begin by applying the principle of conjunction to the two premises, $\sim p$ and $\sim q$. The resulting conclusion will be $\sim p \cdot \sim q$. By negating the conclusion and the second
premise and exchanging the results, we obtain

$$\sim(\sim p \cdot \sim q)$$
$$\underline{\sim p}$$
$$\sim \sim q$$

DeMorgan's theorems and double negation reveal that this form of argument is equivalent to disjunctive syllogism as we just demonstrated. Addition and simplification have a similar, and even simpler, relationship to
each other. We can turn the one form into the other by negating and exchanging premise and conclusion and applying DeMorgan's theorems and
double negation.

We have assumed in the presentation of the basic principles of inference
that there might be some interest in the kind of relationships among them

that have just been illustrated. In fact, they can all be demonstrated directly and independently by appeal to a truth table or evaluation chart. There are complications to this procedure when an indefinite number of constituents are involved. This problem will be taken up in connection with rules for quantified statements, where it has a special significance (see Section 12.8).

11.3 PROOF OF VALIDITY BY INDIRECT INFERENCE

Using one of the basic principles of inference to justify each step, we will now be able to demonstrate, by indirect inference, the validity of any valid argument composed of truth-functional compound statements and their elementary constituents. This is the strategic conception of the present system, as it was the strategic conception of the system using only **A, E, I,** and **O** statements. The construction of an appropriate series of steps leading from the premises to the conclusion is a tactical exercise. Because of the greater number of principles to draw on in the present system, that task presents us with a more complex and difficult problem than it did in the former system. There, we were able to give a general "program" for analysis; now, we shall have to be satisfied with something less than that. There will be a proportionately greater need for insight and ingenuity.

In developing a ready insight into an effective route leading from the premises to the conclusion of an argument, there is no substitute for practice. But the process will be facilitated if there are at least a few guiding principles for us to follow. The first point of reference from which we will work is the conclusion, which is the objective of the proof to be constructed. Its nature will suggest to us what basic principle of inference could be applied in order to derive it directly. We can then ask what are the premises needed in order to apply that principle. If one or more of them is given originally as one of the premises, we need look no further. If any of the needed premises is not given, it becomes an objective itself; we can treat it as if it were a conclusion to be derived. The same process can be repeated until every strand in the proof has made connections with the original premises. The proof itself then becomes merely a matter of retracing the steps that we have ascertained in this way.

We have made no specification for standard form for arguments in the system of compound statements, except that all statements in an argument must fall within the appropriate language. They must be either elementary statements or compounds formed by the truth-functional symbols of the system. (Remember that within this system, the statements of logical English are elementary statements. When we apply the rules of inference for truth-functional compounds, any such statement, although it may have its own kind of internal complexity, functions as if it were a simple letter.) For the traditional system, a complete argument in standard form was in the proper order and pairs of complementary terms and statements beginning with "It is false that" had been eliminated. The elimination of pairs of complementary terms and negations was by far the more important procedure: until we had done that, we could not apply the rules governing validity. The arrangement of the argument's constituents in a standard order was more a matter of convenience than one of principle.

We obtained standard form by replacing statements with their equivalents according to the principles of conversion, obversion, and contradiction. If we could think of these as principles of equivalence functioning under a rule of replacement, we might then think of an argument as in standard form when it is no longer necessary to make use of the rule of replacement. Possibly, we would be stretching the idea of standard form excessively to say that, in the system of compound statements, only those arguments that do not require the replacement of any statement by an equivalent are in standard form. That is a matter of terminology on which we need not linger. Still, it will be useful to begin the study of the technique of devising an appropriate scheme of indirect inference with arguments of that sort. Once the knack of dealing with them has been acquired, it will be easier for us to extend the technique to cases in which the rule of replacement and one or more of the various principles of equivalence required for its application are involved.

As a general rule, an argument will not require the application of the rule of replacement if the same groups of letters in it are combined in the same way with the same connective symbols. For example, if A and B form a compound with a v in one place, they should not form a compound with a $\sim$ and a $\cdot$ somewhere else. This is not without exceptions; it will, however, serve our present purposes, which aim more at practical utility than theoretical precision. In such an argument, the principle of inference required for the direct inference to the conclusion will be determined initially by the conclusion's own logical form. If the conclusion is simple, the principle must be one of those giving such a conclusion. If it is compound, the very same structure may or may not be found somewhere within the premises. If it is, we may treat it as if it were simple. If it is not, the principal connective symbol (that is, the one to which the highest index of complexity must be assigned) determines the principle of inference we must use to derive it. If it is an implication, we are restricted to the principle of hypothetical syllogism; if it is a disjunction, we must choose between addition and dilemma; if it is a conjunction, the principle of conjunction; if a negation, modus tollens.

Where there is a choice, we can usually indicate the correct principle by comparing the conclusion with the premises and noting the role it or its constituents play there. When the conclusion is simple, we are offered a choice of modus tollens, simplification, or disjunctive syllogism. Which we are to apply at the final step will obviously depend on whether the conclusion is the constituent of an implication, a conjunction, or a disjunction somewhere in the premises. The choice between dilemma and addition, where the conclusion is a disjunctive compound, may not be quite so clear in all cases; we can, however, expect it to be so in most of them. Dilemma, for example, seems clearly called for if the constituents of the conclusion are consequents of two implications somewhere in the premises.

Once we have ascertained the nature of the last step in this way, we can determine the sort of premises needed for it. Once they are determined, we are in a position to raise the same question for each of them that we raised originally for the conclusion. Given the nature of each one, simple or a certain type of compound, we can consider which of the basic principles of inference would be likely to produce it. In other words, we have moved our task one step back. By continuing the process, we shall ultimately arrive at a point where whatever premises are needed are supplied in the set originally given; we can retrace the steps in a proof.

The procedure can be understood more easily in terms of an illustrative example than in an abstract description. Here is an indirect inference with all of the steps leading from the premises to the conclusion filled in:

1.	$P \supset (S \cdot M)$	Premise
2.	$S \supset [C \supset (Q \vee L)]$	Premise
3.	$\sim A \supset C$	Premise
4.	P	Premise
5.	$D \vee \sim A$	Premise
6.	$\sim D$	Premise
7.	$\sim A$	5, 6, DS
8.	C	3, 7, MP
9.	$S \cdot M$	1, 4, MP
10.	S	9, SIMP
11.	$C \supset (Q \vee L)$	2, 10, MP
12.	$Q \vee L$	11, 8, MP

The derivation is correct as it stands. Let us consider how it could have been constructed. The process is indicated in the following dialogue.

Q. Look at the conclusion. What sort of statement is it?
            A. Compound, disjunctive.
Q. Does the same compound occur in the premises?
            A. Yes.
Q. Then we may treat it as if it were simple. Where does it occur in the premises?
            A. As the consequent of a hypothetical statement.
Q. Then it will be derived by applying modus ponens. What premises will be needed?
            A. The hypothetical in which the compound is the consequent and the antecedent of that hypothetical.
Q. Which are?
            A. $C \supset (Q \vee L)$ and C.
Q. The last line of the proof will include the conclusion, numbers representing these two statements as premises of the direct inference and the abbreviation MP for the principle of inference that justifies it. Is either of the two statements required as premises originally given as a premise?
            A. No, it will be necessary to derive both of them.
Q. Let us begin with the hypothetical. Does it occur anywhere among the premises?
            A. Yes, as the consequent of Premise 2, a hypothetical statement.
Q. Then we can derive it by applying modus ponens. Beside Premise 2, we shall need its antecedent. What is that?
            A. S.

So far we know what the last two lines of the proof will look like, except that we have not yet determined the proper numbers for statements that we must derive from the original premises. Since we do not know how many steps the entire proof will require, we cannot assign numbers to the last two lines of the proof. Furthermore, we do not know, except for the original premises, the numbers of the statements cited in justifying these lines. For the present, then, we will refer to the last line of the proof as "N," the next to the last line as "N — 1," and so on. In the justifications, those statements for which numbers have not been assigned will be written out in their entirety.

$$N - 1. \quad C \supset (Q \vee L) \qquad 2, S, \text{MP}$$
$$N. \quad Q \vee L \qquad\qquad C \supset (Q \vee L), C, \text{MP}$$

Q. Where does *S* appear in the premises?

      A. As part of a conjunction.

Q. Then it can be derived by simplification. What is the conjunction?

      A. $S \cdot M$.

Q. Then the last three lines will be

$$N - 2. \quad S \qquad\qquad\qquad S \cdot M, \text{SIMP}$$
$$N - 1. \quad C \supset (Q \text{ v } L) \qquad 2, S, \text{MP}$$
$$N. \quad Q \text{ v } L \qquad\qquad\quad C \supset (Q \text{ v } L), C, \text{MP}$$

Q. Does the conjunction $S \cdot M$ occur in the premises?

      A. Yes, as the consequent of Premise 1.

Q. Then it can be derived by modus ponens from Premise 1 and its antecedent. What is that?

      A. *P*.

Q. Is it given as a premise?

      A. Yes, as Premise 4.

Q. Then the fourth line from the bottom will be:

$$N - 3. \quad S \cdot M \qquad\qquad 2, 4, \text{MP}$$

Nothing more is needed for this part of the proof. The other statement needed for the justification of the last step was *C*. Where is it?

      A. It is the consequent of Premise 3.

Q. Then we will have to apply modus ponens again. What is the antecedent of Premise 3?

      A. $\sim A$.

Q. Therefore, we must include this line in our proof:

$$N - 4. \quad C \qquad\qquad\qquad 3, \sim A, \text{MP}$$

Where does *A* appear in the premises?

      A. It is a constituent of a disjunction, which is given as Premise 5.

Q. Then we can derive it by applying the principle of disjunctive syllogism. What is the other constituent of Premise 5?

      A. *D*.

Q. Is the negation of *D* given as a premise?

      A. Yes, in Premise 6.

Q. In that case, $\sim A$ can be derived directly from the premises. Let it and its justification be $N - 5$ or line 7 following the last premise given. We can now assign numbers to the rest of the statements that follow it. We can also replace the statements in the justification by the numbers that now represent them, and the proof is complete and in the form originally given on p. 251.

The preceding example of constructing a proof is a relatively simple one, partly because all of the compound statements needed, either as the final conclusion or somewhere during our construction of the proof, occur as premises or as constituents of premises. Another example, still relatively simple but at least more complicated in this respect, might be the task of deriving the conclusion $Q \vee S$ from the following premises:

1. $P \supset M$ Premise
2. $M \supset Q$ Premise
3. $R \supset S$ Premise
4. $P \vee R$ Premise

We will make use of dialogue again to reach a solution.

Q. What sort of statement is the conclusion?
          A. Compound, disjunctive.
Q. Does the same compound occur in the premises?
          A. No.
Q. Then the last step will be justified by either addition or constructive dilemma or destructive dilemma. Where do the constituents of the conclusion occur?
          A. They are both consequents of hypotheticals.
Q. That suggests constructive dilemma, in which case we will need to fill in the following skeleton for a last line:

N. $Q \vee S$ $(\_ \supset Q), (\_ \supset S), \_ \vee \_,$ CD

The same pair of statements must fill in both sets of blanks. How much of that framework is already provided in the premises?
          A. There is a disjunctive statement in which one of the constituents is the antecedent of the hypothetical statement. S is the consequent of the statement. But the other constituent differs from the antecedent of the statement in which Q is consequent.
Q. Then we could complete the justification of the last line by filling in those statements, but would there be any direct inference from the premises?
          A. No. The disjunctive premise needed is given, but the conjunction of two hypotheticals with the necessary relationship is not.
Q. But we could derive the conjunction of the two hypotheticals by the principle of conjunction, if we had them separately. That would be the next to the last line (N — 1). We have one but not the other, did you say?

A. Yes. We have $R \supset S$ but not $P \supset Q$.

Q. Then we need to derive $P \supset Q$. Is it anywhere in the premises?

A. No.

Q. Then we shall have to use the principle of hypothetical syllogism. This requires as premises two hypothetical statements, one with P as antecedent, the other with Q as consequent, while the other constituents are identical. Have we such a pair of hypotheticals?

A. Yes, in Premises 1 and 2.

Q. Therefore, the first line of the proof will be the derivation of $P \supset Q$ by HS; we have already determined the further steps. We can now write out the completed proof.

1. $P \supset M$	Premise	
2. $M \supset Q$	Premise	
3. $R \supset S$	Premise	
4. $P \lor R$	Premise	To prove: $Q \lor S$
5. $P \supset Q$	1, 2, HS	
6. $(P \supset Q) \cdot (R \supset S)$	4, 3, CONJ	
7. $Q \lor S$	6, 4, CD	

The technique of indirect inference we have been illustrating with these two examples can be used, in this system, to derive the conclusion of any valid argument from its premises. The limitations of the method, except for those of the system itself, do not have to do with its theoretical scope but with the practical problems of applying it as arguments become increasingly complex. Practice in following a systematic procedure (such as the dialogues exemplify) is the best way we can increase our confidence and facility in the construction of proofs of this sort.

11.3 EXERCISES

Complete the following formal proofs. The first five examples require only that the missing justifications be supplied. The last five call for construction of the complete proof, the steps that lead from the premises to the conclusion, as well as their justifications.

A.   1. $\sim(\sim P \lor \sim Q) \lor (R \cdot S)$ Premise
      2. $\sim(P \cdot Q)$ Premise
      3. $\sim P \lor \sim Q$
      4. $\sim\sim(\sim P \lor \sim Q)$
      5. $R \cdot S$
      6. S

B. 1. $P \supset \sim R$ Premise
    2. R Premise
    3. $\sim P \supset S$ Premise
    4. $S \supset T$ Premise
    5. $\sim\sim R$
    6. $\sim P$
    7. S
    8. T
    9. $T \vee W$

C. 1. $\sim P \vee Q$ Premise
    2. $[\sim Q \supset (\sim Q \cdot \sim P)] \supset (R \vee S)$ Premise
    3. $(P \supset Q) \supset \sim R$ Premise
    4. $P \supset Q$
    5. $\sim R$
    6. $\sim Q \supset \sim P$
    7. $\sim Q \supset (\sim Q \cdot \sim P)$
    8. $R \vee S$
    9. S

D. 1. $\sim Q \supset \sim P$ Premise
    2. $R \supset (S \supset T)$ Premise
    3. $(P \vee R) \cdot (P \vee S)$ Premise
    4. $\sim\sim P \supset \sim\sim Q$
    5. $P \supset Q$
    6. $(R \cdot S) \supset T$
    7. $(P \supset Q) \cdot [(R \cdot S) \supset T]$
    8. $P \vee (R \cdot S)$
    9. $Q \vee T$
    10. $T \vee Q$

E. 1. $P \supset Q$ Premise
    2. $\sim R \supset \sim Q$ Premise
    3. $(\sim S \vee \sim T) \supset \sim R$ Premise
    4. $\sim\sim Q \supset \sim\sim R$
    5. $Q \supset R$
    6. $P \supset R$
    7. $\sim\sim R \supset \sim(\sim S \vee \sim T)$
    8. $R \supset \sim(\sim S \vee \sim T)$
    9. $R \supset (S \cdot T)$
    10. $P \supset (S \cdot T)$
    11. $P \supset (T \cdot S)$

F. 1. $(R \vee S) \supset T$ Premise
    2. $T \supset W$ Premise
    3. $\sim W$ Premise   Derive $\sim R$

G. 1. $(K \vee H) \supset (L \cdot M)$ Premise
    2. K Premise   Derive $K \cdot M$

H. 1. $P \supset (Q \supset R)$ Premise
    2. $\sim(\sim P \vee \sim Q)$ Premise
    3. $R \supset S$ Premise   Derive $S \vee T$

I. If March comes in like a lion, it goes out like a lamb. If March comes in like a lion and goes out like a lamb, there are floods in April. But there were no floods in April; therefore March did not come in like a lion.

J. Viola is a liar if and only if her reply was false. Herman is not a liar if and only if he correctly reported Viola's reply. If Viola is a liar and her reply is false, Herman's report of her reply is not correct. The latter holds also if Viola is not a liar and her reply is not false. Therefore, Herman is a liar.

11.4 REDUCTIO AD ABSURDUM AND CONDITIONAL PROOF

There are two special techniques that can be useful to us in expediting the construction of a proof. They are not new rules of inference so much as they are ways of using the established set of rules more effectively. One of these techniques, reductio ad absurdum, was mentioned earlier in connection with the problems posed in demonstrating the validity of certain forms of the syllogism when the principle of obversion was not to be applied (see Section 4.8). The greater complexity of the system we are now studying sometimes makes it a convenient short cut; although wherever it can be applied successfully, we can always use the ordinary method of deriving the conclusion from the premises given.

In the ordinary use of the principles of inference to demonstrate the validity of an argument, we proceed by showing that if the premises are true, the conclusion must be true. In applying the technique of reductio ad absurdum, what we do is to show that if the conclusion is false, at least one of the premises must be false also. Either procedure establishes validity, that is, establishes that it is impossible for all the premises to be true and the conclusion false.

For a reductio ad absurdum demonstration of validity, we negate the conclusion of the argument and add it to the list of premises. However, for the present system, in order to avoid confusion with statements that have been added as a result of *inferences* originating with the premises given—statements that have been established as being true—the negation of the conclusion and every statement derived directly or indirectly from it will be clearly marked off by a bracket labeled "R." The procedure is complete when we have a statement in the "reductio" section of the proof that is the negation of one of the statements in the main section. The conclusion we establish in this way (the negation of which is the first statement in the reductio section) can then be added to the main body of the proof. Its justification should consist of a reference to the reductio section and the premise contradicted at the end of it. An example follows:

$$
\begin{array}{llll}
& 1. & A \supset (B \cdot C) & \text{Premise} \\
& 2. & \sim C & \text{Premise} & \text{Conclusion}: \sim A \\
& 3. & \sim\sim A & \text{Reductio Premise} \\
& 4. & A & 3, \text{DN} \\
R & 5. & B \cdot C & 1, 4, \text{MP} \\
& 6. & C & 5, \text{SIMP} \\
& 7. & \sim A & 2, \text{R3--R6 RED}
\end{array}
$$

As in our demonstration of the validity of certain syllogisms, the use of proofs by reductio ad absurdum would make it possible for us to dispense with certain rules of inference. Modus tollens, for example, would be superfluous; the conclusion could be established by way of a "reductio" column in which the assertion of the consequent of the conditional statement (contradicting the second premise of the modus tollens argument) is derived from the assertion of the antecedent by modus ponens. Not much would be gained by our replacing all applications of modus tollens by the reductio method; in the above example, there is some advantage in doing so. The method of proof using modus tollens would require an application of addition, commutation, and DeMorgan's theorem beforehand.

The second special technique for demonstrating validity is called "conditional proof." We can use it only when the conclusion to be established from a given set of premises is a conditional statement. (Of course, any statement equivalent to a conditional statement can be established using this technique by first deriving the equivalent conditional statement and then applying the rule of replacement.) The procedure in conditional proof is to treat the antecedent of the conclusion as if it were a premise and then show, by the usual procedures, that the consequent of the conclusion is derivable. It is an analogue in proof to the principle of exportation. In other words, conditional proof replaces the proof of a conditional statement with a proof that its antecedent conjoined with the original premises (the original antecedent when exportation is applied) implies its consequent. If arguments were expressed as conditional statements themselves, with the premises as antecedent and the conclusion as consequent, the procedure of conditional proof would still more obviously and directly depend on the equivalence pattern designated as exportation.

As in our application of the reductio method, it is desirable for us to avoid confusing the lines of a conditional proof with the lines derivable from the original set of premises. The conditional proof should constitute a separate section and we should identify the lines in it by a bracket labeled "CP." The conditional formed by taking its first line as antecedent and its last line as consequent can be added to the main body of the proof with its justification to be the numbers of the conditional proof itself. For example:

$$
\begin{array}{lll}
1.\ (P \vee Q) \supset R & \text{Premise} & \\
2.\ A \supset P & \text{Premise} & \\
3.\ C \supset Q & \text{Premise} & \\
4.\ Z \supset (A \vee C) & \text{Premise} & \text{Conclusion: } Z \supset R \\
\end{array}
$$

$$
\text{CP} \begin{cases}
5.\ Z & \text{Conditional Premise} \\
6.\ A \vee C & 4, 5, \text{MP} \\
7.\ P \vee Q & 2, 3, 6, \text{CD} \\
8.\ R & 1, 7, \text{MP}
\end{cases}
$$

$$
9.\ Z \supset R \qquad \text{CP5–CP8}
$$

Of course, both reductio ad absurdum and conditional proof can be used to derive intermediate conclusions within a more extended proof. Whether they are used at all is a matter of convenience, even, it might be said, a matter of taste. They represent refinements in logical technique, lending simplicity and elegance to demonstrations that otherwise might well be equally effective but awkward and of greater length.

11.4 EXERCISES

A. Construct a formal proof using the reductio technique for one of the arguments in the exercises at the end of Section 11.3. Compare the result with the proof using the regular procedure.

B. Which of the arguments in the exercises at the end of Section 11.3 is susceptible to a formal proof using the technique of conditional proof? Construct such a proof and compare it with the regular procedure.

C. One use of the techniques of reductio ad absurdum and conditional proof would be to reduce the number of principles of inference needed. Show that any inference justified by the principles of addition, conjunction, or constructive dilemma could be justified by using the reductio technique and other principles of inference. Show that inferences justified by the principles of hypothetical syllogism and absorption could be justified by using the technique of conditional proof and other principles of inference.

11.5 TAUTOLOGIES AND CONTRADICTIONS

A truth table shows the truth value of a compound statement for each of the possible combinations of truth values that can be assigned to its elementary constituents. Ordinarily, one would expect the column of truth values for the compound statement to show it to be true in some cases and false in others. But this is not always the case. Consider the truth table for $(A \lor B) \lor (\sim A \lor \sim B)$.

A	B	$\sim A$	$\sim B$	$A \lor B$	$\sim A \lor \sim B$	$(A \lor B) \lor (\sim A \lor \sim B)$
T	T	F	F	T	F	T
T	F	F	T	T	T	T
F	T	T	F	T	T	T
F	F	T	T	F	T	T

In the last column, there are only T's. Under none of the possible circumstances definable in terms of the various combinations of truth values for its elementary constituents is the statement false; it is true in all of them. Such statements are called "tautologies."

Consider another truth table, the one for $(A \lor B) \cdot (\sim A \cdot \sim B)$.

A	B	$\sim A$	$\sim B$	$A \lor B$	$\sim A \cdot \sim B$	$(A \lor B) \cdot (\sim A \cdot \sim B)$
T	T	F	F	T	F	F
T	F	F	T	T	F	F
F	T	T	F	T	F	F
F	F	T	T	F	T	F

In this case, the last column contains only F's; the statement is not true in any of the possible circumstances defined by the various combinations of truth values for its constituents. Such statements are called "contradictions."

In tautologies and contradictions, we apparently come upon exceptions to the general rule that logic tells us nothing about the truth or falsity of statements considered by themselves but is concerned solely with their relationships to each other in reasoning. Logic, we have said, can tell us that if a certain premise or set of premises is true, a certain conclusion must be true; it cannot tell us whether any of the statements concerned is simply true. But surely a statement that is true in all possible circumstances must be true, and one that is true in no possible situation must be false.

Therefore, logic does tell us, on truth tables, that at least some statements are true and some statements are false. We can say of tautologies and contradictions that they are *logically true* or *logically false*.

Upon closer examination, statements possessing logical truth or logical falsity turn out to be singularly ineffective as means of communicating information. The simplest form that can be taken by a tautological statement is $p \vee \sim p$. It is logically true either that there are sixteen five-letter words in this paragraph or there are not. One does not need to count in order to determine the truth value of this statement. Unfortunately, however, it does not even provide us with the trivial sort of information that would ordinarily be discovered by counting the words of a certain kind.[1]

That a tautology provides us with no information about the subject matter referred to by its constituents does not mean that it is without interest or importance. Tautologies are interesting not for what they mean or assert but for what they are. The fact that a certain statement is tautologous, logically true, can be of great logical and philosophical significance even though the same fact indicates that it does not make any significant contribution to our information about whatever it seems to describe.

We need not consider the general philosophical significance of tautologies and contradictions, but their possible significance in the determination of the validity of an argument is a matter of direct interest to us as students of logic. An argument is valid when it is impossible for its premises to be true and its conclusion false. This has been our basic definition of validity. We can now explicitly reformulate it in terms of tautology and contradiction. For a definition of validity in terms of tautology, we can consider the argument as having been thrown into the form of a conditional statement, with all the premises conjoined as the antecedent and the conclusion as the consequent. The antecedent will be true if and only if the

---

[1] Another way of expressing an elementary form of tautology would be to say that any statement (at least any statement that could have a truth value at all) is either true or false. Teachers composing true–false examinations must take care in formulating their instructions, therefore. Instructions reading, "Indicate for each of the following statements whether it is true or false," might be complied with by writing "Yes" for each statement. The answers would all be right and yet indicate nothing of the student's knowledge of the subject matter.

A parent wishing to assert authority over a disobedient child could ensure that his commands would be obeyed by issuing tautologies in the imperative mood: "Either go to bed right now or don't!" The child would have no choice but to obey, yet, paradoxically, just as the ordinary tautology is uninformative, the imperative tautology would be totally ineffective in influencing his behavior (except perhaps indirectly, by inducing a mood of perplexity—but then it would not be obedience to the command that made the difference).

premises that are its components are all true. Thus the validity of the argument is related to the truth value of the conditional statement so constituted. To say that it is possible for the premises all to be true and yet the conclusion false is as much as to say that it is possible that the conditional statement is false. The circumstances in which that possibility is excluded are precisely those in which the conditional is a tautology. We can say, therefore, that an argument is valid if and only if the conditional statement formed by making the conjunction of all premises the antecedent and the conclusion the consequent is tautological.

The negation of a tautology is a contradiction, as we have seen. And the negation of a conditional statement is equivalent to the conjunction of the antecedent with the denial of the consequent. This permits another definition of validity, utilizing the concept of a contradiction. The negation of the conditional statement made up of the premises and the conclusion as antecedent and consequent respectively will be a statement that conjoins all of the premises and the denial of the conclusion. If the corresponding conditional is a tautology, its negation, the conjunction just described, must be a contradiction. An argument can be said to be valid if and only if the result of conjoining all of its premises together with the denial of its conclusion is a contradiction. Since contradiction is the criterion of logical impossibility, such a definition of validity is nothing but a slightly more formal equivalent of the original definition: an argument is valid if and only if it is impossible for the premises to be true and the conclusion false.

Concentrating on inconsistency or contradiction as the foundation for determining an argument's validity, it would be of use to us, in the present context, to distinguish among three ways in which inconsistency can arise, although only one of them is of real interest to us. If the joint assertion of the premises is already contradictory, the result when we conjoin it with the denial of the conclusion (no matter what it is) will be a contradiction. In other words, if it is impossible for the premises all to be true in the first place it is impossible for the premises to be true and the conclusion false. Again, if it is impossible for the conclusion to be false, it is impossible for the premises to be true and the conclusion false. That is, if the denial of the conclusion is already a contradiction (as it will be if the conclusion is a tautology), the conjunction of the premises with the denial of the conclusion will be a contradiction, no matter what the premises might be. Notice that while such arguments must be called valid in terms of the definition of validity, they have only a trivial kind of validity. A tautologous conclusion can be validly inferred from any premises whatsoever; it is no longer feasible to discriminate between premises from which it can validly be inferred and premises from which it cannot be validly inferred. Likewise, inconsistent premises validly imply any conclusion at all; we can make no distinction between conclusions that can and those that cannot validly be inferred from those premises.

The interesting, nontrivial cases are those in which the contradiction arises neither in the premises by themselves nor in the denial of the conclusion by itself but in the conjunction of the two. In such cases, it is clear that the nature of the premises and the nature of the conclusion are mutually significant to the validity of the argument. If the premises were to be changed, while the conclusion remained the same, the argument might be rendered invalid. And from the same premises, some other conclusion might not be validly inferred at all. What we are interested in knowing of an argument is not only that it is valid, but also that its validity is of this nontrivial kind.

Following are two valid arguments:

> 1. Either the maid or the butler witnessed the murder. If the maid witnessed it, the victim was alive at 10:15 that morning; if the butler witnessed it, he was alive at 10:40. But the victim was not alive either at 10:15 or at 10:40, having been dispatched the night before. Therefore, he committed suicide.
>
> 2. The maid is in love with the chauffeur, therefore the butler is either guilty or innocent.

The first argument is valid, but only because the premises are themselves inconsistent with each other. It would continue to be valid if the conclusion was replaced with any statement at all: *the victim is not dead,* or *the maid was standing on her head,* or *there were sixteen white mice singing carols at the door,* and so on.

The second argument is valid because there are no circumstances in which the conclusion could be false. Of course the butler is either innocent or guilty. (So are we all.) That will follow as a valid conclusion from any set of premises whatsoever. It is therefore as uninteresting as the first argument.

Omit the first premise of argument 1. From the remaining premises, we can validly infer (by the principle of destructive dilemma) that neither the maid nor the butler witnessed the murder. With different premises or a different conclusion, the argument we have demonstrated in this way to be valid might be made invalid. It is therefore interesting and might serve a purpose.

11.5 EXERCISES

A. Pick out the tautologies and contradictions from among the following statements.

1. $[\sim(A \cdot \sim A) \text{ v} \sim(B \text{ v} \sim B)] \cdot (C \cdot \sim C)$
2. $[(\sim A \text{ v} \sim B) \cdot (A \text{ v } B)] \text{ v } (C \text{ v} \sim C)$
3. $[\sim(A \cdot \sim A) \cdot \sim(B \cdot \sim B)] \text{ v } (C \cdot \sim C)$
4. $[(A \supset \sim A) \text{ v } (B \supset \sim C)] \cdot (C \supset B)$
5. $[(A \supset \sim B) \cdot (A \text{ v } B)] \cdot \sim[(A \cdot \sim B) \text{ v } (\sim A \cdot B)]$

B. Distinguish the trivial from the nontrivial in the following set of valid arguments.

1. $A \supset B$
   $A \text{ v } C$
   $\underline{\sim(B \text{ v } C)}$
   $A \text{ v } D$

2. $A \supset B$
   $A \text{ v } C$
   $\underline{\sim(C \text{ v } D)}$
   $B \text{ v } C$

3. $A \text{ v } B$
   $A \equiv C$
   $\underline{C \supset D}$
   $D \text{ v } B$

4. A
   $B \equiv C$
   $\underline{D \text{ v } (A \supset C)}$
   $(A \text{ v } C) \text{ v } (\sim A \text{ v } B)$

5. $A \text{ v } (B \cdot C)$
   $\sim B \cdot C$
   $\underline{C \supset (A \supset B)}$
   $A \cdot C$

11.6 NORMAL FORM

We can quite easily refine the truth-value methods of determining validity so that we can discriminate between trivially and nontrivially valid forms of argument. When the full truth table is used, we need only first scan the column of values for the conclusion to see if there is any line in which it is false and scan the column for the premises to see if there is any line in which all of them are true. We can do this even before we determine whether or not there is any line in which these conditions are fulfilled together. If the conclusion is not a tautology and the premises are not inconsistent, yet there is no line in which the premises are true and the conclusion false, the argument is valid in a nontrivial way. Similarly, when an evaluation chart is used, we can first check the possibility of a consistent assignment of values with the premises true and the possibility of a consistent assignment of values with the conclusion false before determining whether or not a consistent assignment is possible in which both of these conditions are fulfilled. If a consistent assignment can be made to fulfill either condition separately but not both together, the argument is non-trivially valid.

At this point, however, we are concerned with the use of the basic rules of inference in determining validity, not with the methods that make use of truth-value assignments. The method of normal forms we are now going to introduce resembles even more closely than did the one considered in Sections 11.1 and 11.2 the procedure we used in working with arguments made up of **A, E, I,** and **O** statements. It will be entirely mechanical, that is, the steps followed will not require any ingenuity or insight on our part but only the ability to follow a program. It will provide as clear a distinction between trivial and nontrivial validity as the truth-value methods. Even more important, it will make possible decisions like those introduced in Part One in connection with enthymemes. It will indicate what conclusion, if any, we can nontrivially infer from a given set of premises; it will indicate what additional information must be added to a set of premises in order to infer a conclusion that they do not support by themselves.

In order to develop such a method, we must first impose more stringent restrictions on form than are required by mere standard form. Standard form has been discussed, for arguments involving compound statements as well as for the arguments of Part One, in terms of the use of a rule of replacement. When an argument is in standard form, it is ready for criticism or formal proof by indirect inference using only the basic rules of inference and criticism. This goal is achieved when, after we have replaced some of the statements constituting the original argument by their equivalents, certain relations among the statements are fulfilled (eliminating complementary pairs of terms, for example). The idea of standard form imposes no direct restrictions on the internal form of any of the statements, except that they must be correctly formulated in the language of the system we are using. For the system of symbolic logic, we introduce the concept of "normal form." It is concerned with the internal form of the compound statements that enter into a given argument. A statement is in normal form when the only logical symbols it includes are the ∼, ·, and v; it is built up with these symbols in that order.[2] In other words, it must be

[2] Strictly speaking, what has been introduced here is just one of several kinds of normal form, the one more precisely referred to as "disjunctive normal form." Since this is the only kind of normal form that will be considered in this textbook, it will not be necessary to use the more precise term.

primarily a disjunction (usually a multiple disjunction). The constituents of the disjunction must all be either elementary statements or negations of elementary statements or conjunctions. The constituents of any conjunction must all be either elementary statements or negations of elementary statements. To put the point in still another way, the $\sim$ can apply only to elementary statements, the $\cdot$ can relate only elementary statements and their negations, and the v can relate the constituents made up in this way.

$$A \text{ v } (B \cdot C) \text{ v } (\sim C \cdot \sim D \cdot A) \text{ v } B$$

is a statement in normal form.

$$A \text{ v } \sim (B \cdot C) \text{ v } (\sim C \cdot \sim D \cdot A) \text{ v } B$$

is not, because in the second constituent of the multiple disjunction, a $\sim$ is applied not to an elementary statement but to a compound.

There is a simple mechanical procedure that we can follow in reducing any compound statement to normal form. Naturally, the procedure depends on the application of the rule of replacement and the various equivalences involved. The equivalences can be applied in a definite order so as to replace the statement by an equivalent in normal form. First, all symbols other than $\sim$, $\cdot$, and v must be eliminated; this we accomplish by applying the equivalences given as definitions of material implication and material equivalence.[3] Next, we must fix the hierarchical order of the symbols as prescribed by the definition of normal form. We do this in two stages. First, we apply DeMorgan's theorems wherever a $\sim$ is attached to a compound. When we have completed this procedure, the first condition will have been fulfilled: $\sim$ will apply only to elementary statements. Our next and final task is to eliminate any conjunctions having constituents other than elementary statements and their negations. Since we have already restricted the kinds of compounds to negations, conjunctions, and disjunctions, the only such cases will be conjunctions involving disjunctive constituents. These can all be eliminated if we apply the principle of distribution. The result, after this procedure has been completed, will be a statement in normal form. To sum up these steps:

[3] Of course, it is possible that some elementary statements may be preceded by more than one $\sim$. In that case, the principle of double negation can be applied so that there will remain only an elementary statement or its negation. It is also possible that statements of the form p v p or $p \cdot p$ will occur as constituents. Complications in the next step can be reduced if we apply the principle of tautology to eliminate them.

1. Wherever a ⊃ or a ≡ occurs, apply definition of material implication (MI) or definition of material equivalence (ME), continuing until all such symbols have been eliminated.
2. Whenever a compound is negated, apply DeMorgan's theorems (DeM).
3. Wherever a disjunctive compound occurs as a constituent of a conjunction, apply distribution (DIST).

At any point, if complexity could be reduced by applying the principles of double negation (DN) or tautology (TAUT), do so.

The basic procedures are illustrated, as is simplification by tautology, for the following case:

$$(p \supset q) \cdot \sim(p \cdot q)$$

1. Eliminating ⊃ by applying MI:

$$(\sim p \vee q) \cdot \sim(p \cdot q)$$

2. Eliminating a negated conjunction by applying DeM:

$$(\sim p \vee q) \cdot (\sim p \vee \sim q)$$

3. Rearranging · and v by applying DIST:

$$(\sim p \cdot \sim p) \vee (\sim p \cdot \sim q) \vee (q \cdot \sim p) \vee (q \cdot \sim q)$$

4. Simplifying one component by applying TAUT:

$$\sim p \vee (\sim p \cdot \sim q) \vee (q \cdot \sim p) \vee (q \cdot \sim q)$$

11.6 EXERCISE

Reduce the statements in Exercise 11.5A to normal form.

11.7 THE ANALYSIS OF ARGUMENTS IN NORMAL FORM

An argument is in normal form when all of its premises and either the conclusion or its negation are in normal form. Once we have reduced an argument to normal form by applying the procedure (discussed in Section 11.6) to all of the statements involved, the questions of validity and of triviality and nontriviality can be answered by our use of a procedure equally clear and mechanical. We need use only two principles: (1) the principle of distribution, which has already been introduced among the basic equivalences; (2) in effect, an abbreviated variation of the principle of disjunctive syllogism. It would be appropriate to call this second one the principle of disjunctive simplification. Because they are so closely related, there should be no objection to our using the same abbreviation (DS) for both of them.

The Principle of Disjunctive Simplification

Any contradictory constituent of a disjunction may be eliminated.

The relationship between this principle and disjunctive syllogism can easily be understood. Let the disjunctive statement be represented by $p \vee q$, with the understanding that q is contradictory. If so, $\sim q$ is a tautology and must be true. If $\sim q$ is added as a second premise, disjunctive syllogism permits p alone to be drawn as a conclusion.

What we need in order to apply disjunctive simplification is a way of recognizing a contradiction. Contradictions were defined as statements that turned out to be false on every line of a truth table. If contradictions could be recognized in no other way, we would have to combine the application of rules with truth-value methods in carrying out the procedure we are now trying to develop. This, fortunately, is not necessary. Certain cases of contradiction and tautology can be recognized just by consideration of their logical form. The most primitive type of contradiction is $p \vee p$. A statement and its negation cannot both be true, and so the conjunction of the two must always be false. Furthermore, any multiple conjunction including two such statements among its constituents must be a contradiction too; in order for a multiple conjunction to be true, *all* of its constituents must be true, which in this case is excluded. For purposes of practical application, we can restate the principle of disjunctive simplification to read:

> Any conjunctive constituent of a statement in normal form that is or includes both an elementary statement and its negation may be eliminated.

If we eliminate every constituent of a statement in normal form, this indicates that the statement as a whole is a contradiction. If a disjunction is to be true, at least one of its constituents must be true. If all of its constituents are contradictory, that possibility is excluded.

We are now in a position to construct a program by which the validity of an argument in normal form can be determined. The first step is to apply the principle of disjunctive simplification to the normal form of the *negation* of the conclusion. If this results in the elimination of all constituents, the negation of the conclusion is a contradiction, the conclusion itself a tautology, and the argument is valid; it is so only in the trivial way that holds when it is impossible for the conclusion to be false without any reference to the premises at all.

In the next step, we apply to the premises much the same procedure we applied in Part One to the formal analysis and proof of a sorites: conjoining the first two premises. The result will be a conjunction of two disjunctive statements. We reduce it to normal form by applying the principle of distribution. (Since one or both of the premises may be multiple disjunctions, the most general form of distribution may be required. See p. 244.) We then apply the principle of disjunctive simplification to the result. We conjoin the resulting statement to the next premise and repeat the procedure, continuing until the stock of premises has been exhausted. If at any point we eliminate everything by the application of disjunctive simplification, this is an indication that the premises are inconsistent. If so, the argument is valid but only in the trivial way occurring when it is impossible for all the premises to be true independently of any relationship to the conclusion.

If there is a residue remaining in each case, our last step is to conjoin the residue remaining from the premises with the residue remaining from the negation of the conclusion and then repeat the steps described above. If there is still a residue, it is possible for the premises to be true and the conclusion false. This will be the case for any consistent assignment of truth values we give to the elementary constituents of the residue. If there is no residue, the argument is valid; we have shown that there is no consistent case in which the premises are all true and the conclusion false.

11.7 EXERCISES

A. Use the method of normal forms to establish the validity of the following principles of inference: modus ponens, constructive dilemma, disjunctive syllogism, hypothetical syllogism, and simplification.

B. Use the method of normal forms to determine the validity or invalidity of the first five arguments in Exercise 10.5.

11.8 ENTHYMEMATIC ARGUMENTS

In this system of compound statements, there is no neat method of determining whether or not an argument is complete as it stands; there is nothing comparable to the method of counting terms and statements we used in Part One. Of course, if a set of statements is given, and if a conclusion is to be inferred from them, the incompleteness of the argument owing to the absence of a stated conclusion is obvious. When some premises are given with a conclusion, and it is a conclusion that does not validly follow from them by themselves, the distinction between invalidity and incompleteness breaks down. If the premises do not imply a conclusion attached to them, it is always possible to add further statements to the premises so as to create a valid argument. If all else fails, we add the conclusion to the premises so that it follows from them by the principle of identity. This, too, however, is a trivial kind of validity. For us, the interesting question to be raised in this context is: What additional information, other than the conclusion itself, can be added to a set of premises so as to transform an invalid argument into a valid one?

If a set of premises is given without any stated conclusion, the residue remaining after we have tested the premises for consistency can rightly be regarded as the conclusion. If we conjoined its denial, the result would be the same as the result of the final step in establishing the validity of an argument: every constituent would be eliminated. In many cases, we can simplify and break down the conclusion determined in this way into separate components by applying the various equivalences and the basic rules providing for immediate inferences.

When an argument is invalid, the residue remaining after the final step in testing validity provides a clue to the additional information that we would have to include among the premises if the argument is to be valid. Under any circumstances in which that residual statement is true, the premises will be true and the conclusion false. These are the only circumstances in which this is possible: if they are rendered impossible, the resulting argument must be valid. What is called for, then, is the addition to the premises of a statement formed by negating the residue that remains when we have completed the validity test. When we test the new argument resulting from this addition to the premises, the test will indicate validity, since every constituent of the conjoined normal forms will be eliminated in the process of disjunctive simplification.

11.8   EXERCISES

What additional premise is needed to infer validly the conclusion in the following arguments?

A. $\sim(A \cdot B)$
$\sim A \supset C$
$\underline{C \supset D}$
D

B. $A \supset B$

$\dfrac{(C \vee D) \supset A}{\sim D}$

C. $(A \vee B) \supset (C \cdot D)$

$\dfrac{\sim(D \cdot E)}{\sim A \cdot \sim D}$

Chapter 12

THE LOGIC OF
QUANTIFIED STATEMENTS

We developed in Part One a logical system suitable for the analysis and criticism of arguments formed of simple categorical statements. So far, in Part Three we have developed a system for dealing with arguments that include compound statements. What we will do now is to develop a still more comprehensive system that will bring both forms of argument within the same general framework. To do so, we will need to consider the internal structure of noncompound statements as well as the structures by which compound statements are formed.

12.1 SINGULAR STATEMENTS

We can begin by recalling a kind of statement that entered into our early explorations in Part One and was then abandoned when quantification was introduced: the "singular statement." A singular statement or proposition expresses a judgment concerning a specific individual, identified by name. In English, such statements are ordinarily formed by placing the word "is" (or "is not," if the statement is negative) between a proper name and either an adjective or a general term. Examples are *John is tall* and *John is a man*. When we first introduced the language of Venn diagrams, we noted that such statements could be expressed in that language by writing the name (or a letter serving as an abbreviation for it) inside or outside a circle intended to represent a class. The spatial relation of the letter to the circle corresponds to the logical relationship between the individual named and the class, and it fulfills the function assigned to "is" and "is not" in such contexts in the English language.

Another way of representing this kind of judgment has been generally adopted in modern logical practice. Instead of representing the affirmative judgment by "is," the mere spatial juxtaposition of two marks—one the name of an individual, the other the name of a property being asserted of the individual—suffices for that purpose. Appropriate abbreviations can be used so that *John is tall* can be represented as *Tj*. (It is the convention to use capital letters as abbreviations for names of properties and lower case letters as abbreviations for names of individuals.) For elementary purposes, it is not essential to make a sharp distinction between *John is tall* and *John is a man,* so that the latter would appropriately be expressed as *Mj.* Negative singular statements are expressed by negating the corresponding affirmative form, using the symbol for negation that has already been introduced. We would represent *John is not wealthy* as ~*Wj* and *Imogene is not a man* as ~*Mi.*

12.2 PROPOSITIONAL FUNCTIONS

The pattern into which the simplest singular statements—often called atomic statements—fall, when they are expressed in the way we have been illustrating, can be represented as: [ ]——. The brackets indicate a space in which a capital letter standing for a predicate (that is, the name of a property) is to be filled in, and the line indicates a space to be filled in by a lower case letter representing the name of an individual. We customarily use letters to represent these spaces so that the pattern of a simple singular statement is given as *Fx*. In this expression, *F* does not have the function of an abbreviation; it does not stand for "fat" or "funny" or "faint-hearted." It represents a space to be filled in by a letter standing for a specified predicate term, which *could* be one of those but could be any other predicate term just as well. Likewise, *x* is not the abbreviation for the name of a specific individual, "Xerxes" or "Xenophon" or "Xanthippe." It represents a space to be filled in by a letter that has that function. Consequently, *Fx* is not a statement at all but a form that statements can take. Its constituents are *variables: F* is a predicate variable, and *x* is an individual variable.

There are two parts of such a statement form that we must specify before the mere statement form becomes a statement: the predicate variable and the individual variable must be replaced respectively by the name of a predicate and the name of an individual. The result of carrying out only one half of this process—specifying the predicate but leaving the individual variable—is not a statement, but it plays a very important role in the construction of a common framework for both compound and simple categorical statements. It is called a "propositional function." For example, by replacing the variable F of Fx with W, for "wealthy," we form the propositional function, Wx. In English, we might read this as x *is wealthy,* understanding that we are free to replace the individual variable, x, with the name of any individual in our universe of discourse; until we do so, we have no statement, nothing that could be said to be true or false. Ordinarily, of course, the result will be sometimes a true statement and sometimes a false one, depending on which individual's name is substituted for the variable.

In view of what we have just said, we can see that propositional functions are closely related to the classes we discussed in Part One. A propositional function can be said to divide the universe of discourse into two subsets, composed of those individual items that form a true statement when their names are substituted for the variable and of those individuals who produce a false one. The geometrical pattern used to represent classes and their complements could be reinterpreted to represent a division of the universe into individuals making Fx true and individual elements that make $\sim Fx$ true. The recognition of this relationship takes us a long way toward incorporating into the new system the logic we originally developed in terms of the languages of logical English, Venn diagrams, and algebraic notation.

So far, we have considered only simple statements and propositional functions, but there is no reason why such expressions should not enter into compounds formed with the logical symbols for negation, conjunction, and so on. *John is healthy and wealthy* is a condensed way of expressing a statement in which two singular statements are conjoined. Using appropriate abbreviations, we could represent it as $Hj \cdot Wj$. *Mary is beautiful, but she is not vain* could be represented as $Bm \cdot \sim Vm$. A still more complicated compound, *If Hans is absent, he is either sick or he is out of town* becomes $Ah \supset (Sh \lor Oh)$ when appropriate abbreviations and logical symbols are used. Similar structures can be formed with simple propositional functions as their constituents. We can consider each of the preceding examples as a specific "substitution instance" of a compound propositional function. We produced each by substituting a name for the variable in the propositional function. $Hj \cdot Wj$ can be thought of as the result of replacing the variable x in $Hx \cdot Wx$ by j, the name of a specified individual.

12.3 QUANTIFIED STATEMENTS

Having previously noted the relationship between propositional functions and classes, we may now ask what sort of propositional function has a like relationship to a class product—the class of things belonging to both of two classes (see Section 4.9). It will be a compound one in which the simple propositional functions corresponding to the classes considered separately are conjoined. Something belonging to both of two classes is something that makes both of the corresponding propositional functions true. If the true substitution instances of Hx define the class of healthy individuals and those of Wx, the class of wealthy individuals, the true substitution instances of $Hx \cdot Wx$ define the product of both classes. In the language of algebraic notation, we represent the class product by placing the capital letters representing the two classes involved alongside each other. The corresponding expression in the system of truth-functional compounds is the conjunction of two propositional functions.

Since it was possible for us to treat **A, E, I,** and **O** statements in terms of class products, we are now in a position to translate them into statements involving propositional functions. We need only introduce a way of expressing "There are" and "There are no"—the function of the marks used in Venn diagrams and the equality and inequality signs of algebraic notation. This function in the new system will be based on an expression called the "existential quantifier," written as parentheses enclosing the symbol "∃" alongside a variable: $(\exists x)$. When we place this expression before a propositional function, we take it to assert that there is at least one individual in the universe of discourse for which the propositional function is true. We can easily express the denial that there are any such things, by simply writing the negation sign before the existential quantifier, $\sim(\exists x)$. The correspondence between the Venn diagram formulations of **A, E, I,** and **O** statements and statements formed with the existential quantifier is indicated in figure 12.1.

Unlike propositional functions standing alone, the expressions formed by joining the existential quantifier to a propositional function are genuine

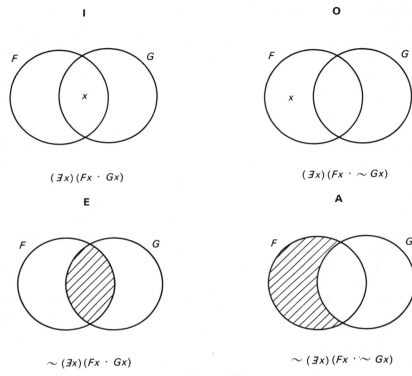

Figure 12.1

statements. As we have just seen, they can provide still another way of expressing the kind of statements previously formulated in one of the three languages of Part One. There is no reason why statements formed by combining the propositional function with the quantifier should be restricted to forms that are equivalent to **A, E, I,** and **O** statements. The existential quantifier can be attached to any propositional function, and it need not be restricted to conjunctions that correspond to class products. Using R and G to stand for "red" and "green," we may write $(\exists x)$ $(Rx \lor Gx)$: *There is something that is either red or green.* This statement does not correspond to anything expressible in logical English. It is, however, as much a statement as any of those that do have such counterparts.

The result we get by attaching a quantifier to a propositional function is a statement. We can get the same result by replacing the variable in the function by a name. We can form statements out of propositional functions in either way. From Hx, by substituting the name j for x, we can form the singular statement *Hj—John is healthy*. From the same propositional function, by attaching the existential quantifier to it, we can form the statement (∃ *x*) *Hx—there is someone who is healthy*. The result of substituting a name for the variable in such a fashion *is* a compound statement, with the same logical structure as the function. It is also a singular statement, that is, it concerns a specific individual identified by name. The result of attaching a quantifier to a compound propositional function is not a compound statement, however, but a simple one. Furthermore, the statement we form by quantification does not mention any specific individual and can therefore be described as a general statement.

One way we have of interpreting the fact that quantified statements are general is by looking on them as being concerned, in a sense, with *all* of the individuals in the universe of discourse instead of with just one specified individual. If we can identify every individual in the universe of discourse, we can even construct a compound statement equivalent to the quantified statement. The name of every individual in the universe will have a part in it. To begin with a very simple example, we can consider a universe of discourse in which there are just two individuals—such as two lights on a signal board. In this universe of discourse, it is obvious that the quantified statement (∃*x*)*Ox—at least one of the lights is on*—is equivalent to the compound statement *Oa* v *Ob*. If there were more than two lights, this would not be so, for the assertion that at least one light is on would be true if both *a* and *b* were off and one of the others on. Even so, there will be *some* compound statement that would be necessarily equivalent to the existentially quantified statement. It would differ from the example here only in the number of individuals concerned. Like *Oa* v *Ob* it would be formed by substituting the name of each individual in the universe of discourse for the variable in the propositional function and then constructing a general disjunction of all the singular statements so formed: *Oa* v *Ob* v *Oc*. . . . If the universe of discourse does not have any finite number of individuals in it—for example, the universe consisting of numbers—it will not even be theoretically possible for us to construct such a statement; we can still conceive the pattern, if not the completed statement, in the same way: a multiple disjunction having for its constituents the distinct singular statements that arise from substituting names of every individual in the universe for the individual variable.

The universal statements of logical English correspond to negations of existentially quantified statements in which the propositional function is a conjunction, the counterpart of the class product. Therefore, we must consider the effect of negation. In the simple two-membered universe we have used as an illustration previously, $\sim(\exists x)Ox$ (which could be read as *There are no lights that are on*) would be equivalent to $\sim(Oa \vee Ob)$. DeMorgan's theorems give $\sim Oa \cdot \sim Ob$ as an equivalent of this expression. For the general case, the negation of a disjunction of any number of constituents is equivalent to a conjunction in which the constituents are the negations of those occurring in the disjunction:

$$\sim(Fa \vee Fb \vee Fc \ldots) \equiv (\sim Fa \cdot \sim Fb \cdot \sim Fc \cdot \ldots)$$

It is useful to have a quantifier that has the same relation to a conjunction that the existential quantifier has to a comparable disjunction. For this purpose, the symbol (x)—a variable enclosed in parentheses—is introduced as the "universal quantifier." It is used to assert that the indicated propositional function becomes true for each substitution of a name for the variable. Because of the relationship determined by DeMorgan's theorem in its generalized form, we can introduce the universal quantifier by defining it in terms of the existential quantifier already introduced:

$$(x)Fx \quad \text{means} \quad \sim(\exists x) \sim Fx$$

When this definition is applied to the special cases of the expressions corresponding to the universal statements of logical English (see figure 12.1), these results emerge:

A: $\sim(\exists x)(Fx \cdot \sim Gx)$ becomes $(x)\sim(Fx \cdot \sim Gx)$ or
                                              $(x)(Fx \supset Gx)$

E: $\sim(\exists x)(Fx \cdot Gx)$ becomes $(x)\sim(Fx \cdot Gx)$ or
                                              $(x)(Fx \supset \sim Gx)$

The alternate forms are produced by use of equivalences depending on the definition of material implication. Replacing F and G with specified predicates for purposes of illustration, we could read them as *Of anyone it is true that if he is healthy, then he is wealthy* and *Of anyone it is true that if he is healthy, then he is not wealthy*. The equivalent expressions in logical English would be *All healthy people are wealthy people* and *No healthy people are wealthy people*.

12.3 EXERCISES

The statements below refer to the preliminary model we gave in Section 1.5 and the problems in Exercise 1.5. Translate them into a form appropriate to the logic of quantified statements as introduced in the preceding sections, using appropriate abbreviations for predicates and proper names. Also, give the conjunctive or disjunctive schematic equivalents, as determined by the universe of discourse, for all quantified statements.

A. Mrs. Chancellor is married.

B. Mr. Allardyce is not a pianist.

C. Viola is a liar.

D. Copperblank is wealthy and famous.

E. Godfrey the Rude was neither wise nor powerful.

F. All the guests at Mrs. Sponsable's party are artists. (Write this two ways, once with a general universe of discourse and once with the universe of discourse understood to include all and only the guests at the party. Give the schematic equivalent of the latter version only.)

G. At least one of them is a liar. (Hogs questioned by the farmer.)

H. All of those who won more than $5000 are either superior or lucky. (The chessplayers in the invitational tournament.)

I. Someone who cannot see has the white pieces and knows it. (The three finalists in the knockout tournament.)

J. All the ladies were beautiful, and one of them who was of royal blood was very proud. (The three ladies in problem 1.5D.)

12.4 QUANTIFICATION AND THE RULE OF REPLACEMENT

We have enriched our systematic language by making provisions for statements based on propositional functions. They are to be formed either by specifying a value of the individual variable ("instantiation") or by attaching a quantifier ("quantification"). We will consequently need to introduce principles of inference applicable to arguments that include such statements. Some of these principles will be entirely new, while others will be adaptations of the principles we have already used with compound statements. We shall begin with the principles with which we are all familiar.

The rule of replacement, since its application depends on a variety of equivalences, calls for separate treatment. Basically, its application within this system involves nothing new. The equivalence patterns represented by commutation, association, DeMorgan's theorems, and the rest impose no conditions on the constituents of the various compounds that enter into them. The equivalence of a doubly negated statement to the unnegated statement, for example, holds whether the statement is a simple statement or a compound of any degree of complexity. Since the equivalences do not depend on the kind of statement substituted for the p's and q's of the equivalence patterns, they will hold just as well if the statements substituted are singular statements or quantified statements. To this extent, no new equivalences nor any extension of the scope of those already accepted, beyond admitting the propriety of new kinds of substitutions for their constituents, is required.

If we wish to extend the application of the rule of replacement to propositional functions, however, we must depart from any procedure we have so far accepted. Propositional functions are not statements, and they have no truth values. Consequently, it is not strictly correct to apply to them the idea of equivalence, which has been defined in terms of truth values. If we wish to apply the rule of replacement to propositional functions, we must modify it to fit the situation. We can make the necessary modification by showing that one propositional function can replace another, if the result of specifying the same value of the variable in each would be a pair of equivalent statements: $\sim(Fx \vee Gx)$ could be replaced by $\sim Fx \cdot \sim Gx$. Any pair of statements created by specifying the same value for x in each of them would be, by DeMorgan's theorems, equivalent. We could justify such a procedure by referring to the principle establishing the equivalence of the statements that are their substitution instances, in this case, DeM. What this means is that as far as the replacement of an expression by its equivalent is concerned, we are permitted to treat propositional functions *as if* they were statements, as if the x were really a name and not just a variable.

So far, we have considered the extension of the rule of replacement to cover three cases: (1) compound statements that include quantified propositional functions, (2) compounds that include substitution instances of propositional functions, and (3) compound propositional functions of which the substitution instances would be equivalent. In all such cases, the practical application of the rule depends only on the recognition of the already familiar equivalence patterns, DeMorgan's theorems, association, commutation, and the rest. There are some other equivalences involving quantified statements that do not depend quite so explicitly on the established equivalences, although the idea of schematic analyses of quantified statements permits us to invoke the established equivalence patterns in justifying them.

Four such quantificational equivalences will be added to the list available for the application of the rule of replacement, all sharing a common abbreviation, QE. The first two, which depend on the application of DeMorgan's theorems to the schematic analyses of the quantified statements concerned, we have already noted in connection with the introduction of the universal quantifier.

Quantificational Equivalences (QE)

    1. $\sim(x)Fx$ is equivalent to $(\exists x) \sim Fx$
    2. $\sim(\exists x)Fx$ is equivalent to $(x) \sim Fx$

The other two depend on the application of commutation and association to the relevant schematic analyses: (3) the conjunction of two universally quantified propositional functions is equivalent to the universally quantified conjunction of the two functions; (4) the disjunction of two existentially quantified propositional functions is equivalent to the existentially quantified disjunction of the two functions.

Quantificational Equivalences (QE)

    3. $(x)Fx \cdot (x)Gx$ is equivalent to $(x)(Fx \cdot Gx)$
    4. $(\exists x)Fx \text{ v } (\exists x)Gx$ is equivalent to $(\exists x)(Fx \text{ v } Gx)$

The justification of these two equivalences is essentially the same, differing only in the application of association and commutation to a complex conjunction on the one hand and to a complex disjunction on the other. It can be illustrated in terms of the equivalence pattern for the universally quantified functions. The schematic analysis of a universally quantified function, as explained in Section 12.2, is the conjunction of all the substitution instances. The left-hand side of the equivalence, then, will be the conjunction of all of the substitution instances of Fx conjoined to all of the substitution instances of Gx. Since the elements of a complex conjunction can be rearranged in any way, such a conjunction is equivalent to the conjunction of a given substitution instance of Fx with the same substitution instance of Gx, this conjoined to another such pair and so on through all the paired substitution instances of each elementary function. But this set of conjoined substitution instances is nothing but the schematic analysis of the universally quantified compound propositional function $Fx \cdot Gx$, which is the right-hand side of the equivalence. Think of all the substitution instances for a certain universe of discourse as arranged in two columns:

$$Fa \quad Ga$$
$$Fb \quad Gb$$
$$Fc \quad Gc$$
$$Fd \quad Gd$$

If the members of the left-hand column are all conjoined and those of the right-hand column conjoined, we have the equivalents of $(x)Fx$ and $(g)(Gx)$. If we conjoin the pair on the first line $(Fa \cdot Ga)$ and so on until we have conjoined all the pairs, we have the equivalent of $(x)(Fx \cdot Gx)$. A similar procedure using disjunction suffices to justify the equivalence of the existentially quantified statements.

12.5   QUANTIFICATION AND OTHER RULES OF INFERENCE

Like the rule of replacement, the other basic rules of inference impose no restrictions on the kind of statement to be substituted in the places represented by the p's and q's we used in expressing their general form. The constituents of a basic argument form may be elementary statements or compound statements, quantified statements or singular statements. In justifying the inference from *If all men are mortal, Socrates is mortal* and *all men are mortal* to *Socrates is mortal,* we simply apply modus ponens. The principle is not affected by the fact that the antecedent of the conditional is in this case a universally quantified statement in the language of logical English, and the consequent is a singular statement.

We can also introduce new rules that depend on the special characteristics of quantified statements. In each case, the rule can be justified by applying the basic rules of inference to the schematic analyses of the quantified statements involved. Rules of this sort will fall into three sets: those permitting inferences between quantified statements and singular statements, those permitting inferences between compounds of quantified statements and elementary quantified statements, and those permitting inferences involving quantified statements only.

We will add two rules of the first type to our list, one for a general statement as premise and a singular statement as conclusion, the other for an inference running from singular premise to general conclusion. We can understand both easily enough as direct applications of the relevant principle of inference for compound statements together with the equivalences between quantified statements and exhaustive conjunctions or disjunctions of substitution instances for each member of the universe of discourse.

A universal statement is equivalent to some set of conjoined singular statements, in which each member of the universe is represented; it is the conjunction of every substitution instance of the propositional function. The principle of simplification permits us to infer any member of a set of conjoined statements from the conjunction. We can state a special application of simplification to the case of the universally quantified statements. Although it is, as suggested here, just a special application of simplification, it is convenient to have a special name for it:

> *The Principle of Universal Instantiation* (UI)
> From a universally quantified propositional function, it is possible to infer any of its substitution instances. In abbreviated form:

$$\frac{(x)Fx}{Fy}$$

The symbol y could be any of the individual names in the universe of discourse.

The other principle of this type permits us to make inferences from a singular statement to a general statement. We can justify it by an appeal to the principle of addition. That principle permits us to add by disjunction to any statement any other statement we choose. If the given statement is true, any disjunction of which it is a constituent will be true, since all that is required for the truth of the disjunction is that one of its constituents be true. The special application of addition we are interested in here is one that proceeds by adding to a singular statement by disjunction every other substitution instance of the corresponding propositional function. We can therefore state the rule, again with a special name of its own, although it is in effect only an application of the principle of addition:

> *The Principle of Existential Generalization* (EG)
> From any substitution instance of a propositional function it is possible to infer the existential quantification of the function.

$$\frac{Fy}{(\exists x)Fx}$$

Again, y is meant to represent any of the individual names belonging to the universe of discourse.

We next introduce two rules for the second of the three types we distinguished above. They are rules relating a compound of two quantified statements to a single quantified statement operating on a compound propositional function. Like UI and EG, the justification of these two rules depends on the application of SIMP and ADD respectively to the corresponding schematic analyses; here we must apply *DIST* also.

> *The Principle of Universal Consolidation* (UC)
> From the disjunction of two universally quantified statements, it is possible to infer the universally quantified disjunction of their respective propositional functions.

$$\frac{(x)Fx \text{ v } (x)Gx}{(x)(Fx \text{ v } Gx)}$$

If we replace the premise and the conclusion with their corresponding schematic analyses for a given universe of discourse, the result, in the case of the premise, will be a disjunction of two multiple conjunctions. In the case of the conclusion, it will be a multiple conjunction of the substitution instances of the disjunctive propositional function. But if distributional equivalence is applied to the premise, the result will be a complex conjunction and among its constituents will be all of the constituents of the conclusion, plus a number of others. We can rearrange the longer conjunction by using commutation and association and bring about a situation in which the shorter one is identical with one of its components, so that it can be inferred by simplification. The procedure is illustrated below for a universe containing just two individuals:

1. $(Fa \cdot Fb) \text{ v } (Ga \cdot Gb)$	The premise analyzed for two items.
2. $(Fa \text{ v } Ga) \cdot (Fa \text{ v } Gb) \cdot (Fb \text{ v } Ga) \cdot (Fb \text{ v } Gb)$	1, DIST
3. $[(Fa \text{ v } Ga) \cdot (Fb \text{ v } Gb)] \cdot (Fa \text{ v } Gb) \cdot (Fb \text{ v } Ga)$	2, COMM, ASSOC
4. $(Fa \text{ v } Ga) \cdot (Fb \text{ v } Gb)$	3, SIMP

The conclusion is $(x)(Fx \text{ v } Gx)$, analyzed for the two items, a and b.
There is another rule falling into this classification.

> *The Principle of Existential Dissociation* (ED)
> From the existential quantification of a conjunction of propositional functions, it is possible to infer the conjunction of the

existential quantification of each of the two propositional functions.

$$\frac{(\exists x)(Fx \cdot Gx)}{(\exists x)Fx \cdot (\exists x)Gx}$$

In this case, if we replace the quantified statements with their equivalents for any given universe of discourse and apply distributional equivalence to the conclusion, we will produce a complex disjunction as conclusion. Part of it will be identical (upon appropriate rearrangement) with the premise, and the inference becomes a matter of applying the principle of addition. We should be able to construct an illustration, say for a universe containing just two members, with no difficulty:

1. $(Fa \cdot Ga) \vee (Fb \cdot Gb)$ The premise
     analyzed
     for two items

2. $[(Fa \cdot Ga) \vee (Fb \cdot Gb)]$
     $\vee [(Fa \cdot Gb) \vee (Fb \cdot Ga)]$ 1, ADD

3. $(Fa \cdot Ga) \vee (Fa \cdot Gb)$
     $\vee (Fb \cdot Ga) \vee (Fb \cdot Gb)$ 2, COMM

4. $(Fa \vee Fb) \cdot (Ga \vee Gb)$ 3, DIST

Line 4 is the equivalent, for the universe of two individuals, of $(\exists x)Fx \cdot (\exists x)Gx$.

12.6 QUANTIFIED FORMS OF THE BASIC RULES OF INFERENCE

What remains for us to consider are the rules of inference that will permit quantified conclusions to be drawn from quantified premises. It is by rules such as these that we can provide, in this system, for the valid inferences of the so-called traditional system we examined in Part One. A useful set of rules is available by transformation of the basic rules of inference themselves. There are two steps in the procedure:

1. For the statement variables in the basic rule of inference, substitute propositional functions.
2. Quantify all lines of the argument form in one of the following ways:
   a. Attach the universal quantifier to all of the premises and to the conclusion.

   b. Attach the existential quantifier to one of the premises and to
   the conclusion and attach the universal quantifier to all of
   the other premises.

These procedures for transforming the premises and conclusions of the
basic argument forms into quantified statements permit at least two such
principles to be derived from each. When there are two premises, there
will be three derivative forms, depending on which premise is existentially
quantified.

From the principle of simplification, for example, we can derive these
forms:

Basic Argument Form (SIMP)	Quantified Form (1)	Quantified Form (2)
$p \cdot q$	$(x)(Fx \cdot Gx)$	$(\exists x)(Fx \cdot Gx)$
p	$(x)Fx$	$(\exists x)Fx$

From the principle of hypothetical syllogism, these three forms may be
constructed:

Basic Argument Form (HS)	Quantified Form (1)	Quantified Forms (2)	
		(a)	(b)
$p \supset q$	$(x)(Fx \supset Gx)$	$(\exists x)(Fx \supset Gx)$	$(x)(Fx \supset Gx)$
$q \supset r$	$(x)(Gx \supset Hx)$	$(x)(Gx \supset Hx)$	$(\exists x)(Gx \supset Hx)$
$p \supset r$	$(x)(Fx \supset Hx)$	$(\exists x)(Fx \supset Hx)$	$(\exists x)(Fx \supset Hx)$

In using such principles in proofs, we shall distinguish them from the
basic argument forms by adding Qun or Qex to the title assigned to the
form. The Q indicates that it is a quantified form derived according to
the procedure just described and the adjoined *un* or *ex* indicates which of
the two rules governing the attachment of quantifiers has been applied—
the one providing for a universally quantified conclusion or the one
providing for an existentially quantified one.

A systematic justification of these procedures for constructing quantified
versions of the basic argument forms can be presented in terms of the
schematic equivalents for quantified statements. The universally quantified
forms are justified very simply. The premise or premises will correspond
to a set of conjoined singular statements that exhaust the universe. By
applying the principle of simplification, we can isolate the premise or
premises for any given individual in the universe and draw a conclusion
justified by the basic argument form itself. By conjoining all of the con-

clusions so derived, we form a statement that is the schematic equivalent of the universal conclusion of the argument in its quantified form.

The forms we derive by attaching the existential quantifier to one premise and to the conclusion require a somewhat more complex process of justification. We make use of a procedure resembling what is called "mathematical induction." We show first that a given argument form is valid for a universe with a stated number of individuals, say one. We then show that if the argument form is valid for a universe with n individuals, it must also be valid for a universe containing $n + 1$ individuals. With both of these points established, it follows that the argument form must be valid for any universe, no matter how many individuals it contains.

Let us begin with the simple case of immediate inference from an existentially quantified premise to an existentially quantified conclusion. An example would be the Qex form of simplification.

$$\frac{(\exists x)(Fx \cdot Gx)}{(\exists x)(Fx)}$$

For any given universe, each existentially quantified statement will be equivalent to the disjunction of all of its substitution instances. Now let us suppose that for a universe of n individuals, it is impossible for the disjunction of substitution instances formed from the propositional function in the premise to be true and the corresponding disjunction of substitution instances for the conclusion to be false. Now we raise the question: Would the addition of one more substitution instance, that is, the addition of one more individual to the universe of discourse, create a situation in which this would no longer be impossible? Under what conditions would it become possible for the premise to be made true while the conclusion remains false? We have assumed that when the conclusion as it originally stood is false, the premises must be false. We now attach to each, by disjunction, an additional statement. The premise will become true only if the statement added on is true; the conclusion will remain false only if the statement added onto it is false. Whether this combination is possible depends on the application of the basic argument forms to the substitution instances introduced by the additional individual. The validity of the quantified argument form in a universe containing only one individual can also be established directly by reference to the basic argument form. From there, we can proceed to a two-membered universe, then to a three-membered one, and so on indefinitely.

This form of proof can easily be illustrated in terms of an evaluation chart used in the ordinary way to establish validity. In the next chart,

P represents the disjunction of n substitution instances in the premise function; Q represents the disjunction of the same substitution instances in the conclusion function for a certain universe of n members, that is, they are respectively the disjunctive equivalents of existentially quantified functions in that universe.

Premise	*Conclusion*
P v $(Fx_{n+1} \cdot Gx_{n+1})$	Q v Fx_{n+1}
F | $\cdot$	F v
F v	F
T	

If, when Q is false, P must be false, the addition of the substitution instances indicated for x_{n+1} does not alter the situation and permit the premise side to become true while the conclusion side remains false. This is excluded by the validity of the principle of simplification in its basic nonquantified form. Therefore, once we have established the validity of the principle for a given number of substitution instances, we can always establish its validity for a set including one more. That it is valid for just one substitution instance can be proved by substituting Fx_1 and Gx_1 in the principle of simplification. The argument form in which we are interested

$$\frac{(\exists x)(Fx \cdot Gx)}{(\exists x)Fx}$$

is valid when there is just one substitution instance for each function. But if it is valid for a universe in which it has n substitution instances, it is also valid for a universe in which it has $n + 1$ substitution instances. Therefore, it is valid for a two-membered universe. By applying the same procedure again, however, we move on to a universe in which there are three substitution instances, and from there to four, and ultimately to any number we please. This permits us to assert the existentially quantified version of simplification without any restriction.

When there are two premises, one of them must be universally quantified. For any given universe, the schematic equivalent of that premise will be the conjunction of all the substitution instances for that universe. The only interesting case is the one in which for n instances, the conclusion is false, the conjunction corresponding to the universally quantified premise is true, and the disjunction corresponding to the existentially quantified premise is false (according to the supposition that for n instances, the premises cannot be true and the conclusion false). We now ask whether the addition of one more instances, to provide for a universe of $n + 1$ members, will make it possible for both premises to become true while the conclusion remains false. Since the additional substitution instance in the conclusion is disjoined, it must be false if the conclusion is to remain false. The substitution instance added to the conjunctive premise must be true if that premise is to remain true, and the substitution instance attached to the disjunctive premise must be true if that premise is to become true. If the argument composed of just the substitution instances for x_{n+1} is valid, this combination is impossible. The rest of the reasoning proceeds along the lines we have already suggested for the simpler case.

12.6 EXERCISE

Prepare a complete list of the quantified principles of inference that can be derived from the basic principles given on pages 245–248. Compare your results with the list in Appendix 3.

12.7 RULES OF INFERENCE
FOR TRADITIONAL LOGIC

We are now prepared to incorporate the principles of immediate inference and the syllogism of traditional logic into the new system. There is one exception: the principle of limitation, which was introduced to take account of inferences that are bound up with the usage of universal statements in English so that the rules of logical English would conform as closely as possible to the rules governing reasoning with the same types of statement in ordinary discourse. Because the language we are now using is an artificial language in which the ordinary quantifiers of the English language have been supplanted by special symbolic expressions, no such rule has been included. It would be possible for us to add such a rule for special purposes, just as it was possible to add one in working within the equally artificial languages of Venn diagrams and algebraic notation.

We begin with the rule of replacement, whose application will suffice to introduce counterparts of the principles of immediate inference. The principle of contradiction has its counterpart in the quantificational equivalences which are special applications of DeMorgan's theorems. For example, *All S are P* and *Some S are not P* have as their counterparts $(x)(Sx \supset Px)$ and $(\exists x)(Sx \cdot \sim Px)$. The former, as we have seen, is equivalent to

$\sim(\exists x)$ $(Sx \cdot Px)$. Obversion is accomplished by applying double negation to the propositional function which corresponds to the predicate term of the statement in its logical English form. *Some S are P,* for example, reformulated as $(\exists x)(Sx \cdot Px)$, is equivalent to $(\exists x)(Sx \cdot \sim \sim Px)$, which we can then read as *Some S are not NonP.* The conversion of an **I** statement is, in the new language, the application of commutation; the conversion of an **E** statement is accomplished by applying transposition and double negation. (There is a direct inference to the complement converse of an **A** statement in the new formulation, incidentally, by application of transposition.)

The justification of syllogistic reasoning requires the use of the special quantified versions of the basic principles. Of the four basic forms of the syllogism in the first figure, **AAA, AII, EAE,** and **EIO,** we need consider only the first two separately, since the other two, in the new language, differ only in that $\sim Px$ stand in the place of Px. 1-**AAA** involves a particularly simple and direct application.

1. $(x)(Mx \supset Px)$
2. $\underline{(x)(Sx \supset Mx)}$
   $(x)(Sx \supset Px)$

We need add only the justification, since this argument is (except for order) an example of the quantified form of hyopthetical syllogism already used in illustrating the generation of quantified principles. The justification would be, simply: 2, 1, Qun HS. The justification of 1-**AII** requires more than one step but is still quite simple:

1. $(x)(Mx \supset Px)$
2. $(\exists x)(Sx \cdot Mx)$
3. $(x)[(Sx \cdot Mx) \supset (Sx \cdot Px)]$ 1, Qun ABS
4. $(\exists x)(Sx \cdot Px)$ 3, 2, Qex MP

There is no reason to restrict the application of the rules of inference to arguments translated from the repertoire of valid forms expressible in logical English. Earlier, in Chapters 3 and 4, we pointed out that the greater flexibility of the Venn diagrams and algebraic notation in comparison with logical English enabled us to construct argument forms and rules of inference in languages that were outside the compass of the rules restricted to the range of logical English. The same is true of the new notation. We can translate the statements of logical English into the present systematic language and so make its rules fall within the scope of those relating quantified statements formed in the new way. But that is not all. Other statements, and rules appropriate to them that cannot even be formulated in terms of logical English, can also be expressed in the new notation. Inferences involving such statements are just as susceptible to analysis according to the procedures we have developed in the preceding sections as are arguments having counterparts in logical English. These inferences occupy no privileged position. Here is an example of an obviously valid argument not demonstrable in logical English with the rules available in Part One:

> All the lights that are on are red or green.
> None of the lights that are on are red.
> _____
> All the lights that are on are green.

The argument eludes the rules for logical English because in logical English there is no way of significantly representing the relationship between the three predicate terms. Since this can be done in our new notation for quantified statements, in the system we are now using we can demonstrate the argument's validity by a formal proof.

1. $(x)[Ox \supset (Rx \text{ v } Gx)]$ Premise
2. $(x)(Ox \supset \sim Rx)$ Premise
3. $(x)[\sim(Rx \text{ v } Gx) \supset \sim Ox]$ 1, TRANS
4. $(x)[(\sim Rx \cdot \sim Gx) \supset \sim Ox]$ 3, DeM
5. $(x)[\sim Rx \supset (\sim Gx \supset \sim Ox)]$ 4, EXP
6. $(x)[Ox \supset (\sim Gx \supset \sim Ox)]$ 2, 5, Qun HS
7. $(x)[Ox \supset (Ox \supset Gx)]$ 6, TRANS
8. $(x)[(Ox \cdot Ox) \supset Gx]$ 7, EXP
9. $(x)(Ox \supset Gx)$ 8, TAUT

12.7 EXERCISE

Work out proofs within the system presented in this chapter for all of the valid forms of the syllogism in Part One, except those that derive a particular conclusion from two universal premises.

12.8 PROOF OF INVALIDITY

The evaluation chart can be adapted to use as a test of validity for arguments involving quantified statements. Its application, as might be expected, is more complex than in the case of arguments in which only truth-functional compounds are involved. Fundamentally, of course, the chart is still being applied for truth-functional compounds. It was designed for that and that alone. The technique becomes applicable to quantified statements only if we regard them as schematically analyzed into multiple conjunctions or disjunctions.

For any specified universe, a universally quantified statement is truth-functionally equivalent to the multiple conjunction of all of its substitution instances. An existentially quantified statement is equivalent to their multiple disjunction. The question of validity depends on whether or not there is a possible universe that contains individuals with characteristics such that the premises of the argument are true, yet the conclusion is false. Validity and invalidity do not vary from one universe of discourse to another. Therefore, if we can establish the possibility of premises being true and conclusion false in a relatively simple universe containing only a small number of individuals, that is sufficient to establish invalidity without qualification. To establish validity, it must be shown that there is no such possible universe.

The chart is set up as for testing the validity of an argument with compound statements, with one exception: at the head of each column there should be two lines. The top line is intended for the premises and the conclusion of the argument in its original form. The line below is intended for an equivalent argument (for an appropriate universe of discourse) in which all quantified statements have been replaced by exhaustive disjunctions of their substitution instances. From our study of arguments in logical English, we know that the following argument is invalid (since it violates one of the rules of quality and distribution):

> Some fanatics are guerillas.
> No guerillas are householders.
> _____
> Some householders are not fanatics.

When the argument is reformulated in the language of quantified propositional functions, using appropriate abbreviations, it reads:

$$(\exists x)(Fx \cdot Gx)$$
$$\underline{(x)(Gx \supset {\sim}Hx)}$$
$$(\exists x)(Hx \cdot {\sim}Fx)$$

These premises are now to be written across the top line of an evaluation chart. They are to be given the value T. The conclusion is to be written at the top right of the top line and assigned the value F. See the following chart for the initial assignment of values for a validity test:

	Premise 1	Premise 2	Conclusion
	$(\exists x)(Fx \cdot Gx)$	$(x)(Gx \supset \sim Hx)$	$(\exists x)(Hx \cdot \sim Fx)$
0			
1			
2			
3	T	T	F

Notice first of all that a sufficient number of levels for truth values have been provided to accommodate multiple disjunctions and conjunctions that have substitution instances of the propositional functions as their constituents. This can be done at the outset if we permit such compounds to occupy a single block on the chart.

In the second place, notice that as matters now stand, no further marks are determined on the chart. This reflects the fact that the premises and the conclusion of the argument are all elementary statements. In order to apply the technique of determining truth values on the chart, we must introduce truth-functional compounds. This can be done by replacing quantified statements with substitution instances of their functions, according to the following rules:

> 1. An existentially quantified statement over a T or a universally quantified statement over an F may be replaced by a single substitution instance, using an individual name that has not yet been introduced on the chart.
> 2. All other quantified statements are to be replaced by multiple conjunctions or disjunctions that include their substitution instances for every name that already appears on the chart and that provide for the addition of still other substitution instances.

The second rule is a restatement of the truth-functional equivalence between quantified statements and their schematic analyses in a universe of discourse that may be partly specified as containing certain individuals. The first rule requires some explanation, but the point is really a simple one. The minimal condition for the truth of an existentially quantified statement is that there be one individual in the universe for which the propositional function it quantifies becomes true upon substitution. We can assign that individual, although we do not know which one it is, a name. Of course, it must not be a name that has already been used to designate some individual, for that would illegitimately presuppose that the individual already designated by the name is the very one that results in a true substitution instance of the existentially quantified function. Exactly parallel reasoning applies in the replacement of a false, universally quantified statement by a single substitution instance, using a name not previously used. The minimal condition for the falsity of a universal is that one of its substitution instances be false. We write down that substitution instance, taking care to avoid illegitimate assumptions of identity by making use of a new name.

In the example we introduced, we are permitted by the first rule to replace the existentially quantified premise, $(\exists x)(Fx \cdot Gx)$, with a single substitution instance. Since no names appear on the chart, we have complete freedom of choice. Let $Fa \cdot Ga$ be one, possibly the only one, of the substitution instances of $Fx \cdot Gx$ that is true. If the existentially quantified statement is to be true, there must be such a one, and we are in a position to use whatever name we please in writing it. Corresponding substitution instances for the other quantified statements must be written in beneath them, leaving open the possibility of adding further substitution instances in a multiple conjunction or disjunction as called for. From here we can set up the chart in the usual fashion:

	Premise 1	Premise 2	Conclusion
	$(\exists x)(Fx \cdot Gx)$	$(x)(Gx \supset {\sim}Hx)$	$(\exists x)(Hx \cdot {\sim}Fx)$
	$Fa \cdot Ga$	$(Ga \supset {\sim}Ha)\cdot$	$(Ha \cdot {\sim}Fa)\text{v}$
0	$\cdot$	$\vert \; {\sim} \; \vert$	$\vert \; {\sim} \; \vert$
1		$\supset \quad \vert$	$\cdot \quad \vert$
2		$\cdot$	v
3	T	T	F

On this chart, the truth values for $Fa,\ Ga,$ and Ha are all determined, and consistently so, by the initial assignment of truth to the premises and falsity to the conclusion. The student should be familiar enough with the procedure to complete the determination of truth values himself. What this result shows is that even in a universe containing only one individual, it is possible for the premises of the argument to be true and the conclusion false. Of a universe consisting of just one man, a fanatic, a guerilla, but not a householder, we could assert the premises and deny the conclusion of the argument without even being false to the facts, to say nothing of committing an inconsistency. Invalidity is therefore demonstrated very simply in this case.

Another example will bring out somewhat more plainly the distinctive features of the validity test when it is applied to arguments involving quantified statements. Again, we shall use an argument that has a counterpart in logical English:

> Some fanatics are guerillas.
> No guerillas are householders.
> ———————————————
> No householders are fanatics.

This argument violates the same rule as the preceding one. It is, however, impossible for the premises to be true and the conclusion false in a universe containing only one individual. More generally, it is impossible for the *same* individual to be specified, without inconsistency, in the substitution instances that minimally assure these truth values for premises and conclusion. The following chart has nevertheless been filled in consistently and shows the argument to be invalid:

	Premise 1	Premise 2				Conclusion	
	$(\exists x)(Fx \cdot Gx)$	$(x)(Gx \supset \sim Hx)$				$(x)(Hx \supset \sim Fx)$	
	$Fa \cdot Ga$	$(Ga \supset \sim Ha) \cdot (Gb \supset \sim Hb)$				$Hb \supset \sim Fb$	
0	$T \cdot T$	T	$\sim F$	F	$\sim T$	T	$\sim T$
1	T	$T \supset T$		$F \supset F$		$T \supset F$	
2	T	T	$\cdot$	T		F	
3	T		T			F	

First the existentially quantified premise, assumed to be true, was replaced by a single substitution instance. Substitution instances for the same individual were specified in the universal premise, also assumed to be true, and values filled into the chart as required. The universally quantified conclusion, assumed to be false, was replaced by a single substitution instance, *using a different name, b,* and the same procedure carried out. The result is a completed chart, showing that in a universe of two individuals (one fanatic guerilla who is not a householder and one householder who is neither a fanatic nor a guerilla) the premises of the argument would be true and the conclusion false.

When the first rule, permitting the replacement of a true existentially quantified statement or a false universally quantified statement by a single substitution instance is not directly applicable, we introduce a sample individual and apply rule 2. If the resulting chart is filled in completely and consistently, invalidity is demonstrated. If an inconsistency is generated for one individual, we must consider whether the inconsistency could be avoided by introducing additional individuals. Whether rule 1 has been applied or not, this possibility must be considered before a final judgment is rendered about the argument's validity. Essentially, we can follow a procedure similar to the one outlined in Section 12.8. The crucial question is this: Could what is impossible in a universe containing n items be made possible by adding another individual to the collection? After the procedures we have already outlined have been applied, we add to the multiple disjunctions and conjunctions that remain open still another substitution instance, using a name not used before; then we test for validity on the resulting chart.

The examples considered in this discussion had quantified statements as premises and conclusion. In fact, they were both counterparts of arguments in logical English. No change in technique is required to prove invalidity when one or more of the constituents of the argument is a singular statement or a compound with singular or quantified statements among its components. Rule 1 applies quite generally and rule 2 requires only some increased caution to ensure that every name that appears is represented among the substitution instances filling in the multiple conjunctions or disjunctions it calls for.

12.8 EXERCISES

A. Determine the validity or invalidity of the following arguments:

1. $(x)(Hx \supset Ax)$
   $\sim(\exists x)(Ax \cdot Sx)$
   $\overline{(x)(Hx \supset \sim Sx)}$

2. $(x)(Fx \supset Bx)$
   $\underline{(x)(Fx \supset Dx)}$
   $(x)(Dx \supset Bx)$

3. $\sim(\exists x)(Ax \cdot Bx)$
   $(x)(Cx \supset \sim Dx)$
   $\underline{(x)[Bx \supset (Dx \lor \sim Ax)]}$
   $(x)(Ax \supset \sim Cx)$

4. Everyone who knew Brutus admired him, and everyone who knew him also respected Caesar, so those who admired Brutus respected Caesar.

5. Only harmful creatures were driven from Ireland by St. Patrick, and he drove all the snakes living there away. But all creatures that are neither poisonous nor large and carnivorous are harmless. The snakes that were living in Ireland, therefore, were either poisonous or large and carnivorous.

6. There are men who know how to reason who are not wise. No wise men deny the difference between good and evil. If a man denies the difference between good and evil or does not know how to reason, he is unable to solve moral problems. Therefore, either there are wise men who cannot solve moral problems or no one who knows how to reason denies the difference between good and evil.

7. Any region in which there is snow on the ground after the vernal equinox has either a cold or a temperate climate. Minnesota is a region in which the temperature is often below zero and in which there is snow on the ground after the vernal equinox. The climate of a region where the temperature is often below zero is not temperate. It follows that Minnesota has a cold climate.

8. If cold climates are stimulating, the vigor of Minnesota's natives is easily explained. If there is such an easy explanation and none has been offered, either the Department of Anthropology or the Department of Psychology is at fault. All cold climates require bodily exertion, and climates requiring bodily exertion are stimulating. It is true, therefore, that if the Department of Anthropology is not at fault, the Department of Psychology is; for no explanation of Minnesota's vigor has been offered.

B. Complete the following proofs, and construct proofs for any of the arguments in Part A that are valid.

1.   1. $(x)(Px \supset Ex)$ Premise
      2. $\sim(Ea \text{ v } Rb)$ Premise
      3. $\sim Pa \supset (x)[Sx \supset (Mx \text{ v } Lx)]$ Premise
      4. $(x)[(Mx \text{ v } Lx) \supset Rx]$ Premise
      5. $Pa \supset Ea$
      6. $\sim Ea \cdot \sim Rb$
      7. $\sim Ea$
      8. $\sim Pa$
      9. $(x)[Sx \supset (Mx \text{ v } Lx)]$
      10. $(x)(Sx \supset Rx)$
      11. $\sim Rb$
      12. $(\exists x) \sim Rx$
      13. $(\exists x) \sim Sx$
      14. $(\exists x)(\sim Sx \text{ v } \sim Ox)$
      15. $(\exists x) \sim (Sx \cdot Ox)$

2.   1. $C \supset (x)[Bx \supset (Dx \cdot Fx)]$ Premise
      2. $(\exists x)(Gx \cdot Hx) \supset (Ba \cdot \sim Da)$ Premise
      3. Gb Premise
      4. Hb Premise
      5. $Gb \cdot Hb$
      6. $(\exists x)(Gx \cdot Hx)$
      7. $Ba \cdot \sim Da$
      8. $(Ba \cdot \sim Da) \text{ v } (Ba \cdot \sim Fa)$
      9. $Ba \cdot (\sim Da \text{ v } \sim Fa)$
      10. $Ba \cdot \sim(Da \cdot Fa)$
      11. $\sim\sim[Ba \cdot \sim(Da \cdot Fa)]$
      12. $\sim[Ba \supset (Da \cdot Fa)]$
      13. $(\exists x) \sim [Bx \supset (Dx \cdot Fx)]$
      14. $\sim(x)[Bx \supset (Dx \cdot Fx)]$
      15. $\sim C$

Appendix 1

THE ABERDEEN DEBATE

INTRODUCTION

It is the fashion, even in the case of prose that is plainly argumentative, for style to camouflage logical structure. In the following text of a debate held in 1675, this is not so; many of the arguments advanced are cast explicitly in what must be counted as a kind of standard form even if it is not precisely the form we have established in this book. Throughout the debate, even when the form of the argument is not explicit to such a degree, the play of logical stroke and counterstroke is never so obscured as not to be easily accessible. It offers, therefore, a rich store of logical material for our analysis and evaluation, which is all the more remarkable because it is encountered during the course of an extemporaneous debate.

Throughout the body of the debate, there are portions of the text appearing in brackets. They represent marginal comments made by those who prepared this account of the debate for publication. The numbers in parentheses following certain sentences refer to the exercises that follow the debate itself.

BACKGROUND OF THE DEBATE

Robert Barclay was a young man of twenty-six at the time of the debate and George Keith a little less than ten years his senior. Barclay had recently published a series of theological theses, and these were the occasion of the debate. The

A

True and Faithful
ACCOMPT
OF

The moſt material Paſſages of
a Diſpute betwixt ſome *Students of Divinity* (ſo called) of the Univerſity of *Aberdene*, and the People called *Quakers*; held
in *Aberdene* in *Scotland*, in *Alexander Harper*
his Cloſe (or Yard) before ſome hundreds of
Witneſſes, upon the fourteenth day of the
ſecond Month called *April*, 1675. There being

Opponents $\left\{\begin{array}{l}\textit{John Leſly.}\\ \textit{Alexander Shirreff.}\\ \textit{Paul Gellie.}\end{array}\right\}$ Maſt. of Art.

And Defendants upon the *Quakers* part.
Robert Barclay. and *George Keith.*

Præſes for moderating the meeting,
choſen by them, *Andrew Thomſone* Advocate:
and by the *Quakers*, *Alexander Skein*, ſom-
time a Magiſtrate of the City.

Publiſhed for preventing miſreports,
by *Alexander Skein*, *John Skein*, *Alexander Harper*, *Thomas Merſer*, and *John Cowie.*

To which is added, *Robert Barclay's*
offer to the Preachers of *Aberdene*, renewed
and re inforced.

Act. 4. 27 *For of a truth, againſt thy holy Child
Jeſus, whom thou haſt anointed; both Herod,
and* Pontius Pilate, *with the Gentiles, and
the People of* Iſrael *were gathered together.*

London Printed, in the Year, 1675.

issues involved were at the time matters of bitter controversy; in the following year, both Barclay and Keith found themselves imprisoned, as were a number of members of the Society of Friends (Quakers) in Aberdeen. Less than ten years later, however—a sidelight that will be of interest to American readers— under a patent issued to twelve members of the Society by the Duke of York (later James II), Barclay was made nominal governor of the province of East New Jersey. He held the title from 1682 to 1688. George Keith, in fact, emigrated to East New Jersey in 1684 but ultimately renounced Quakerism for the Church of England and wrote critical works against Barclay and William Penn.

The text of the debate reproduced here is, with very slight omissions and no corrections, the entirety of the debate as published in Vol. III of *Barclay's Works* (Philadelphia, 1831). It first appeared a few months after the debate itself, but it was not the last published item to have been inspired by the occasion. The theological students published their own version of the proceedings, titled *Quakerism Canvassed*; Barclay replied with a lengthy critique, *Quakerism Confirmed,* which appeared in the same year he was jailed. Those were unquiet times.

THE EPISTLE

Friendly Readers,

Forasmuch as our opposers threatened, they would print an account of the debate, and boasted of a victory; we thought it our concernment for the truth's sake, and to undeceive those that may be abused by such reports, to give this True and Faithful Account of what passed; which we are confident, all the impartial and attentive auditors will affirm to be a true account: neither is there any one argument omitted, that we can remember of, or any thing added. There were many things spoken extrinsic from the matter; and sometimes confusedly, two or three of our opposers speaking often at once, and also some others, that were not concerned; as particularly, one *Brown,* the bishop's chaplain, who though he refused to subscribe the articles, and so was excluded from speaking, did often most impertinently interrupt and intrude himself: but these being only transient, and no arguments insisted on, we have not inserted them; studying to keep to the matter. And we do faithfully declare, that we have herein dealt impartially, according to our memory; as we hope, such serious auditors, as may read this, will acknowledge. So leaving you to the perusal hereof, we rest

Your souls' well-wishers,

Alexander Skein,
John Skein,
Thomas Mercer,
John Cowie.

AN ACCOUNT
OF A
DISPUTE AT ABERDEEN

In the first place the articles were read which are as followeth,

I. It is hereby declared, that this is to be a private conference betwixt the students of Divinity (so called) of the colleges of Aberdeen, and the people called Quakers, as a fulfilling of any challenge, wherein these students may be included within the Theses set forth by *Robert Barclay* (or may have received from any of that people) but abstract from the public challenge given to the preachers in general in the end of the English Theses; because it is offered with particular conditions, of having the public places to dispute in, before the auditories, before whom they conceive they have been misrepresented.

II. It is provided, that when any of either party is speaking, if any of their company offer to speak, he that is speaking, is to be silent; but if two of a party speak at once, he that is seen to obtrude himself, shall be judged impertinent, and excluded thereby from farther access.

III. That each speaker on any of the sides have full liberty and time to speak, without interruption of the contrary party; and that he that interrupts, shall be debarred from farther speaking.

IV. That each side abstain from school-terms and distinctions (as much as possible) but if any use them, that they may be opened to the people in plain English; so that any of ordinary capacity (that are not educated in colleges) may understand them.

V. As for *Retortions,* they must not be impertinent, and from the purpose: and none shall be so insisted on, as to divert us from the point, or turn the *Opponent* into the *Respondent.*

VI. The day appointed for the Conference, is the fourteenth of April, in the year one thousand six hundred seventy-five, (being the day called Wednesday) the place is to be at *Alexander Harper's* house or close (in case the Gray-Fryers Church (so called) cannot be obtained) and that the conference is to continue from two to five a clock in the afternoon.

VII. Both parties shall endeavour to procure a *Praeses* to moderate, but not to have any *decisive judgment;* yet if such a one cannot be procured, the conference is not to be broken up.

VIII. And it is hereby declared, that both parties intend this for *mutual edification;* and therefore intend to abstain from any thing, that may obstruct so good an event.

IX. It is likewise agreed, that none shall have liberty to speak, but those that have, or shall subscribe, before the dispute begin, these aforesaid articles.

Here *Alex. Skein,* one of our Friends, chosen *Praeses* for us (because we could not at that time procure another) standing up with the other *Praeses—Student:* It was condescended, that no Quaker should be a *Praeses.*

Quaker: We are wronged; for we never condescended to any such thing: and seeing ye have chosen one of your way, how can we be hindered to choose one of ours?

Andr. Thomson (their *Praeses*): There needs no debate in this matter; for we are chosen not to have any decisive judgment, but only for the moral part, to take notice if the rules be observed; or whether ye keep to the purpose.

Then *John Leslie* had a long and tedious discourse, concerning what was fit to be done, and how we ought to dispute.

G.K.: Praeses, I suppose we came not to this place to hear from this young man a long logic discourse.

R.B.: I desire to be heard: we being a people so generally misrepresented, as heretical and erroneous, did conceive ourselves obliged to give a true and faithful account of our principles, which I did in a certain paper now under debate. And, that our innocency therein might appear, there was a challenge added to the end of it, offering to defend these our principles, if we might be allowed so to do, in these public places, where we have been so much misrepresented, and against these persons, who had there so often traduced us. To which having received no answer, some of the students of divinity came to us, and signified, that they looked upon themselves as concerned; because mention is made of such in the beginning of that paper. To whom we answered, that they were not the persons challenged by us; as not being the public preachers that had misrepresented us: but seeing they were desirous to debate the matter, we were not unwilling to render to any a reason of the hope that is in us; and therefore should not decline it. And forasmuch as some did object, that we were at a loss, as engaging with them; because there would be little advantage, in case we had any victory; and a greater reflection, should we appear to be at any loss. To such we had, and have this to say, that as we are not afraid to meet with the greatest and ablest of the preachers themselves; so the truth leads us not to despise any.

As R.B. was going on, he was interrupted.

Alex. Shirreff. If it were pertinent, I could easily disprove much of what is said; but to be short: R.B. having given *Theses,* provoking all the scholars of Europe and Great Britain (though R.B. pretends in his preface to be against school-divinity; yet his *Theses* are full of it: and there are many other contradictions, which I will not now take notice of) the preachers and ministers of the word not finding themselves concerned, we young men, and but students, have offered to dispute. In the articles the Quakers have been very unreasonable; and particularly G.K. did refuse, any article should be put in against railing; because he said, that might be railing in me, which was not in him, because he (to wit, G.K.) was immediately led by the Spirit. We have concluded, that being young men, in case the Quakers should have any advantage, it will not be of great consequence; and if we have advantage, we hope it may be useful: because these are the great prophets and preachers of the Quakers.

G.K.: I could take notice of many things not true in that young man's long discourse; as particularly, that R.B. hath provoked all Europe: but I pass them by, because I am here exceedingly abused; and therefore desire to be heard. For I declare in God's fear, and in singleness of my heart, I never said any such thing, as is by that young man, alleged upon me; as I can appeal to the auditors, who were there present. But what I said was this; I cannot bind myself not to rail, because I'm bound already, that I should not rail, by the righteous law of God in my conscience; and may perhaps speak that, as believing it to be true, which ye may call railing.

[And it may here be observed, that afterwards J.L. speaking reflectingly against the Quakers said, it was no railing to speak the truth; which was all he pleaded for.]

A. Shir.: I being chiefly concerned, and having mostly occasioned this Debate, am employed by the rest to speak first; and therefore I will impugn the *Second Thesis*. Which R.B. read, and is as followeth:

Seeing "No man knoweth the Father, but the Son, and he to whom the Son revealeth him," Mat. 11. 27. And seeing, the Revelation of the Son is in and by the spirit; therefore the Testimony of the Spirit is that alone, by which the true knowledge of God hath been, is, and can be only revealed; who, as by the moving of his own spirit, converted the chaos of this world into that wonderful order, wherein it was in the beginning, and created man a living soul to rule and govern it; so by the revelation of the same Spirit he hath made manifest himself all along unto the sons of men, both Patriarchs, Prophets and Apostles: which Revelations of God by the Spirit, whether by outward voices and appearances, dreams, or inward objective manifestations in the heart, was of old the formal object of their faith, and remaineth yet so to be, since the object of the saints' faith is the same in all ages, though set forth under divers administrations. Moreover, these Divine inward revelations, which we make absolutely necessary for the building up true faith, neither do, nor can ever contradict the outward testimony of the Scriptures, or right and sound reason; yet from hence it will not follow, that the divine revelations are to be subjected to the examination either of the outward testimony of the scriptures, or of the natural reason of man, as to a more noble, or certain rule and Touchstone. For this divine revelation and inward illumination is that, which is evident and clear of itself; forcing by its own evidence and clearness the well disposed understanding to assent, irresistably moving the same thereunto, even as the common principles of natural truths move and incline the mind to a natural assent."

R.B.: People, this is that which we affirm, and which these young men are about to dispute against as false. Notwithstanding that *A. Shir.* had thus offered himself first to dispute, yet J.L. intruding himself, put him to silence, beginning as followeth:

J.L.: That which is not to be believed, as the rule of faith, is not to be the rule of faith:

But the spirit is not to be believed, as the rule of faith;

Therefore the spirit is not to be the rule of faith. (1)

R.B.: (Having repeated the argument) I deny the minor, or second proposition.

J.L.: I prove it;

That which hath not a sufficient evidence, to evidence itself to be a rule, is not to be a rule:

But the spirit in the Quakers hath not a sufficient evidence, whereby to evidence itself to be a rule;

Therefore the spirit in the Quakers is not to be our rule. (2)

R.B.: (Having repeated the argument) I distinguish that second proposition, if thou meanest any spirit in the Quakers, which they peculiarly assume to themselves, as Quakers, or say they have as a part of themselves, or of man's nature; we concede, that such have no evidence; neither do we say, that any such spirit is to be our rule. But if thou meanest that universal spirit of God, a manifestation whereof is given to every one to profit withal; we affirm, it hath a sufficient evidence in us, and in all men. (3)

J.L.: I urge that distinction;

If the Spirit hath a sufficient evidence, either this evidence is from your own declaration, or some other.

But it is neither from your own declaration, nor from some other;

Therefore it hath not a sufficient evidence. (4)

R.B.: It is from both.

J.L.: What is it then?

R.B.: That it teacheth us to deny ungodliness and worldly lusts, and to live soberly, righteously and godly in this present world: this is an evidence to all men.

J.L.: I prove, that is not a sufficient evidence; thus:

That is not a sufficient evidence, which heretics may pretend unto, as a sufficient ground for their heresy:

But heretics may pretend this as a sufficient ground for their heresy;

Therefore it is not a sufficient evidence. (5)

R.B.: I answer this first by a retortion; this is the same argument upon the matter which the Jesuit, Dempster, used against your master, viz. John Menzies; for the Jesuit pressing him to assign a ground for the protestant religion, which heretics could not pretend unto; J.M. named the scripture: and the Jesuit further urged, that heretics could and did pretend unto the scriptures. (6) Now, what evidence can ye give from the scriptures, which we cannot give? Yea, and greater from the Spirit, that heretics cannot justly lay claim to.

Stud.: (with one voice) We will not have retortions.

R.B.: Praeses, read the Articles, which contain a particular provision for retortions, as being lawful, if not insisted too much on.

So the fifth article above-mentioned was read.

G.K.: I offer to answer directly to his argument without retortion, though I pass not from the retortion; for it stands over your heads, which ye will never get over. Then I say, we have a two-fold evidence, which no heretic can justly lay claim to. The one is, the inward evidence of the Spirit of God, by its own immediate testimony in our hearts: the other is, the testimony of the scriptures, which I affirm in the name of the People called Quakers, is the best external and outward evidence and rule, that can be given. And my reason, why we have the testimony of the scriptures, as an evidence, that we have the inspiration of the Spirit is this:

All men have a measure of the inspiration of the Spirit of God according to the scriptures testimony, that Christ the true light enlighteneth every man, that cometh into the world; and that a manifestation of the Spirit is given to every man to profit withal: but this universal illumination or manifestation is inspired; and if all men be in measure inspired, then consequently we, who are men, are inspired. (7)

J.L.: I prove, ye have not the testimony of the scriptures for a sufficient evidence:

That which is fallacious, is not a sufficient evidence:

But, the scripture's testimony, according to the Quakers, without the indwelling of the Spirit, is fallacious;

Therefore, the scriptures testimony is not a sufficient evidence. (8)

R.B.: (Having repeated the argument) I deny the second proposition.

G.K.: The argument is wrong in its structure, and vicious, as consisting of four terms which no right syllogism should have.

Stud.: Is it not in forma? For it hath not four terms.

G.K.: It hath four terms; and this I offer to prove before either your masters, or any other judicious logicians of any university in this nation. I say it hath four terms, because it subsumes that in the second proposition, which was not in the first proposition. (9)

[I appeal to all logicians, if when any thing is subsumed in a syllogism, which is neither in the first proposition, nor in the conclusion, whether that syllogism hath not four terms?]

At this the students fell a laughing, and so provoked the people to lightness.

Al. Skein: (one of the Praeses). I am sorry to see those, who profess to study divinity, behave themselves so lightly, and so far from seriousness in such weighty matters, as concern the truths of God.

G.K.: I am ready still to prove, that the syllogism hath four terms: but this being not so proper here for this auditory, ye proceed to prove the second proposition, which R.B. hath denied.

J.L.: I prove the second proposition;

That which may beguile a man, is fallacious:

But, according to the Quakers, the scriptures may beguile a man, without the indwelling of the Spirit:

Therefore, according to the Quakers, the scriptures are fallacious. (10)

G.K.: This argument is also wrong in the structure, having four terms.

R.B.: But waving that, I deny thy second proposition: for the scripture cannot beguile any man, although men may or have beguiled themselves by a wrong use of it.

A. Shir.: Take notice people! the Quakers say, the scriptures cannot beguile you.

R.B.: Speak louder yet; for we do and have constantly affirmed it; and we hope, it will help to clear us of those misrepresentations, as if we despised or spake evil of the scriptures.

G.K.: I would, my words could reach from the one end of the world to the other, when I say, the scriptures cannot beguile any man; for the scripture is innocent, and a true testimony in itself; but men do beguile themselves oft, by making perverse glosses upon the scriptures: the scripture cannot be fallacious, because according to you, it is your principal rule of faith; and if we can prove from your own principal rule, that we are inspired, then the scripture's testimony is not fallacious, else your principal rule would be fallacious. (11)

Stud.: But that is not according to your principle.

G.K.: But it is an argument ad hominem which ye know, is lawful (12): and besides, though we do not acknowledge them to be the principal rule of our faith; yet we affirm, that they are a true testimony, and the best outward testimony and rule in the world. And besides, here is a manifestation of the spirit in many, where there is not an in-dwelling of the spirit, and by this manifestation of the spirit all men may understand the Scriptures, as they do improve it.

Stud.: We will go to another argument.

R.B.: People take notice, this argument is left upon this point, that according to the Quakers' principle these young men say, the scriptures may beguile people; which we utterly deny, as proved, or that can be proved.

Al. Shir.: I argue against the latter part of the second thesis, where ye affirm; "that inward immediate revelations are necessary to the building up of true faith." We confess that subjective revelation is necessary; but we deny that objective revelation is necessary, which ye affirm.

G.K.: Explain, what ye mean by subjective and objective revelation, that the people may understand according to the articles.

Al. Shir.: I explain it from this scripture, Luke 24. 17. "And beginning at Moses and all the prophets, be expounded unto them in all the scriptures the things concerning himself." Here is the objective revelation, to wit, the Scriptures, so that they needed not any new objective revelation, but only that which was before; but needed a subjective revelation, or divine illumination, to make them understand the objective revelation, to wit, the Scriptures.

G.K.: That is not a sufficient explanation of objective and subjective revelation; therefore I desire to be heard, that I may open it more sufficiently, according as is provided in the articles of agreement.

Objective revelation, or the object of our faith is twofold, to wit, first, the material object, secondly, the formal object.

Stud.: Do the people understand this?

G.K.: I shall explain to them, for it is necessary to the matter in hand. The material object is that, which is to be believed: the formal object is that, for which principally we are to believe, or the principal motive of credibility. (13) Now to apply, I say; The scriptures are the material object, or a part of the material object of our faith; but not the formal object of our faith.

Al. Shir.: I prosecute my argument against such objective revelations, as being necessary to faith.

G.K.: We confess, the scriptures are sufficient to move us to an historical faith, and that to a more excellent degree of historical faith, than any other book in the world; because it hath more excellent outward motives of credibility, as the consent of all ages, since they were written, and of all Christians, however differing among themselves, &c. But they are not sufficient to beget in us a saving faith, without inward objective revelation. (14)

Al. Shir.: I prove, such inward objective revelations are not necessary to beget saving faith, by this argument:

If there be no such seed in men, as the Quakers maintain, then there are no such revelations, as the Quakers maintain:

But there is no such seed in men as the Quakers maintain:

Therefore there are no such revelations, &c. (15)

R.B. (After he had repeated the argument): I deny that second proposition.

Al. Shir.: I prove it.

If there be such seed in men, as a substantial, living principle, distinct from the soul, that can be heard, seen, savoured, tasted and felt, then there is no such seed in men, as the Quakers maintain:

But the first is true; therefore the last. (16)

And then the said *Alexander Shirreff* read a passage at length out of G.K. his book of Immediate Revelation, page 6, 7. That the seed was such a living, substantial principle, and that in the seed these revelations were only received.

R.B.: This is a digression from the matter, and a passing from the Theses (which should have been the subject of this day's debate) to G.K. his book of Immediate Revelation.

G.K.: I must now appear to defend my book, and apologize to R.B. because I am necessitated to put my hand in another's harvest: therefore I distinguish upon the word *such,* in the first proposition. If by *such,* thou meanest a substantial principle, &c. I say, that is altogether extrinsic to the subject of the debate; and besides it will engage us into the greatest niceties and obscurities of philosophy and school-divinity, that is not proper for this auditory: but if by such thou meanest, an universal principle of God's saving grace in men, whereby they are capacitated both to know and do the will of God; I affirm and am ready to maintain, there is such a principle in all men.

Al Shir.: But I prove, That that seed in men is not of a substance, or substantial principle.

G.K.: I am ready to defend, That it is a substantial principle: but that belonging to the second proposition, we ought not to come to it, before the distinction of the first proposition be discussed. Here the students make a great noise; and G.K. appealed to the Praeses *And. Thomson:* who answered discreetly, that G.K. did not refuse to defend, that the seed of God was a substantial principle; but this was not its proper place, until the distinction of the former proposition be discussed.

Al. Shir.: I shall wave the word *substantial,* &c. and I offer to prove, that there is not a seed of God in men, as the Quakers affirm:

If there be such a seed, it is either created or uncreated,

But it is neither created, nor uncreated; choose you whether. (17)

G.K. (After he had repeated the argument): I distinguish the word *seed,* as being either a concrete term, or an abstract term.

J.L.: Doth the people understand this distinction?

G.K.: I hope ye understand it; and I shall explain it to them, who understand it not. A concrete term comprehendeth two things; the one *in recto,* (as they say) the other *in obliquo,* that is to say, the one hath the other belonging to it. As merciful is a concrete term, which is as much as to say, one that had mercifulness in him; and so mercifulness is the abstract, which signifieth that one thing belonging to the concrete. Now to apply: If we understand seed as the concrete, it is both uncreated and created; for it is God himself discovering himself to the creature's capacity in his work of manifestation, which work is created; but He, who doth manifest himself in that manifestation, is uncreated. And because he manifests himself at first in a low and small degree unto the soul; therefore he in that manifestation is compared unto a *seed;* even as *Clemens Alexandrinus* saith, That Christ compared himself to a grain of mustard-seed in his inward appearance in men's hearts.

Al. Shir.: The seed is not a substantial principle, because it is the manifestation of God: but the manifestation of God is not a substantial principle, but accidental. (18)

G.K.: That may be substantial or a substance, which in another respect is accidental; as gold is a substance, so silver, houses, lands are substances; but they are accidental to me, because I may want them.

Al. Shir.: He saith, his seed is a substance or substantial principle.

G.K.: This is an abuse: I speak not of my seed, or of the seed of man; but of the seed of God in men.

Al. Shir.: I prove, that manifestation is not a substance.

R.B.: That brings us again into a philosophical debate, which is here to be avoided.

J.L.: I prove, that manifestation is not created.

Whatsoever is of God, is God: but

This manifestation is of God,

Therefore it is God. (19)

G.K.: Take notice of this young man's blasphemy; for if whatsoever is of God, be God, then all the creatures are God, as stones, horses, &c. (20) For the Scripture says; "Of him, and through him, and to him are all things." Here the students made a noise, and fell a laughing to cover this: some of them speaking irreverently of God.

G.K.: I beseech you, yea, I charge you all in God's fear, that when you speak of that holy and dreadful Being, ye do it with fear and reverence.

Al. Shir.: Ye say then, this Seed is God in a manifestation; I prove, it is not.

That is not God which can be measured in measures, and can grow from a lesser measure to a great, can be formed and grow up in men.

But God cannot be measured in measures, nor grow, &c.

Therefore this Seed is not God in a manifestation. (21)

G.K. (After he had repeated the argument): I answer; God as in himself, or as in his own Being, cannot be measured or grow up, it is true; but as in respect of his manifestation, *quoad nos,* (or as to us) that is to say, as he comes forth as to us, discovering himself, He or his Spirit may be said to have measures. (22) And this I shew from scripture: as where it is said in John concerning Christ; "God gave not the Spirit by measure unto him;" implying, he gave it forth in measures unto others: and where Elisha said unto Elijah, "Let a double portion of thy spirit be upon me." (23)

J.L.: He saith, God cometh forth into the creatures: I prove, he cannot come forth into the creatures, because he is in himself. (24)

G.K.: He doth come forth into the creatures, and yet is still in himself; for he is not limited, as creatures are, who go from one place to another: but he is in all creatures, and in himself also. (25) But this young man, as I perceived by him the other day, is a *nullibist* in his opinion, as they term them: so that according to his principle, the soul of *John Lesly* is as much in France, even now, as in his body, or in this place; that is to say, neither here, nor there. But herein I speak according to scripture words, which saith, 'God boweth the heavens, and cometh down;' yet not that he leaveth his one being; but it is spoken after the manner of men, who is every where in all his creatures; but manifesteth himself in several measures unto them.

Al. Shir.: There is nothing in the Seed, but God; therefore God in his own being is measured forth according to the Quakers' doctrine, for the Seed is nothing, but God and his manifestation.

G.K.: The manifestation is in itself, and not out of itself. Can *Al. Shir.* be out of himself? or can any thing be out of itself?

R.B.: If some of them be not without themselves, it is like they are beside themselves. (26)

G.K.: In a moral way of speaking, when a man is a madman, or beside his purpose, he is beside himself. Upon this the students fell to debate among themselves, whether they should prosecute the argument, or not, some being for it, and some against it: and those who were for it, boasting of their advantage?

G.K.: I see no strength in your reasoning to glory in, it hath not the strength of a cobweb; but if you think it hath, produce it: and if any more water remain in your bottle, bring it out.

Al. Shir.: Yea, we have water enough yet in our bottle to quench your Spirit.

R.B.: Come on with it then.

We will go from this to the Eleventh *Thesis* which R.B. read out, and is as followeth.

> All true and acceptable worship to God is offered in the inward and immediate moving and drawing of his own Spirit, which is neither limited to places, times, or persons. For, though we be to worship him always, in that we are to fear before him; yet as to the outward signification thereof in prayer, praises or preachings, we ought not to do it, where and when we will, but where and when we are moved thereunto by the secret inspirations of his Spirit in our hearts, which God heareth and accepteth of, and is never wanting to move us thereunto, when need is; of which he himself is the alone proper judge. All other worship then, both praises, prayers and preachings, which man sets about in his own will, and at his own appointment, which he can both begin and end at his pleasure, do or leave undone, as himself sees meet, whether they be a prescribed form, as a liturgy, or prayers, conceived *ex tempore,* by the natural strength and faculty of the mind, they are all but superstition, will-worship, and abominable idolatry in the sight of God, which are to be denied, rejected and separated from in this day of his spiritual arising. However it might have pleased him, who winked at the times of ignorance, with respect to the simplicity and integrity of some, and his own innocent seed, (which lay, as it were, buried in the hearts of men under the mass of superstition) to blow upon the dead and dry bones, and to raise some breathings, and answer them; and that until the day should more clearly dawn and break forth.

Al. Shir.: By this thesis ye affirm, that no man ought to go about any duty without a particular impulse of the Spirit.

R.B.: Impulse is not a word used by me, but an obscure word; therefore say, inspiration or influence.

Al. Shir.: Either this inspiration ye have it in all things, or in some things: choose you whether. (27)

R.B.: We have it in these things relating to our duties of worship towards God.

Al. Shir.: This contradicts G.K. who in his book of Immediate Revelation saith, that in all things whatsoever, we ought to have an inspiration of the Spirit for the doing of the same; otherwise we cannot do in faith. (28)

R.B.: This is another digression and going from the purpose: for the question is not, how far I contradict another; but what in reason ye can say, against what I have here affirmed? For when I shewed you before, how you contradicted your master, viz. *John Menzies* in another matter, ye would not admit it as relevant, though the case be alike; alledging, it was a retortion. Ye undertook to dispute against the theses; but it seems you find not room enough there, but ye must run to G.K.'s book for further matter.

G.K.: I see it is more against G.K. than R.B. his theses, that you set yourselves: and therefore G.K. must defend G.K. But I say, in this there is no contradiction between R.B. and me; for there is a two-fold sort of inspirations or influences, the one general, the other special. The general influences are given in general or common, for the doing of all common and ordinary actions; and by the special influences of the Spirit we are enabled to go about those special duties, as of prayer, thanksgiving, &c. Now of these special inspirations or influences R.B. in his theses is to be understood; and thus there is no contradiction betwixt him and me.

[Note divers of the auditors were displeased with their going from the theses.]

R.B.: To which I have this to add; there is a difference betwixt the influences of the Spirit, as we are particularly acted by them in singular and particular acts of worship, and as we are generally influenced by the Spirit, in so far as we come habitually to live and walk in the Spirit: for in that respect we may be said to do every thing in the Spirit, as we grow up into that state; though there be more particular influences requisite in matters of worship.

G.K.: I say further; particular influences or inspirations of the Spirit are of several sorts, which are analogous or proportional to the several sorts of duties; as preaching and praying are several sorts of duties; now the particular influence to pray, it is not to preach, and so on the contrary. Also the influences, which serve to duties only inward, or to wait, fear and love God, do not serve without a superadded influence to the performance of outward duties. Therefore every influence is to respect the duty, that it is given unto. (29)

Al. Shir.: I prove, that such particular influences are not needful to acts of worship.

Thus: if such particular influences of the Spirit were needful unto outward acts of worship, then they were needful unto inward duties, as to waiting, desiring, loving and feeling God:

But the last is absurd; therefore the first. (30)

R.B. (Having repeated the argument): I deny that the last is absurd.

G.K.: Come on with that argument: I confess it hath some acumen or sharpness in it; but *ex tua pharetra nunquam venit illa sagitta,* this arrow hath not come out of thy quiver, but out of thy master's who hath formerly used this argument against us.

Al. Shir.: I prove that last absurd:

If the inspiration of the Spirit be necessary to inward duties, as to wait, desire, &c. then we must not wait without them;

But this is absurd; therefore is the other. (31)

G.K. (Having repeated the argument): I deny that this is absurd: For we cannot suppose, that ever at any time an influence or inspiration can be wanting to wait upon God, to desire, and fear and love him, and the particular influences to particular duties, such as, Praying, Preaching, Thanksgiving, is not wanting, whenever the season cometh to go about them. (32)

Al. Shir.: If ye have these particular Influences, why do ye not make use of them? why do ye not say the grace?

R.B.: It will not follow, that we do not pray, nor make use of those particular influences, because at sometime we do not take off our hats, or speak words, which are not essential to true prayer.

J.L.: I prove, That that distinction concerning general and particular influences is not sufficient.

That which may be a ground for an heretic to forbear praying for a whole year, is not a sufficient distinction;

But this may be a ground for an heretic to forbear prayer for a whole year;

Therefore it is not a sufficient distinction. (33)

G.K. (Having repeated the argument): I deny the second proposition.

J.L.: I prove it; for an heretic may pretend, he hath not those particular influences for a whole year. (34)

G.K.: Though an heretic may pretend, yet he hath no ground from our principle to pretend to any such thing, because these particular influences cannot be wanting, neither for one year, nor for any time, that the particular duties ought to be gone about; and if any did pretend the want of particular influences, to pray, &c. they are to be judged as guilty and deceitful, as giving that for an excuse, which is not sufficient, although all have not the utterance of prayer, so as to pray in words; nor can any pray truly in words; but by a particular influence. (35)

Al. Shir.: This influence or inspiration is either commanding or forbidding; so G.K. understood it; but because of the great confusion, or noise, he cannot certainly say: And upon this understanding G.K. answered, It is not a sufficient enumeration; for there is a midst. (36)

Praeses A.T.: Master Keith, ye know we say *non datur medium.*

Stud.: There is no midst betwixt contradictory propositions.

G.K.: But these propositions are not contradictory; for there is a midst betwixt commanding and forbidding.

Al. Shir.: Either he doth command, or not command; there is no midst here, choose you whether. (37)

G.K.: He doth not command us in all things, in which we are inspired; for some inspirations are mandatory and commanding, some permissory or permitting; and some forbidding; so betwixt commanding and forbidding, the midst is permitting. (38)

J.L.: But a permission cannot be an inspiration, otherwise ye might say, a stone doth inspire you as much as God, because a stone doth permit or not hinder you. (39)

G.K.: I deny the consequence; for I offer to shew from Scripture, that Paul, when he did a thing by permission, was inspired: as when he said; I speak this by permission, and not by commandment: here he was writing Scripture by inspiration in the very time. And again, where he said; I assayed to go to such a place, but the Spirit permitted not.

Al. Shir.: This was not a permission, but a hindering, or not a permitting him.

G.K.: But I gather out of these words by the rules of contraries, that if the Spirit did not permit Paul at sometimes, it did permit him at other times; and this permission was by inspiration (40): and I hope, it is lawful for me to make this observation or note upon this Scripture, seeing, your masters will make half a dozen not so much to the purpose. But for the further opening of this matter, I distinguish of permission thus: There is a negative permission, and a positive permission. A negative permission is a simple forbearance, or not meddling in any case; and such a negative permission is no sufficient warrant to us to do any thing. The positive permission is, when God by some inward evidence or signification of his Spirit by words or otherwise, maketh us know, that he alloweth us to do such a thing, although he command it not. (41) As for example; if a scholar should go forth, out of the school, without getting of his master's leave, this is a negative permission, and is not a sufficient ground for the scholar to go forth: but when the scholar cometh, and saith, Let me go forth; and the master answereth, Thou mayest go; this is a positive permission, and not a command.

Praeses A. Th.: Examples are not demonstrations.

G.K.: But they may be used to illustrate.

Praeses A. Th.: But the master saith to the scholar, *exi,* go forth, which is in the imperative, and that signifieth to command. (42)

G.K.: That is but a grammaticism: for the imperative mood doth not always signify to command; but sometimes to command, and sometimes to permit: which I refer to the judgment of schoolmasters, who teach the grammar.

[As in the third person in the imperative *exeat,* let him go, is permissive.]

Praeses A. Th.: This is rather like a debate about grammatications of imperative moods, than about the matter intended; therefore come to the purpose.

Al. Shir.: In the prosecution of this argument against this *Thesis* alleged on G.K. he will not pay his debt, because he may pretend, he wants an inspiration to do it. (43)

G.K.: I hope, none can blame me for refusing to pay my debt; and I pay my debt, as well as any of you; nor can any be supposed, that men can want an inspiration to do any such thing. (44) And we refer ourselves to the judgment of discretion in all sober persons here present. (45)

Paul Gelly: I have an argument to propose for *Water-Baptism.*

R.B.: Then let me read the *Thesis;* which was read, and is as followeth:

> As there is one Lord, and one faith, so there is one baptism, Ephes. 4, 5. which is not the putting away of the filth of the flesh, but the answer of a good conscience before God, by the resurrection of Jesus Christ, 1 Pet. 3. 21. And this baptism is a holy and spiritual thing (to wit) the baptism of the Spirit and fire, by which we are buried with him, Col. 2. 12. That being washed and purged from our sins, we may walk in newness of life, Rom. 6. 4. of which the baptism of John was a figure, which was commanded for a time, and not to continue forever. As to the baptism of infants, it is a mere human tradition, for which neither precept nor practice is to be found in all the scripture.

R.B.: What hast thou against this *Thesis,* is it not the express words of scripture? (46)

P.G.: It is true, and therein we agree; but I oppose your meaning of it.

[Note, That while this young man was prosecuting his argument, J.L. did insolently intrude himself, and interrupted him, and they spoke of them three at some times.]

R.B.: We make no meaning in the case, for the scripture declareth our meaning.

G.K.: Ye have a large field to dispute in, in the last part of the *Thesis,* if you please, where he positively affirms, "that sprinkling of infants is a mere human tradition."

Stud.: We will not meddle with that at this time.

P.G.: Either you mean by this *Thesis,* that water-baptism is ceased, or not ceased. (47)

R.B.: Come on, we mean, it is ceased. (48)

P.G.: I prove it is not ceased, thus:

If the presence of Christ is to continue with his church forever, then water-baptism is to continue for ever.

But the first is true:

Therefore the second. (49)

G.K.: People take notice, he saith water-baptism is to continue forever; if so, then we must be baptized in heaven after this life with water-baptism.

Stud.: He means by forever, to the end of the world.

R.B. (Having repeated the argument): I deny the sequel of the first proposition.

P.G.: I prove it from Matth. 28. "Go teach and baptize all nations," &c. Here Christ commanding them to baptize, sheweth, he will be with them to the end of the world; therefore as long as he was to be with them, that baptism was to continue.

R.B.: I grant the whole: but the question is, if that baptism be by water? which I deny.

P.G.: I prove, it was by water.

If the apostles baptized with water, then they were commanded to baptize with water.

But the apostles baptized with water:

Therefore, they were commanded to baptize with water. (50)

R.B. (Having repeated the argument): I deny the consequence of the proposition. (51)

P.G.: I prove it thus: Either the apostles did baptize with water by the command of Christ, Matth. 28. or they were ignorant of the meaning of that command; choose you whether.

G.K.: It is not a sufficient enumeration; for they might have known the meaning of the command, and yet baptized with water, not for that command, but in condescension to the weaknesses of the Jews.

P.G.: If they condescended to baptize with water for the weakness of the Jews, though without a command, then ye ought to baptize now with water, to condescend to people's weakness now; seeing ye confess, that there are, who are weak both among us and yourselves. (52)

G.K.: That will not follow, more than in the case of circumcision; for the apostle *Paul* did circumcise without a command in condescension to the Jews, yet it followeth not, that any now should circumcise to condescend to the people, who should require it. (53)

Stud.: The parity is not alike, because baptism with water was commanded to the apostles, so not circumcision; for *John Baptist* was sent to baptize with water. (54)

R.B.: *John Baptist* was not an *apostle,* and so not concerned in that commission, Matt. 28. And his baptism was to decrease, that the baptism of Christ by the Holy Ghost might increase. (55)

Al. Shir.: It must be water-baptism, because the baptizing of the Holy Ghost is ceased now.

G.K.: People, take notice, he saith, "The baptism of the Holy Ghost is ceased now."

Al. Shir.: It is ceased to be given by men; for do ye give the Holy Ghost by the laying on of hands?

G.K.: The Holy Ghost may be given without the laying on of hands; and holy men now are instruments in conveying the gifts of the Holy Ghost to others.

R.B.: Did not *Paul* say, Rom. 1. 11. "That he longed to see them to communicate some spiritual gift?" And besides, as to the matter of condescendence, abstaining from blood and things strangled, though particularly commanded by the apostles, yet is not now to be practised by any condescension, as yourselves confess. (56)

G.K.: Hear what *Augustine* saith in the case of *circumcision, observing of meats, drinks, washing, sacrifices,* &c. They are to be considered in a threefold respect, viz. first, as living under the law; secondly, as dead, after the death of Christ; thirdly, as deadly, as being once buried; and being once buried, they are not to be again raised up out of their grave, out of condescension to any. So I say the same, as of *water-baptism,* it being once *dead* and *buried,* is not again to be raised up now, after the apostacy.

P.G.: I prove, that water-baptism was thought needful even to those, that were baptized with the Holy Ghost: *Can any man forbid water,* &c. as *Paul* said Acts 10.

G.K.: Say *Peter,* not *Paul.*

P.G.: *Peter,* I say, not *Paul.*

R.B.: That proves not at all, that it was done by necessity; but to condescend to their weakness.

About this time the *Praeses A. Th.* going forth, said, It was now five a clock, the time appointed for the continuance of the dispute; and so went away: nor was there any argument farther urged.

G.K.: Praeses Al. Skein; I see there is like to be no more here, but confusion, seeing the other *Praeses* is gone. I shall only propose this just and reasonable desire to these students, that since we have given them a fair opportunity to impugn and oppose our principles, they also will promise us another day, to impugn and oppose theirs.

Stud.: When we set out *Theses,* then ye shall have an opportunity to impugn them.

G.K.: Your *Theses* are set out already, for your confession of faith is your *Theses,* which I offer to impugn.

Stud.: Our faith is established by the law of God, and of the nation, and therefore ought not to be called in question. (57)

R.B.: That it is established by the law of God, is the thing under debate (58); and as for the law of the nation, so is the Popish faith in Italy and Spain, and Mahometanism in the Turk's dominions; will it therefore follow, that Popery and Mahometanism are not to be called in question or oppugned? (59)

Stud.: We will come to your meetings, and debate further with you.

R.B.: Our meetings are not for debate; but to wait upon God and worship Him; but if ye please to meet us here again to-morrow, we are satisfied.

Stud.: We will not.

R.B.: It seems, ye need a longer time to prepare you; for your present strength is all exhausted.

Stud.: We will come to your meeting, and wait til it be done, and then oppose you.

R.B.: I have told you before, that is not proper; but on this condition I will admit it, that when I see meet, I may have the like opportunity to come to your meetings, and when your preachers have done, that I be allowed to oppose and impugn your principles.

Stud.: No, no.

The confusion and tumult increasing, through the removing of the *Praeses, A. Th.* and divers of the soberest people: and the students vainly boasting of their victory, laughing, clamouring and making a noise, and telling, they would cause to be published in print their (imaginary) victory, occasioned such lightness and rudeness in a rabble of the grossest sort, that were without the bar, that laying hold on a heap of turfs, they threw many of them against us, without offering the least violence to our opposers on the other side. So that having beat divers with hard turfs, peats, and also with stones, R.B. with divers other Friends, received several knocks in his head, and was wounded in his hand with a stone (60); while as the students (the masters of art) and their companions, who had been disputing in matters of religion, instead of interposing themselves to prevent, stood divers of them laughing, hallowing and clamouring thereat; and so the meeting broke up.

EXERCISES

1. Analyze the structure of the argument.
2. Analyze the structure of the argument.
3. What is the point of making a distinction of this sort here?
4. Analyze the structure of the argument.
5. Analyze the structure of the argument.
6. What sort of defense does R. B. offer here?
7. Analyze the structure of the argument.
8. Analyze the structure of the argument.
9. Is G. K. correct or is the argument correct (or neither)?
10. Analyze the structure of the argument.
11. What sort of an argument is G. K. offering here? Explain.
12. What do you think G. K. means by saying that an argumentum ad hominem is lawful?
13. Comment on this distinction, keeping in mind the discussion of truth and evidence in Chapter 8.
14. Evaluate G. K.'s argument for the credibility of the scriptures.
15. Analyze the structure of the argument.
16. Analyze the structure of the argument.
17. How do you think Al. Shir. intends to continue? What would be the structure of his complete argument?
18. Analyze the structure of the argument.
19. Analyze the structure of the argument.
20. How should G. K.'s response be classified?
21. Complete the argument and describe its form.
22. What is the point of G. K.'s response here?
23. Is there a fallacy here, or not?

24. What is presupposed by this argument?
25. Explain how this is intended to serve as a rebuttal to J. L.'s argument.
26. A pun or an argument?
27. Describe Al. Shir.'s apparent logical strategy here. Has it been used before?
28. What sort of an argument is Al. Shir. advancing at this point?
29. Explain how the distinctions made by G. K. and R. B. in the preceding comments are intended to evade Al. Shir.'s strategy.
30. Analyze the structure of the argument.
31. Analyze the structure of the argument.
32. Evaluate the cogency of G. K.'s reply.
33. Analyze the structure of the argument.
34. What does J. L.'s argument presuppose?
35. How does G. K.'s reply relate to J. L.'s argument?
36. Analyze the logical structure of the issue which now develops and decide who is correct.
37. What is the point of the reformulation?
38. Analyze the structure of the argument. Is it to the point?
39. What about this argument?
40. What about this argument?
41. Relate this distinction to the immediately preceding discussion. At what argument is it aimed?
42. Evaluate A. Th.'s argument.
43. To what previous point in the discussion is this claim related?
44. Does G. K.'s protest reply to the issue raised by A. Shir.?
45. Would you classify this as a fallacy?
46. What kind of an argument does R. B.'s rhetorical question suggest?
47. What form of argument does P. G. seem about to embark upon?
48. Compare R. B.'s response with the response in similar situations earlier in the discussion.
49. Analyze the structure of the argument.
50. Analyze the structure of the argument.
51. The import of R. B.'s comment is obscure. In the light of what follows, what sort of attack on P. G.'s argument may have been intended?
52. How is P. G.'s argument to be classified?
53. What is the point of G. K.'s analogy?
54. With what fallacy does the Student charge G. K. here?
55. Evaluate R. B.'s reply.
56. Classify the last point made by R. B.
57. Classify the Student's argument.
58. What is the logical point of the first part of R. B.'s response?
59. What is the logical point of the second part of R. B.'s response?
60. Classify the final argument.

Appendix 2

===

AN APPROACH TO
MACHINE APPLICATION

We have called attention to the relevance of systematic logic to the development and application of computing devices and "thinking machines." Once a formal system has been constructed, the application of its rules can be (in principle, at least) an essentially mechanical procedure. When we solve problems and work out proofs, we frequently take short cuts such as condensing a number of distinct steps into one and often without any clear awareness that we are doing so. A machine cannot exercise this sort of ingenuity. It does only what it is told to do, and its instructions must be precise and detailed.

A completely analyzed procedure according to which a machine is supposed to carry through some task is called a "program." For the program to be useful in directing the operations of the machine, it must be written in a language to which the machine is able to respond, a "machine language." This is ordinarily constructed in columns of positions on a punch card, or in an array of magnetic cores, or on a magnetic disk or tape. Each position, called a "bit," can take either of two values; combinations of bits make up the vocabulary of the machine language. In the preliminary stages of programming a machine, it is useful (for all practical purposes, indispensable) to prepare a program in the form of a "block diagram" or "flow chart." The block diagram breaks the entire procedure down into its successive steps, as must be done if the machine is to function; the steps, however, are indicated in English instead of in the machine language. Once the block diagram for a particular procedure has been

320

prepared, it can then be translated into machine language and used to direct the machine's operations.

Of course, the block diagram can also serve to provide a detailed sequence of instructions for the human mind. The completion of a complicated procedure then becomes the essentially mechanical one of a step-by-step performance of a series of minute directives. This is illustrated in the following two diagrams. They constitute a program for determining the logical relationship of any two statements in logical English. Some added refinements would be needed for these diagrams to be directly adaptable as directions for a machine, but the way in which the task is approached with a view to mechanizing the procedure is sufficiently clear.

DETERMINING LOGICAL RELATIONSHIP

A. Clearing Complementary Terms

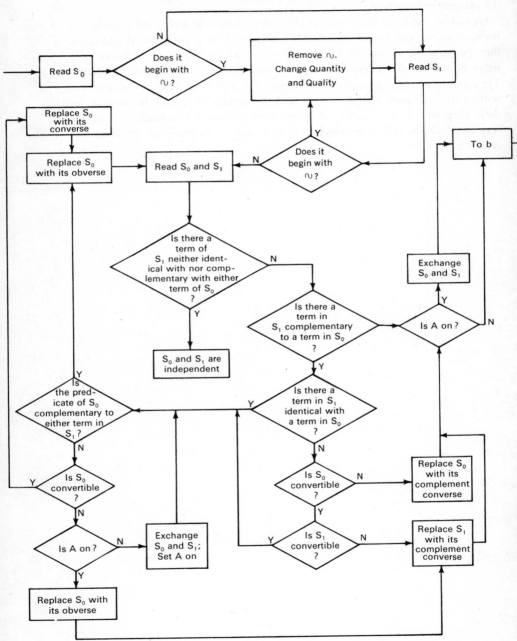

B. Test

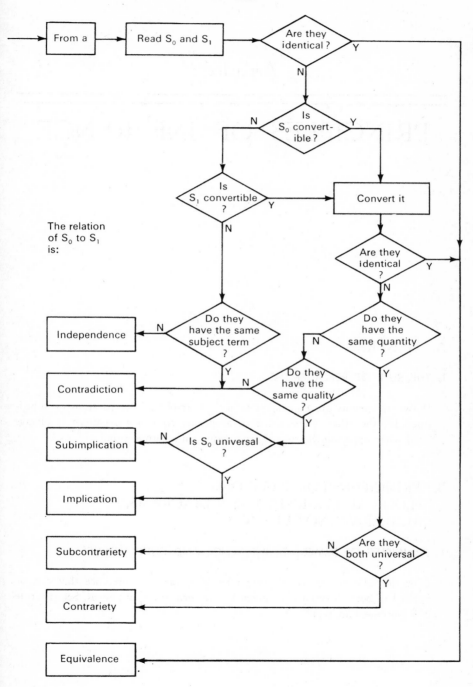

Appendix 3

PRINCIPLES OF INFERENCE

A. GENERAL

1. THE RULE OF REPLACEMENT

If two statements are equivalent either one may be inferred from or substituted for the other. (The name of a specific equivalence pattern is always cited when applying the rule of replacement in a formal proof.)

B. PRINCIPLES FOR PART ONE (LOGICAL ENGLISH, VENN DIAGRAMS, ALGEBRAIC NOTATION)

1. PRINCIPLES OF IMMEDIATE INFERENCE AND EQUIVALENCES

(For the sake of brevity, all principles of immediate inference that can be applied in both directions are given in the form of equivalences. See the rule of replacement above.)

a. The Principle of Contradiction (CONTRAD)

1. LOGICAL ENGLISH   If two statements differ in both quantity and quality, they differ in truth value also. (If the negation sign is added to one member of such a pair, the result is a pair of equivalent statements.)

All S are P.	is equivalent to	$\sim$ (Some S are not P).
$\sim$ (All S are P).	is equivalent to	Some S are not P.
No S are P.	is equivalent to	$\sim$ (Some S are P).
$\sim$ (No S are P).	is equivalent to	Some S are P.

2. VENN DIAGRAMS   An x and shading mutually exclude each other. Changing from one to the other changes the truth value.

3. ALGEBRAIC NOTATION   An equality and an inequality with the same terms have opposite truth values. (The result of attaching the negation sign to either member of such a pair is a pair of equivalent statements.)

$SP = 0$	is equivalent to	$\sim SP \neq 0)$
$\sim (SP = 0)$	is equivalent to	$SP \neq 0$
$S\bar{P} = 0$	is equivalent to	$\sim (S\bar{P} \neq 0)$
$\sim (S\bar{P} = 0)$	is equivalent to	$S\bar{P} \neq 0$

b. The Principle of Limitation (LIM)

1. LOGICAL ENGLISH $$\frac{\text{All } S \text{ are } P.}{\text{Some } S \text{ are } P.} \qquad \frac{\text{No } S \text{ are } P.}{\text{Some } S \text{ are not } P.}$$

2. VENN DIAGRAMS   A circle representing a subject term must not be entirely shaded out, that is, it must contain an x somewhere inside it.

3. ALGEBRAIC NOTATION $$\frac{S\bar{P} = 0}{SP \neq 0} \qquad \frac{SP = 0}{S\bar{P} \neq 0}$$

c. The Principle of Conversion (CONV)

1. LOGICAL ENGLISH   The terms of an **E** or an **I** statement may be reversed

No S are P.	is equivalent to	No P are S.
Some S are P.	is equivalent to	Some P are S.

2. VENN DIAGRAMS   Any diagram may be reversed.

3. ALGEBRAIC NOTATION   The terms of any equality or inequality may be reversed.

$SP = 0$	is equivalent to	$PS = 0$
$SP \neq 0$	is equivalent to	$PS \neq 0$

d. The Principle of Complement Conversion (CC)

1. LOGICAL ENGLISH   The terms of an **A** or an **O** statement may be replaced by their complements and reversed.

All S are P.   is equivalent to   All $\bar{P}$ are $\bar{S}$.

Some S are not P is equivalent to Some $\overline{P}$ are not $\overline{S}$
(Not applicable in Venn Diagrams and Algebraic Notation)

e. The Principle of Obversion (OBV)

1. LOGICAL ENGLISH The predicate term of any statement may be replaced by its complement, if the quality of the statement is also changed.

All S are P.	is equivalent to	No S are $\overline{P}$.
No S are P.	is equivalent to	All S are $\overline{P}$.
Some S are P.	is equivalent to	Some S are not $\overline{P}$.
Some S are not P.	is equivalent to	Some S are $\overline{P}$.

2. VENN DIAGRAMS A circle may be relabeled to represent the complementary class, if the marks inside it are moved outside and the marks outside it moved inside.

3. ALGEBRAIC NOTATION An even number of bars may be added to any term.

(The following two principles of immediate inference are applicable only to Algebraic Notation. Their most important use is in formal proofs of the validity of syllogisms.)

f. The Principle of Simple Addition (SA)

Any term can be added to a term (or terms) set equal to O.

Simple Addition

$$\frac{S = O}{SP = O}$$

g. The Principle of Simple Elimination (SE)

Any term can be eliminated from a group of terms set unequal to O.

Simple Elimination

$$\frac{SP \neq O}{S \neq O}$$

2. SYLLOGISTIC INFERENCE

a. Rules for Testing the Validity of Syllogisms

1. THE RULES OF QUALITY
   First Rule of Quality (Q1): There can be only one negative premise.
   Second Rule of Quality (Q2): If there is one negative premise, the conclusion must be negative; if there is a negative conclusion, one premise must be negative.

2. THE RULES OF DISTRIBUTION
   First Rule of Distribution (D1): The middle term must be distributed at least once.

Second Rule of Distribution (D2): If a term is distributed in the conclusion, it must be distributed in the premise in which it occurs.

b. Principles of Syllogistic Inference

1. LOGICAL ENGLISH   *The Principle of Syllogism* (SYL)
In the first figure, when the major premise is universal and the minor premise is affirmative, a conclusion may be drawn that has the quantity of the minor premise and the quality of the major premise.

All M are P.	All M are P.	No M are P.	No M are P.
All S are M.	Some S are M.	All S are M.	Some S are M.
All S are P.	Some S are P.	No S are P.	Some S are not P.

2. VENN DIAGRAMS   When the premises of a valid syllogism are written on a Venn diagram, the conclusion appears on the diagram.

3. ALGEBRAIC NOTATION   *The Principle of Complementary Elimination* (CE)
If two class products are both set equal to O and differ only in sharing a pair of complementary terms, the pair of complementary terms may be eliminated.

$$\frac{\begin{array}{c} SP = O \\ S\bar{P} = O \end{array}}{S = O}$$

The Principle of Complementary Addition (CA)
If a term set unequal to O by itself is part of a class product set equal to O, the complement of the other member of the class product may be added to the inequality.

$$\frac{\begin{array}{c} S \neq O \\ SP = O \end{array}}{S\bar{P} \neq O}$$

C. PRINCIPLES FOR COMPOUND STATEMENTS

1. EQUIVALENCES

(For the sake of brevity, logical equivalence is represented by the = sign.)

a. Association (ASSOC)

All compound statements in which the same constituents are related by v only or by · only are equivalent, no matter in what way they are associated in groups by parentheses.

$$[(p \lor q) \lor r] = [p \lor (q \lor r)] = (p \lor q \lor r)$$
$$[(p \cdot q) \cdot r] = [p \cdot (q \cdot r)] = (p \cdot q \cdot r)$$

b. Commutation (COMM)

All compound statements in which the same constituents are related by v only or by · only are equivalent no matter in what order they appear.

$$(p \lor q) = (q \lor p) \qquad (p \cdot q) = (q \cdot p)$$

c. Tautology (TAUT)

$$(p \lor p) = p = (p \cdot p)$$

d. Double Negation (DN)

$$p = \sim\sim p$$

e. DeMorgan's Theorems (DeM)

$$\sim (p \lor q) = (\sim p \cdot \sim q)$$
$$\sim (p \cdot q) = (\sim p \lor \sim q)$$

f. Definition of Material Implication (MI)

$$(p \supset q) = (\sim p \lor q)$$

g. Definition of Material Equivalence (ME)

$$(p \equiv q) = [(p \supset q) \cdot (q \supset p)]$$
$$(p \equiv q) = [(p \cdot q) \lor (\sim p \cdot \sim q)]$$

h. Distribution (DIST)

The conjunction of two disjunctions is equivalent to the disjunction of all the conjunctions formed by pairing each constituent of the one with each constituent of the other. Similarly, the disjunction of two conjunctions is equivalent to the conjunction of all the disjunctions formed by pairing each constituent of the one with each constituent of the other.

$$[(p \lor q) \cdot (r \lor s)] = [(p \cdot r) \lor (p \cdot s) \lor (q \cdot r) \lor (q \cdot s)]$$
$$[(p \cdot q) \lor (r \cdot s)] = [(p \lor r) \cdot (p \lor s) \cdot (q \lor r) \cdot (q \lor s)]$$

i. Exportation (EXP)

$$[(p \cdot q) \supset r] = [p \supset (q \supset r)]$$

j. Transposition (TRANS)

$$(p \supset q) = (\sim q \supset \sim p)$$

2. PRINCIPLES OF INFERENCE

a. Simplification (SIMP)

$$\frac{p \cdot q}{p} \qquad (\text{or } q)$$

b. Conjunction (CONJ)

$$\frac{\begin{array}{c} p \\ q \end{array}}{p \cdot q}$$

c. Addition (ADD)

$$\frac{p}{p \lor q}$$

d. Absorption (ABS)

$$\frac{p \supset q}{(p \cdot r) \supset (q \cdot r)}$$

e. Hypothetical Syllogism (HS)

$$\frac{\begin{array}{c} p \supset q \\ q \supset r \end{array}}{p \supset r}$$

f. Modus Ponens (MP)

$$\frac{\begin{array}{c} p \supset q \\ p \end{array}}{q}$$

g. Modus Tollens (MT)

$$\frac{\begin{array}{c} p \supset q \\ \sim q \end{array}}{\sim p}$$

h. Constructive Dilemma (CD)

$$\frac{\begin{array}{c} (p \supset r) \cdot (q \supset s) \\ p \lor q \end{array}}{r \lor s}$$

i. Destructive Dilemma (DD)

$$\frac{\begin{array}{c} (p \supset r) \cdot (q \supset s) \\ \sim r \lor \sim s \end{array}}{\sim p \lor \sim q}$$

j. Disjunctive Syllogism (DS)

$$\frac{\begin{array}{c} p \lor q \\ \sim p \end{array}}{q}$$

D. PRINCIPLES FOR QUANTIFIED STATEMENTS

1. EQUIVALENCES

(The equivalences for compound statements are extended to apply to compound propositional functions as well.)

a. Quantifier Equivalences (QE)

$$\sim(\exists x)Fx = (x) \sim Fx$$
$$\sim(x)Fx = (\exists x) \sim Fx$$
$$(x)(Fx \cdot Gx) = [(x)Fx \cdot (x)Gx]$$
$$[(\exists x)Fx \text{ v } (\exists x)Gx] = (\exists x)(Fx \text{ v } Gx)$$

2. SPECIAL PRINCIPLES OF INFERENCE

a. Universal Instantiation (UI)

$$\frac{(x)Fx}{Fy}$$

b. Existential Generalization (EG)

$$\frac{Fy}{(\exists x)Fx}$$

c. Universal Consolidation (UC)

$$\frac{(x)Fx \text{ v } (x)Gx}{(x)(Fx \text{ v } Gx)}$$

d. Existential Dissociation (ED)

$$\frac{(\exists x)(Fx \cdot Gx)}{(\exists x)Fx \cdot (\exists x)Gx}$$

3. QUANTIFIED FORMS OF THE BASIC PRINCIPLES OF INFERENCE

(These principles are derived from the principles of inference for compound statements by replacing the propositional variables by propositional functions and then either (a) attaching the universal quantifier to each line or (b) attaching the existential quantifier to the conclusion and one premise and the universal quantifier to all other premises.)

a. Simplification (SIMP)

Qun SIMP

$$\frac{(x)(Fx \cdot Gx)}{(x)Fx}$$

Qex SIMP

$$\frac{(\exists x)(Fx \cdot Gx)}{(\exists x)Fx}$$

b. Conjunction (CONJ)

Qun CONJ

$$\frac{\begin{array}{c}(x)Fx\\(x)Gx\end{array}}{(x)(Fx \cdot Gx)}$$

Qex CONJ

$$\frac{\begin{array}{c}(\exists x)Fx\\(x)Gx\end{array}}{(\exists x)(Fx \cdot Gx)} \qquad \frac{\begin{array}{c}(x)Fx\\(\exists x)Gx\end{array}}{(\exists x)(Fx \cdot Gx)}$$

c. Addition (ADD)

Qun ADD

$$\frac{(x)Fx}{(x)(Fx \vee Gx)}$$

Qex ADD

$$\frac{(\exists x)Fx}{(\exists x)(Fx \vee Gx)}$$

d. Absorption (ABS)

Qun ABS

$$\frac{(x)(Fx \supset Gx)}{(x)[(Fx \cdot Hx) \supset (Gx \cdot Hx)]}$$

Qex ABS

$$\frac{(\exists x)(Fx \supset Gx)}{(\exists x)[(Fx \cdot Hx) \supset (Gx \cdot Hx)]}$$

e. Hypothetical Syllogism

Qun HS

$$\frac{\begin{array}{c}(x)(Fx \supset Gx)\\(x)(Gx \supset Hx)\end{array}}{(x)(Fx \supset Hx)}$$

Qex HS

1. $$\frac{\begin{array}{c}(\exists x)(Fx \supset Gx)\\(x)(Gx \supset Hx)\end{array}}{(\exists x)(Fx \supset Hx)}$$

2. $$\frac{\begin{array}{c}(x)(Fx \supset Gx)\\(\exists x)(Gx \supset Hx)\end{array}}{(\exists x)(Fx \supset Hx)}$$

f. Modus Ponens

Qun MP

$$\frac{\begin{array}{c}(x)(Fx \supset Gx)\\(x)Fx\end{array}}{(x)Gx}$$

Qex MP

1. $$\frac{\begin{array}{c}(\exists x)(Fx \supset Gx)\\(x)Fx\end{array}}{(\exists x)Gx}$$

2. $$\frac{\begin{array}{c}(x)(Fx \supset Gx)\\(\exists x)Fx\end{array}}{(\exists x)Gx}$$

g. Modus Tollens

Qun MT

$(x)(Fx \supset Gx)$
$(x) \sim Gx$
─────────
$(x) \sim Fx$

Qex MT

1. $(\exists x)(Fx \supset Gx)$
    $(x) \sim Gx$
    ─────────
    $(\exists x) \sim Fx$

2. $(\exists x)(Fx \supset Gx)$
    $(x) \sim Gx$
    ─────────
    $(\exists x) \sim Fx$

h. Constructive Dilemma

(In constructing quantified versions of the dilemmatic principles, the two hypothetical constituents are treated separately. This offers greater flexibility in application.)

Qun CD

$(x)(Fx \supset Lx)$
$(x)(Gx \supset Mx)$
$(x)(Fx \text{ v } Gx)$
─────────
$(x)(Lx \text{ v } Mx)$

Qex CD

1. $(\exists x)(Fx \supset Lx)$
    $(x)(Gx \supset Mx)$
    $(x)(Fx \text{ v } Gx)$
    ─────────
    $(\exists x)(Lx \text{ v } Mx)$

2. $(x)(Fx \supset Lx)$
    $(\exists x)(Gx \supset Mx)$
    $(x)(Fx \text{ v } Gx)$
    ─────────
    $(\exists x)(Lx \text{ v } Mx)$

3. $(x)(Fx \supset Lx)$
    $(x)(Gx \supset Mx)$
    $(\exists x)(Fx \text{ v } Gx)$
    ─────────
    $(\exists x)(Lx \text{ v } Mx)$

i. Destructive Dilemma

Qun DD

$(x)(Fx \supset Lx)$
$(x)(Gx \supset Mx)$
$(x)(\sim Lx \text{ v } \sim Mx)$
─────────
$(x)(\sim Fx \text{ v } \sim Gx)$

Qex DD

1. $(\exists x)(Fx \supset Lx)$
    $(x)(Gx \supset Mx)$
    $(x)(\sim Lx \text{ v } \sim Mx)$
    ─────────
    $(\exists x)(\sim Fx \text{ v } \sim Gx)$

2. $(x)(Fx \supset Lx)$
    $(\exists x)(Gx \supset Mx)$
    $(x)(\sim Lx \text{ v } \sim Mx)$
    ─────────
    $(\exists x)(\sim Fx \text{ v } \sim Gx)$

$$(x)(Fx \supset Lx)$$
$$3. \quad (x)(Gx \supset Mx)$$
$$\underline{(\exists x)(\sim Lx \text{ v } \sim Mx)}$$
$$(\exists x)(\sim Fx \text{ v } \sim Gx)$$

j. Disjunctive Syllogism

Qun DS

$$(x)(Fx \text{ v } Gx)$$
$$\underline{(x) \sim Fx}$$
$$(x)Gx$$

Qex DS

$$1. \quad (\exists x)(Fx \text{ v } Gx)$$
$$\underline{(x) \sim Fx}$$
$$(\exists x)Gx$$

$$(x)(Fx \text{ v } Gx)$$
$$2. \quad \underline{(\exists x) \sim Fx}$$
$$(\exists x)Gx$$

SELECTED ANSWERS

Chapter 1

1.5 EXERCISE

A: Jewel was sold. Herman's report on Viola's answer was truthful and establishes him as a veracious pig. He vouches for Viola's veracity. Jewel, since she contradicts him, is a liar. **B:** Keningson Dish has black pieces. If he had white, one of his opponents would know the color of his own pieces. If only one had black, he would know immediately, both white sets being visible to him. If both had black, either of them would be able to draw the correct conclusion by taking account of the fact that his sighted opponent did not know immediately and so could not have been looking at another white set besides the one at Dish's place. With a random assignment of colors, the odds are distinctly in the blind man's favor. Once the combination of three white sets is excluded, seven possibilities remain. In four of them (when he had black) Mr. Dish would be the only one who could know the color of his own pieces. For each of the sighted contestants, there are only two combinations in which they could know (and one of these they share).

Chapter 2

2.3 EXERCISES

		Subject term	Predicate term	Quality	Quantity	Form
A:	1.	*A*	*P*	univ.	neg.	**E**
	3.	*S*	*P*	part.	neg.	**O**
	5.	*P*	*S*	part.	neg.	**O**
	7.	*A*	*B*	univ.	neg.	**E**
	9.		Not in standard form			
B:	1.	piemen	simpletons	univ.	affirm.	**A**
	3.	nonsimpletons	piemen	part.	affirm.	**I**
	5.	piemen	nonsimpletons	univ.	neg.	**E**
	7.	people who are seeking unjustly to deprive their fellow citizens of their rights	misguided but sincere patriots	part.	affirm.	**I**
	9.	sincere but misguided patriots	possessors of outstanding logical capacities	univ.	neg.	**E**

2.4 EXERCISES

A:

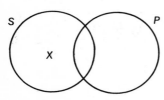

1. No *A* are *P*.

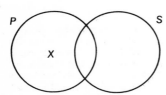

3. Some *S* are not *P*.

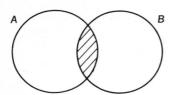

5. Some *P* are not *S*.

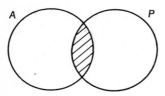

B:

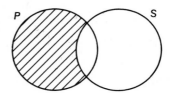

1. All *P* are *S*.

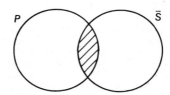

3. Some non-$\bar{S}$ are *P*.

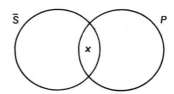

5. No *P* are non-$\bar{S}$.

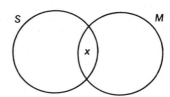

7. Some *S* are *M*.

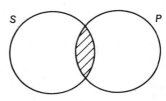

9. No *S* are *P*.

7. No *A* are *B*.

9. Not in standard form

2.5 EXERCISES

A: 1. $AP = 0$. 3. $S\bar{P} \neq 0$. 5. $PS \neq 0$. 7. $AB = 0$. 9. Not in standard form. **B:** 1. $P\bar{S} = 0$. 3. $SP \neq 0$. 5. $P\bar{S} = 0$. 7. $SM \neq 0$. $SP = 0$.

2.6 EXERCISES

(The terms listed below are distributed; those unlisted are not, but only for odd-numbered problems.)

A: 1. *A*, *P*. 3. *P*. 5. *S*. 7. *A*, *B*. 9. Not in standard form. **B:** 1. piemen. 3. none. 5. piemen, nonsimpletons. 7. none. 9. misguided patriots, possessors of outstanding logical capacities.

Chapter 3

3.3 EXERCISE

		Position on the square	Truth value of *A, E, I, O,* if true	Truth value of *A, E, I, O,* if false	Truth can be inferred from	Falsity can be inferred from
B:	1.	lower left	? *F* — ?	*F* *T* — *T*	All *A* are *B*. ~(No *A* are *B*). ~(Some *A* are not *B*).	No *A* are *B*
	3.	upper left	— *F T F*	— ? ? *T*	~(Some *R* are not *W*).	No *R* are *W*. ~(Some *R* are *W*). Some *R* are not *W*.
	5.	upper left	— *F T F*	— ? ? *T*	~(Some *V* are not *M*).	No *V* are *M*. ~(Some *V* are *M*). Some *V* are not *M*.
	7.	lower right	*F* ? ? —	*T* *F T* —	No *S* are *P*. ~(All *S* are *P*). ~(Some *S* are *P*).	All *S* are *P*.
	9.	upper left	— *F T F*	— ? ? *T*	~(Some *P* are not *S*).	No *P* are *S*. ~(Some *P* are *S*). Some *P* are not *S*.

3.5 EXERCISES

A: 1. No *P* are *A*; All *A* are *P̄*. 3. Some *P̄* are not *S̄*; Some *S* are *P̄*. 5. Some *S̄* are not *P̄*; Some *P* are *S̄*. 7. No *B* are *A*; All *A* are *B̄*. 9. Not in standard form. **B:** 1. All nonsimpletons are nonpiemen; No piemen are nonsimpletons. 3. Some piemen are nonsimpletons; Some nonsimpletons are not nonpiemen. 5. No nonsimpletons are piemen; All piemen are simpletons. 7. Some *M* are *S*; Some *S* are not *M̄*. 9. No *P* are *S*; All *S* are *P*.

3.8 EXERCISES

The following statements can be formed: All *L* are *B*; No *L* are *B*; Some *L* are *B*; Some *L* are not *B*; All *L̄* are *B*; No *L̄* are *B*; Some *L̄* are *B*; Some *L̄* are not *B*; All *L* are *B̄*; No *L* are *B̄*; Some *L* are *B̄*; Some *L* are not *B̄*; All *L̄* are *B̄*; No *L̄* are *B̄*; Some *L̄* are *B̄*; Some *L̄* are not *B̄*; All *B* are *L*; No *B* are *L*; Some *B* are *L*; Some *B* are not *L*; All *B* are *L̄*; No *B* are *L̄*; Some *B* are *L̄*; Some *B* are not *L̄*; All *B̄* are *L*; No *B̄* are *L*; Some *B̄* are *L*; Some *B̄* are not *L*; All *B̄* are *L̄*; No *B̄* are *L̄*; Some *B̄* are *L̄*; Some *B̄* are not *L̄*.

A: 1. ?. 3. False. 5. ?. 7. True. 9. False. **B:** 1. ?. 3. True. 5. ?. 7. False. 9. ?. **C:** 1. Independence. 3. Contradiction. 5. Independence. 7. Equivalence. 9. Contrariety.

Chapter 4

4.2 EXERCISES

A: 1–AEE. **C:** 1–AEE. **E:** 4–AOO. **G:** 4–IAA. **I:** 3–OAO.

4.3 EXERCISES

A: D2. **C:** D2. **E:** D1. **G:** D2. **I:** Valid.

4.4 EXERCISES

A:

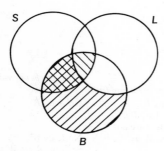

C:

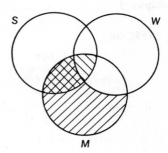

E:

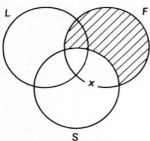

G:

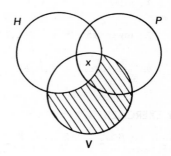

I:

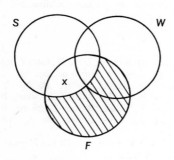

4.8 EXERCISES

A:
1. No *P* are *M*.   Premise
2. Some *S* are *M*.   Premise
3. No *M* are *P*.   1, CONV
4. Some *S* are not *P*.   3, 2, SYL

C:
1. All *P* are *M*.   Premise
2. No *S* are *M*.   Premise
3. No *M* are *S*.   2, CONV
4. No *P* are *S*.   3, 1, SYL
5. No *S* are *P*.   4, CONV

E:
1. Some M are N. — Premise
2. All N are Y. — Premise
3. Some M are Y. — 2, 1, SYL
4. Some Y are M. — 3, CONV

I:
1. All O are A. — Premise
2. Some O are H. — Premise
3. Some H are O. — 2, CONV
4. Some H are A. — 1, 3, SYL

G:
1. No M are P. — Premise
2. All S are M. — Premise
3. Some S are M. — 2, LIM
4. Some S are not P. — 1, 3, SYL

4.9 EXERCISES

A:
1. $PM = 0$. — Premise
2. $SM \neq 0$. — Premise
3. $PMS = 0$. — 1, SA
4. $MSP = 0$. — 3, CONV
5. $MS \neq 0$. — 2, CONV
6. $MS\overline{P} \neq 0$. — 4, 5, CA
7. $S\overline{P}M \neq 0$. — 6, CONV
8. $S\overline{P} = 0$. — 7, SE

E:
1. $MN \neq 0$. — Premise
2. $N\overline{Y} = 0$. — Premise
3. $MN\overline{Y} = 0$. — 2, SA
4. $MNY \neq 0$. — 1, 3, CA
5. $MY \neq 0$. — 4, SE
6. $YM \neq 0$. — 5, CONV

I:
1. $O\overline{A} = 0$. — Premise
2. $OH \neq 0$. — Premise
3. $OH\overline{A} = 0$. — 1, SA
4. $OHA \neq 0$. — 2, 3, CA
5. $HA \neq 0$. — 4, SE

C:
1. $P\overline{M} = 0$. — Premise
2. $SM = 0$. — Premise
3. $SP\overline{M} = 0$. — 1, SA
4. $SPM = 0$. — 2, SA
5. $SP = 0$. — 3, 4, CE

G:
1. $MP = 0$. — Premise
2. $S\overline{M} = 0$. — Premise
3. $SM \neq 0$. — 2, LIM
4. $SMP = 0$. — 1, SA
5. $SM\overline{P} \neq 0$. — 3, 4, CA
6. $S\overline{P} \neq 0$. — 5, SE

4.10 EXERCISES

E: 2-**AOO**; valid
1. All T are E. — Premise
2. Some $\overline{L}$ are not E. — Premise
3. All $\overline{E}$ are $\overline{T}$. — 1, CC
4. Some $\overline{L}$ are $\overline{E}$. — 2, OBV
5. Some $\overline{L}$ are $\overline{T}$. — 3, 4, SYL
6. Some $\overline{L}$ are not T. — 5, OBV

Chapter 5

5.3 EXERCISES

	Argument	*An Equivalent*	*Result of Test*
A:	All $\overline{P}$ are $\overline{M}$.	All M are P.	
	All M are $\overline{S}$.	All M are $\overline{S}$.	Q2, D2
	No $\overline{S}$ are P.	No $\overline{S}$ are P.	
C:	Some M are not $\overline{P}$.	Some M are P.	
	All M are S.	All M are S.	Q2, D2
	Some S are not P.	Some S are not P.	

	Argument	*An Equivalent*	*Result of Test*
E:	Some $\overline{P}$ are not M.	Some $\overline{M}$ are not P.	
	All $\overline{M}$ are S.	No $\overline{S}$ are $\overline{M}$.	Q1
	Some $\overline{S}$ are not P.	Some $\overline{S}$ are not P.	
G:	All P are N.	All P are N.	
	All S are $\overline{N}$.	No S are N.	Valid
	No S are P.	No S are P.	
I:	Some M are $\overline{C}$.	Some M are $\overline{C}$.	
	No $\overline{M}$ are W.	All W are M.	D1
	Some W are not C.	Some W are $\overline{C}$.	

5.4 EXERCISES

A: (Some M are P).
All M are S.

Some S are P.

G: (All $\overline{P}$ are M).
No S are M.

Some S are P.

C: All M are P.
(Violates D2).

No S are P.

I: (Some F are M).
All F are H.

Some H are M.

E: All P are M.
Some M are S.

(Violates D1).

5.5 EXERCISES

A: valid

1.	Some P are R.	Premise
2.	All P are Q.	Premise
3.	All R are S.	Premise
4.	Some R are P.	1, CONV
5.	Some R are Q.	2, 4, SYL
6.	Some Q are R.	5, CONV
7.	Some Q are S.	3, 6, SYL
8.	Some S are Q.	7, CONV

C: invalid (D2)

E: valid

1.	Some Q are not T.	Premise
2.	All Q are W.	Premise
3.	All W are V.	Premise
4.	All Y are T.	Premise
5.	No Y are $\overline{T}$.	4, OBV
6.	No $\overline{T}$ are Y.	5, CONV
7.	Some Q are $\overline{T}$.	1, OBV
8.	Some Q are not Y.	6, 7, SYL
9.	All Q are V.	3, 2, SYL
10.	Some Q are $\overline{Y}$.	8, OBV
11.	Some $\overline{Y}$ are Q.	10, CONV
12.	Some Y are V.	9, 11, SYL
13.	Some V are $\overline{Y}$.	12, CONV
14.	Some V are not Y.	13, OBV

5.6 EXERCISES

A: valid

1.	Some A are $\bar{B}$.	Premise
2.	All C are B.	Premise
3.	No D are $\bar{C}$.	Premise
4.	All D are C.	3, OBV
5.	All D are B.	4, 2, SYL
6.	All $\bar{B}$ are $\bar{D}$.	5, CC
7.	Some A are $\bar{D}$.	6, 1, SYL
8.	Some A are not D.	7, OBV

G: valid

1.	All U are W.	Premise
2.	No $\bar{E}$ are W.	Premise
3.	No F are G.	Premise
4.	All M are U.	Premise
5.	All E are G.	Premise
6.	No G are F.	3, CONV
7.	No E are F.	6, 5, SYL
8.	No W are $\bar{E}$.	2, CONV
9.	All W are E.	8, OBV
10.	No W are F.	7, 9, SYL
11.	No U are F.	10, 1, SYL
12.	No M are F.	11, 4, SYL
13.	All M are $\bar{F}$.	12, OBV

C: valid

1.	All O are S.	Premise
2.	Some B are not $\bar{O}$.	Premise
3.	No S are U.	Premise
4.	Some B are O.	2, OBV
5.	Some B are S.	1, 4, SYL
6.	Some B are not U.	3, 5, SYL

E: (Some S are O)

I: valid

1.	Some T are not S.	Premise
2.	All $\bar{S}$ are R.	Premise
3.	All R are $\bar{U}$.	Premise
4.	All $\bar{S}$ are $\bar{U}$.	3, 2, SYL
5.	Some T are $\bar{S}$.	1, OBV
6.	Some T are $\bar{U}$.	4, 5, SYL
7.	Some T are not U.	6, OBV

Chapter 6

6.7 EXERCISES

A: 1. valid. 3. invalid (construct an equivalent standard form argument that violates D2). 5. invalid (construct an equivalent standard form argument that violates Q1). 7. invalid (construct an equivalent that violates Q1). 9. invalid (construct an equivalent that violates D1). **B:** 1. No one besides John knows what it is about. (No J are K.) 3. No valid conclusion. 5. Add premise: Logic puzzles me. (All L are P.) 7. Add premise: No one who has a cold can lecture effectively today. (No C are L.) 9. People who do not carry plenty of small change lose their luggage. (All $\bar{C}$ are L.)

C:

1. All D are $\bar{L}$.
   No C are $\bar{R}$.
   No $\bar{L}$ are R.
   ─────────────
   (No D are C.)

3. No E are $\bar{C}$.
   Some L are B.
   No C are B.
   ─────────────
   (Some L are not E.)

5. No B are S.
   No $\bar{L}$ are M.
   No $\bar{B}$ are L.
   ─────────────
   (No S are M.)

7. No $\bar{F}$ are G.
   All F are G.
   All A are R.
   All R are P.
   No $\bar{A}$ are F.
   ─────────────
   (All G are P.)

9. No N are I.
   All M are P.
   No H are K.
   All G are N.
   No $\bar{K}$ are $\bar{I}$.
   All $\bar{M}$ are H.
   ─────────────
   (All G are P.)

Chapter 7

7.12 EXERCISE

1. Equivocation. 3. Reification. 5. Amphiboly. 7. Accent. 9. Composition.

Chapter 8

8.6 EXERCISE

A: 1. *Ad misericordiam.* 3. *A dicto secundum quid ad dictum simpliciter.* 5. *Ad misericordiam.* 7. *Petitio principii.* 9. *A dicto simpliciter ad dictum secundum quid.* 11. Appeal to authority (illegitimate extension of authority). 13. *Ad baculum.* 15. Retortion. 17. *A dicto simpliciter ad dictum secundum quid.* 19. *Ad populum.*

Chapter 9

9.3 EXERCISE

B: 1. $\sim(\sim p \vee \sim q)$. 3. $\sim(p \cdot \sim q)$. 5. $(\sim p \vee q) \cdot (\sim q \vee p)$. 7. $\sim(\sim p \cdot \sim q)$.

9.4 EXERCISE

A: 3 1 0 2 1 0. **C:** 3 1 0 2 1 0. **E:** 0 3 0 2 1 0. **G:** 0 1 0 2 0 1 0. **I:** 3 0 2 1 0.

9.5 EXERCISES

A: $\sim(\sim p \vee \sim q)$

0	$\sim T$	$\sim F$
1	$F \vee T$	
2	$\sim$ T	
3	F	

C: $\sim(\sim p \cdot \sim q)$

0	$\sim T$	$\sim F$
1	$F \cdot T$	
2	$\sim$ F	
3	T	

E: $p \supset (q \cdot \sim q)$

0	T	F	$\sim F$
1	T	$F \cdot T$	
2	$T \supset$ F		
3	F		

G: $(p \supset q) \cdot (q \supset p)$

0	$T \supset F$	$F \supset T$
1	$F \cdot T$	
2	F	

I:

	$\sim(p \supset \sim q)$
0	T $\sim F$
1	$T \supset T$
2	$\sim$ T
3	F

9.6 EXERCISES

A:

p	q	$\sim p$	$\sim q$	$\sim p \vee \sim q$	$\sim(\sim p \vee \sim q)$
T	T	F	F	F	T
F	T	T	F	T	F
T	F	F	T	T	F
F	F	T	T	T	F

C:

p	q	$\sim p$	$\sim q$	$\sim p \cdot \sim q$	$\sim(\sim p \cdot \sim q)$
T	T	F	F	F	T
F	T	T	F	F	T
T	F	F	T	F	T
F	F	T	T	T	F

E:

p	q	$\sim q$	$q \cdot \sim q$	$p \supset (q \cdot \sim q)$
T	T	F	F	F
F	T	F	F	T
T	F	T	F	F
F	F	T	F	T

G:

p	q	$p \supset q$	$q \supset p$	$(p \supset q) \cdot (q \supset p)$
T	T	T	T	T
F	T	T	F	F
T	F	F	T	F
F	F	T	T	T

I:

p	q	$\sim q$	$p \supset \sim q$	$\sim(p \supset \sim q)$
T	T	F	F	T
F	T	F	T	F
T	F	T	T	F
F	F	T	T	F

Chapter 10

10.5 EXERCISES

A: valid.

	$O \supset (P \cdot M)$		$M \supset \sim P$		$\sim O$
0	O T	$T \cdot T$	T	$\boxed{\sim T}$	$\sim T$
1	$T \supset$	T	$T \supset \boxed{T}$		F
2		T		T	

B: invalid.

	$A \supset (B \vee C)$		$B \supset (A \vee C)$		$\sim C$		A
0	F	$F \vee F$	F	$F \vee F$	$\sim F$		F
1	$F \supset$	F	$F \supset$	F	T		
2		T		T			

C: valid.

	$A \vee B$	$C \cdot \sim A$		$B \vee D$
0	$T \vee F$		$\sim T$	$F \vee F$
1	T	$\boxed{\cdot\ F}$		F
2		$\boxed{T}$		

Chapter 11

11.3 EXERCISES

A:
1. $\sim(\sim P \vee \sim Q) \vee (R \cdot S)$ — Premise
2. $\sim(P \cdot Q)$ — Premise
3. $\sim P \vee \sim Q$ — 2, DeM
4. $\sim\sim(\sim P \vee \sim Q)$ — 3, DN
5. $R \cdot S$ — 1, 4, DS
6. S — 5, SIMP

C:
1. $\sim P \vee Q$ — Premise
2. $[\sim Q \supset (\sim Q \cdot \sim P)] \supset (R \vee S)$ — Premise
3. $(P \supset Q) \supset \sim R$ — Premise
4. $P \supset Q$ — 1, MI
5. $\sim R$ — 3, 4, MP
6. $\sim Q \supset \sim P$ — 4, TRANS
7. $\sim Q \supset (\sim Q \cdot \sim P)$ — 6, ABS
8. $R \vee S$ — 2, 7, MP
9. S — 5, 8, DS

E:
1. $P \supset Q$ — Premise
2. $\sim R \supset \sim Q$ — Premise
3. $(\sim S \vee \sim T) \supset \sim R$ — Premise
4. $\sim\sim Q \supset \sim\sim R$ — 2, TRANS
5. $Q \supset R$ — 4, DN
6. $P \supset R$ — 1, 5, HS
7. $\sim\sim R \supset \sim(\sim S \vee \sim T)$ — 3, TRANS
8. $R \supset \sim(\sim S \vee \sim T)$ — 7, DN
9. $R \supset (S \cdot T)$ — 8, DeM
10. $P \supset (S \cdot T)$ — 6, 9, HS
11. $P \supset (T \cdot S)$ — 10, COMM

G:
1. $(K \vee H) \supset (L \cdot M)$ — Premise
2. K — Premise
3. $K \vee H$ — 2, ADD
4. $L \cdot M$ — 1, 3, MP
5. M — 4, SIMP
6. $K \cdot M$ — 2, 5, CONJ

I:
1. $C \supset G$ — Premise
2. $(C \cdot G) \supset F$ — Premise
3. $\sim F$ — Premise
4. $\sim(C \cdot G)$ — 2, 3, MT
5. $C \supset (C \cdot G)$ — 1, ABS
6. $\sim C$ — 5, 4, MT

11.4 EXERCISES

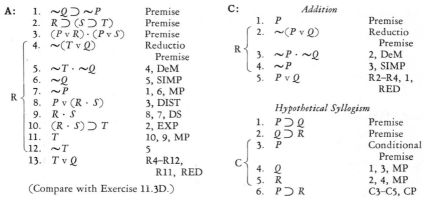

A:
1. $\sim Q \supset \sim P$ — Premise
2. $R \supset (S \supset T)$ — Premise
3. $(P \vee R) \cdot (P \vee S)$ — Premise
4. $\sim(T \vee Q)$ — Reductio Premise
5. $\sim T \cdot \sim Q$ — 4, DeM
6. $\sim Q$ — 5, SIMP
7. $\sim P$ — 1, 6, MP
8. $P \vee (R \cdot S)$ — 3, DIST
9. $R \cdot S$ — 8, 7, DS
10. $(R \cdot S) \supset T$ — 2, EXP
11. T — 10, 9, MP
12. $\sim T$ — 5
13. $T \vee Q$ — R4–R12, R11, RED

(Compare with Exercise 11.3D.)

Constructive Dilemma
1. $P \supset R$ — Premise
2. $Q \supset S$ — Premise
3. $P \vee Q$ — Premise
4. $\sim(R \vee S)$ — Reductio Premise
5. $\sim R \cdot \sim S$ — 4, DeM
6. $\sim R$ — 5, SIMP
7. $\sim P$ — 1, 6, MT
8. Q — 3, 7, DS
9. S — 2, 8, MP
10. $\sim S$ — 5, SIMP
11. $R \vee S$ — R4–R10, R9, RED

C:

Addition
1. P — Premise
2. $\sim(P \vee Q)$ — Reductio Premise
3. $\sim P \cdot \sim Q$ — 2, DeM
4. $\sim P$ — 3, SIMP
5. $P \vee Q$ — R2–R4, 1, RED

Hypothetical Syllogism
1. $P \supset Q$ — Premise
2. $Q \supset R$ — Premise
3. P — Conditional Premise
4. Q — 1, 3, MP
5. R — 2, 4, MP
6. $P \supset R$ — C3–C5, CP

11.5 EXERCISES

A: 1. Contradiction. 3. Tautology. 5. Contingent. **B:** 1. trivial: inconsistent premises. 3. nontrivial. 5. trivial: inconsistent premises.

11.6 EXERCISES

1. $(\sim A \cdot C \cdot \sim C) \vee (A \cdot C \cdot \sim C) \vee (\sim B \cdot B \cdot C \cdot \sim C)$.
3. $(\sim A \cdot \sim B) \vee (\sim A \cdot B) \vee (A \cdot \sim B) \vee (A \cdot B) \vee (C \cdot \sim C)$.
5. $(\sim A \cdot B) \vee (\sim A \cdot A) \vee \sim A \vee (\sim B \cdot B) \vee (\sim B \cdot A) \vee (B \cdot A)$.

11.7 EXERCISES

A: *Modus ponens*

$$\begin{array}{l} p \supset q \\ p \\ \hline q \end{array} \quad [(\sim p \vee q) \cdot p \cdot \sim q] \equiv [(\sim q \cdot p \cdot \sim p) \vee (\sim q \cdot p \cdot q)]$$

B: 1. $O \supset (P \cdot M)$
              $M \supset \sim P$
              $\overline{}$
              $\sim O$

Valid: The conjunction of the premises with the negation of the conclusion is equivalent to $(O \cdot P \cdot M \cdot \sim M) \vee (O \cdot P \cdot M \cdot \sim P)$.

11.8 EXERCISES

A: *B.*   **C:** *E.*

Chapter 12

12.3 EXERCISES

A: *Mc.*   **C:** *Lv.*   **E:** $\sim Wg \cdot \sim Pg.$ **G:** $(\exists x)Lx;$ *Lh* v *Lv* v *Lj.*   **I:** $(\exists x)(\sim Sx \cdot Hx \cdot Kx).$

12.6 EXERCISE

See Appendix 3.

12.7 EXERCISES

Answers are for only *some* of the valid forms of the syllogism.

1–AAA

1. $(x)(Mx \supset Px)$	Premise
2. $(x)(Sx \supset Mx)$	Premise
3. $(x)(Sx \supset Px)$	2, 1, Qun HS

1–AII

1. $(x)(Mx \supset Px)$	Premise
2. $(\exists x)(Sx \cdot Mx)$	Premise
3. $(x)[(Mx \cdot Sx) \supset (Px \cdot Sx)]$	1, Qun ABS
4. $(x)[(Sx \cdot Mx) \supset (Sx \cdot Px)]$	3, COMM
5. $(\exists x)(Sx \cdot Px)$	4, 2, Qex MP

2–EAE

1. $(x)(Px \supset \sim Mx)$	Premise
2. $(x)(Sx \supset Mx)$	Premise
3. $(x)(\sim\sim Mx \supset \sim Px)$	1, Trans
4. $(x)(Mx \supset \sim Px)$	3, DN
5. $(x)(Sx \supset \sim Px)$	2, 4, Qun HS

2–AOO

1. $(x)(Px \supset Mx)$	Premise
2. $(\exists x)(Sx \cdot \sim Mx)$	Premise
3. $(x)(\sim Mx \supset \sim Px)$	1, Trans
4. $(x)[(\sim Mx \cdot Sx) \supset (\sim Px \cdot Sx)]$	3, Qun ABS
5. $(x)[(Sx \cdot \sim Mx) \supset (Sx \cdot \sim Px)]$	4, COMM
6. $(\exists x)(Sx \cdot \sim Px)$	5, 2, Qex MP

3–AII

1. $(x)(Mx \supset Px)$	Premise
2. $(\exists x)(Mx \cdot Sx)$	Premise
3. $(x)[(Mx \cdot Sx) \supset (Px \cdot Sx)]$	1, Qun ABS
4. $(\exists x)(Px \cdot Sx)$	3, 2, Qex MP
5. $(\exists x)(Sx \cdot Px)$	4, COMM

3–IAI

1. $(\exists x)(Mx \cdot Px)$	Premise
2. $(x)(Mx \supset Sx)$	Premise
3. $(x)[(Mx \cdot Px) \supset (Sx \cdot Px)]$	2, Qun ABS
4. $(\exists x)(Sx \cdot Px)$	3, 1, Qex MP

4–AEE			4–IAI	
1. $(x)(Px \supset Mx)$	Premise		1. $(\exists x)(Px \cdot Mx)$	Premise
2. $(x)(Mx \supset \sim Sx)$	Premise		2. $(x)(Mx \supset Sx)$	Premise
3. $(x)(Px \supset \sim Sx)$	1, 2, Qun HS		3. $(x)[(Mx \cdot Px) \supset (Sx \cdot Px)]$	2, Qun ABS
4. $(x)(\sim\sim Sx \supset Px)$	3, Trans		4. $(\exists x)(Mx \cdot Px)$	1, COMM
5. $(x)(Sx \supset Px)$	4, DN		5. $(\exists x)(Sx \cdot Px)$	3, 4, Qex MP

12.8 EXERCISES

A: 1. valid.

	$(x)(Hx \supset Ax)$		$\sim(\exists x)(Ax \cdot Sx)$		$(x)(Hx \supset \sim Sx)$	
	$(Ha \supset Aa) \cdot$		$(Aa \cdot Sa) \vee$		$Ha \supset \sim Sa$	
0	$T \supset F$		$F \cdot T$		T	$\sim T$
1	T	$\cdot$	F	$\vee$	$T \supset F$	
2		T	$\sim$	F	F	
3		T				

3. invalid.

	$\sim(\exists x)(Ax \cdot Bx)$		$(x)(Cx \supset \sim Dx)$		$(x)[Bx \supset (Dx \vee \sim Ax)]$			$(x)(Ax \supset \sim(x)$	
	$(Aa \cdot Ba) \vee$		$(Ca \supset \sim Da) \cdot$		$[Ba \supset (Da \vee \sim Aa)] \cdot$			$Aa \supset \sim Ca$	
0	$T \cdot F$		T	$\sim F$	F	F	$\sim T$	T	$\sim T$
1	F	$\vee$	$T \supset T$		F	$F \vee F$		$T \supset F$	
2	$\sim$	F	T	$\cdot$	$F \supset$	F		F	
3	T			T	T		$\cdot$		
4							T		

5. valid.

	$[(x)(Dx \supset Hx)] \cdot [(x)(Sx \supset Dx)]$				$(x)\{\sim[Px \vee (Lx \cdot Cx)] \supset \sim Hx\}$			$(x)Sx \supset [Px \vee (Lx \cdot Cx)]$		
	$(Da \supset Ha) \cdot$		$(Sa \supset Da) \cdot$		$\{\sim[Pa \vee (La \cdot Ca)] \supset \sim Ha\} \cdot$			$Sa \supset [Pa \vee (La \cdot Ca)]$		
0	$I \supset T$		$T \supset T$		F	$T \cdot T$	$\sim T$	T	F	$T \cdot T$
1	T	$\cdot$	T	$\cdot$	$F \vee$	T	F	T	$F \vee$	F
2		$T \cdot$		T	T	$\supset F$		$T \supset$	F	
3		T			$\sim$	F		F		
4					T					
5						T				

7. valid.

$(x)[Sx \supset (Cx \vee Tx)]$	$Bm \cdot Sm$	$(x)(Bx \supset \sim Tx)$	Cm
$[Sm \supset (Cm \vee Tm)] \cdot$	$Bm \cdot Sm$	$(Bm \supset \sim Tm) \cdot$	Cm
0 T $\quad F \vee T$	$T \cdot T$	$T \quad \sim T$	F
1 $T \supset \quad T$	T	$T \supset F$	
2 $\quad T \qquad \cdot$		T $\qquad \cdot$	
3 $\qquad\qquad T$	T	$\qquad\qquad T$	T

B:
1. $(x)(Px \supset Ex)$ — Premise
2. $\sim(Ea \vee Rb)$ — Premise
3. $\sim Pa \supset (x)[Sx \supset (Mx \vee Lx)]$ — Premise
4. $(x)[(Mx \vee Lx) \supset Rx]$ — Premise
5. $Pa \supset Ea$ — 1, UI
6. $\sim Ea \cdot \sim Rb$ — 2, DeM
7. $\sim Ea$ — 6, SIMP
8. $\sim Pa$ — 5, 7, MT
9. $(x)[Sx \supset (Mx \vee Lx)]$ — 3, 8, MP
10. $(x)(Sx \supset Rx)$ — 9, 4, Qun HS
11. $\sim Rb$ — 6, SIMP
12. $(\exists x) \sim Rx$ — 11, EG
13. $(\exists x) \sim Sx$ — 10, 12, Qex MT
14. $(\exists x)(\sim Sx \vee \sim Ox)$ — 13, Qex ADD
15. $(\exists x) \sim (Sx \cdot Ox)$ — 14, DeM

Selected valid arguments from 12.8A.

1.
1. $(x)(Hx \supset Ax)$ — Premise
2. $\sim(\exists x)(Ax \cdot Sx)$ — Premise
3. $(x) \sim (Ax \cdot Sx)$ — 2, QE
4. $(x)(\sim Ax \vee \sim Sx)$ — 3, DeM
5. $(x)(Ax \supset \sim Sx)$ — 4, MI
6. $(x)(Hx \supset \sim Sx)$ — 1, 5, Qun HS

7.
1. $(x)[Sx \supset (Cx \vee Tx)]$ — Premise
2. $Bm \cdot Sm$ — Premise
3. $(x)(Bx \supset \sim Tx)$ — Premise
4. $Sm \supset (Cm \vee Tm)$ — 1, UI
5. Sm — 2, SIMP
6. $Cm \vee Tm$ — 4, 5, MP
7. $Bm \supset \sim Tm$ — 3, UI
8. Bm — 2, SIMP
9. $\sim Tm$ — 7, 8, MP
10. Cm — 6, 9, DS

Index

St. Vincent de Paul Library

102596   BC 71 T325
Logic